Skills in Numeracy

By the same author

A Complete GCSE Mathematics — General Course
A Complete GCSE Mathematics — Basic Course
A Complete GCSE Mathematics — Higher Course

A Complete O-level Mathematics
New Comprehensive Mathematics for O-level
CSE Mathematics 1 The Core Course
CSE Mathematics 2 The Special Topics
A Concise CSE Mathematics

Arithmetic for Commerce
A First Course in Statistics

Revision Practice in Algebra
Revision Practice in Arithmetic
Revision Practice in Geometry and Trigonometry
Revision Practice in Multiple-Choice Maths Questions
Revision Practice in Short-Answer Questions in O-level Maths
Revision Practice in Statistics

with S. Llewellyn   Mathematics The Basic Skills

with G. W. Taylor   BTEC First Mathematics for Technicians
                      BTEC National NII Mathematics for Technicians
                      BTEC National NIII Mathematics for Technicians

Skills in Numeracy

A. Greer
Formerly Senior Lecturer,
Gloucestershire College of Arts and Technology

Stanley Thornes (Publishers) Ltd

First published in 1989 by:
Stanley Thornes (Publishers) Ltd
Old Station Drive
Leckhampton
CHELTENHAM GL53 0DN
England

British Library Cataloguing in Publication Data

Greer, A. (Alex)
    Skills in numeracy.
    1. Arithmetic
    I. Title
    513

    ISBN 0-7487-0081-1

Typeset by Tech-Set, Gateshead, Tyne & Wear in 10/12 Melior
Printed and bound in Great Britain at The Bath Press, Avon

Contents

Preface

This is a complete revision course in arithmetic and it covers all of the topics required for the following:

R.S.A. – Numeracy stages I and II and Vocational Certificates
London Chamber of Commerce and Industry – Arithmetic
A.E.B. – Proficiency in Arithmetic and similar courses offered by other examination boards

It is also suitable for courses such as BTEC First Certificate in Business Studies and City and Guilds Numeracy.

Nothing has been assumed and the book starts with a chapter on operations in arithmetic which introduces the student to the basic ideas of counting.

Throughout the book the emphasis is on a simple but thorough approach. The contents have been arranged in a logical sequence and hence a teacher and the class may work, if desired, through the book chapter by chapter.

A very large number of graded exercises have been provided in each chapter together with answers. Students therefore should find it possible to work from relatively easy problems to much harder ones.

At the end of most chapters there is a miscellaneous exercise followed by a mental test. The miscellaneous exercises contain questions which are of the type usually found in examinations for which this book caters. The idea is that the student is given the opportunity of answering examination type questions thus gaining experience in examination techniques. The mental tests consist of basically simple problems which will take only a few seconds to answer. Nevertheless they will help to bring out the important points contained in the chapter.

Finally I would like to thank my son David for his invaluable help in correcting the manuscript and checking the answers to the exercises. It is probably too much to hope that despite rigorous checking there are no errors and the publishers and myself would be pleased to hear from anyone who finds an error in either the text or in the answers to the exercises.

A. Greer   Gloucester 1989

Acknowledgement

The author and publishers are grateful to British Rail for permission to reproduce the timetable on page 111.

CHAPTER 1

Operations in Arithmetic

PLACE VALUE

As young children we start learning about numbers by counting objects: 1, 2, 3, 4, 5, 6, 7, 8, 9, 10. Hence these numbers are called counting numbers or natural numbers.

Whole numbers are the same as counting numbers but they also include zero. So the whole numbers are 0, 1, 2, 3, 4, 5, etc.

The positions of the figures in a number give the value of that number.

Hundreds	Tens	Units
5	9	3

593 is the number five hundred and ninety-three.

Each figure in the number has a place value because it is so many hundreds, tens or units.

In the number 357 the 7 means 7 units.
In the number 375 the 7 means 7 tens.
In the number 735 the 7 means 7 hundreds.

In these three numbers the 7 stands for a different value when it is in a different place.

It is important to remember that the figure with the smallest value is always written on the extreme right of the number. The figure with the greatest value is always written on the extreme left of the number. So in the number 689, 6 has the greatest value because it means 6 hundreds (i.e., 600) and 9 has the smallest value because it means 9 units.

Zero (sometimes called nought) plays a very important part in our number system.

306 means 3 hundreds and 6 units. The zero keeps the place for the missing tens. 360 means 3 hundreds and 6 tens. The zero keeps the place for the missing units.

999 (nine hundred and ninety-nine) is the largest number that can be obtained by using hundreds, tens and units. For larger numbers we use thousands and millions:

    1000 is one thousand
   10 000 is ten thousand
  100 000 is one hundred thousand
 1 000 000 is one million

The number 63 587 means sixty-three thousand five hundred and eighty-seven.

The number 8 763 928 means eight million seven hundred and sixty-three thousand nine hundred and twenty eight.

When writing large numbers a gap is left between each group of three figures counting from the right. However, care must be taken when there are noughts in the middle of the number.

    5006 is five thousand and six
   18 013 is eighteen thousand and thirteen
  603 507 is six hundred and three thousand
           five hundred and seven

1

THE NUMBER LINE

Whole numbers can be shown on a number line (Figure 1.1). As we move to the right along the line the numbers increase in value.

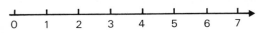

Figure 1.1

EXERCISE 1.1

Write the following numbers in figures:

1. Forty-nine

2. Three hundred and seventy-five

3. Seven hundred and five

4. Two hundred and forty

5. Three thousand five hundred and twenty-three

6. Eight thousand three hundred and twenty-six

7. Ninety-one thousand

8. Thirty-five thousand two hundred and forty

9. Six hundred thousand

10. Seven hundred and thirty-five million

11. Five hundred and thirty-seven million three hundred and fifty thousand four hundred and seven

12. Nine hundred and seventy-six million

Write the following numbers in words:

13. 374
14. 805
15. 404
16. 270
17. 350
18. 82 000
19. 862 000
20. 807 000
21. 97 609

22. 304 069
23. 790 068
24. 6 893 039
25. 8 013 709

26. Put the following numbers in order of size, smallest first: 321, 213, 123, 132, 231, 312.

27. Write down the value of the figure 7 in each of the following numbers:
    (a) 706 (b) 227 (c) 371
    (d) 738 091 (e) 47 836 060

ADDING WHOLE NUMBERS

+ is the addition sign, meaning plus. Thus $5 + 3 = 8$ which is read as 'five plus three equals eight'.

(1) To add a line of numbers:

Example 1

Add 5, 3, 6 and 9.

$$5 + 3 + 6 + 9 = 23$$

Working in your head add the first two numbers $(5 + 3 = 8)$. Then add the third number $(8 + 6 = 14)$. Finally add the fourth number $(14 + 9 = 23)$.

The order in which the numbers are added does not affect the answer.

(2) To add a column of figures:

Example 2

By forming a column, add 9, 4, 6 and 5.

$$
\begin{array}{r}
9 \\
4 \\
6 \\
+5 \\
\hline
24 \\
\hline
\end{array}
$$

Working in your head start at the bottom and add the first two numbers $(5 + 6 = 11)$. Next add the third number $(11 + 4 = 15)$. Finally add the fourth number $(15 + 9 = 24)$. To check the answer start at the top and add downwards.

There are many ways in which the process of addition may be specified. Some of these ways are shown in Example 3.

Example 3

(a) Add 7, 6 and 5.

$$7 + 6 + 5 = 18$$

(b) Find the sum of 6, 7 and 9.

$$6 + 7 + 9 = 22$$

Hence the sum of 6, 7 and 9 is 22.

(c) Find the total of 3, 5 and 8.

$$3 + 5 + 8 = 16$$

Hence the total of 3, 5 and 8 is 16.

(d) Increase 5 by 7.

$$5 + 7 = 12$$

So 5 increased by 7 is 12.

EXERCISE 1.2

This exercise should be tackled mentally. Work out:

1. $3 + 2 + 5 + 7$
2. $8 + 4 + 6 + 7$
3. $11 + 8 + 7 + 2$
4. $14 + 5 + 3 + 4$
5. $14 + 8 + 7 + 6 + 4$
6. Find the sum of 3, 8 and 9.
7. Add 4, 8, 6 and 9.
8. Find the total of 7, 6, 4 and 2.
9. Add 6 to 8.
10. What is the sum of 6, 9, 5 and 3?
11. Increase 4 by 9.
12. Calculate 6 plus 3 plus 4 plus 5.
13. Add 3, 6, 8, 7 and 5.
14. If 9 is added to 4, what is the total?
15. Work out the sum of 7, 2, 6, 3 and 8.

ROUNDING NUMBERS

When numbers greater than 10 have to be added, subtracted, multiplied or divided a calculator is often used. A calculator in good condition does not make mistakes but human beings do. We need, therefore, a method for making sure that the answer produced by a calculator is sensible. One way of doing this is to round off the numbers.

It is usual to round off:

a number between 10 and 100 to the nearest number of tens

a number between 100 and 1000 to the nearest number of hundreds

a number between 1000 and 10 000 to the nearest number of thousands

and so on.

3

Example 4

(a) 29 would be rounded up to 3 tens, i.e., to 30.

(b) 643 would be rounded down to 6 hundreds, i.e., to 600.

(c) 6748 would be rounded up to 7 thousands, i.e., to 7000.

When a number is half-way between tens, hundreds, thousands, etc. the number is always rounded up.

Example 5

(a) 7500 would be rounded up to 8000.

(b) 650 would be rounded up to 700.

EXERCISE 1.3

Round off the following numbers to the nearest number of tens:

1. 52	**3.** 65	**5.** 86
2. 7	**4.** 93	

Round off the following numbers to the nearest number of hundreds:

6. 589	**8.** 76	**10.** 785
7. 603	**9.** 450	

Round off the following numbers to the nearest number of thousands:

11. 3631	**13.** 7289	**15.** 6875
12. 892	**14.** 7500	

THE ELECTRONIC CALCULATOR

There are many different types of calculators on sale but one like that shown in Figure 1.2 is good enough for most purposes.

The keyboard on this calculator has ten number keys marked 0, 1, 2, 3, 4, 5, 6, 7, 8 and 9 and there

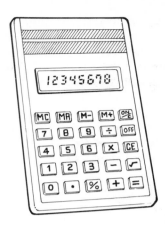

Figure 1.2

are six function keys marked $+$, $-$, $\times$, $\div$, $\sqrt{}$ and %. In addition there are four memory keys M+ (memory plus), M− (memory minus), MR (memory recall) and MC (memory clear). There is an = key and two clear keys marked CE (correct error) and C (clear the calculator). In some calculators it is necessary to press the function keys in a different order to get the same answer. You can check the method of working of your calculator using some of the numbered examples in this chapter.

ADDING LARGER NUMBERS

When adding using pen and paper it is important to make sure that all the unit figures are placed beneath each other by lining up the figures on the right hand sides of the numbers.

Example 6

Add 87, 2348 and 976.

$$\begin{array}{r} 87 \\ 2348 \\ 976+ \\ \hline 3411 \\ \hline \end{array} \qquad 87 + 2348 + 976 = 3411$$

Start by adding the right hand column and add upwards (6 + 8 is 14 and 7 is 21, so write 1 in the units column and carry 2 over to the tens column. Now add the tens column, 2 and 7 is 9 and 4 is 13 and 8 is 21. Write 1 in the tens column and carry 2 over to the hundreds column. Carry on in this way until the addition is completed.) The figures which have been carried can be written underneath the bottom line to remind you to add them in.

Because the order in which the numbers are added is unimportant we can check the result of an addition by adding in the reverse direction.

Thus in Example 6 we added upwards to obtain the answer. To check the answer we add downwards.

More often than not a calculator will be used to add numbers greater than 10. However before attempting to use the calculator we should make a rough estimate of the answer to make sure that the answer produced by the calculator is sensible. To obtain this rough estimate we round off the numbers involved to the nearest ten, hundred, thousand, etc.

Example 7

Use a calculator to find the sum of 63, 72 and 348.
Rough estimate $= 60 + 70 + 300 = 430$

Input	Display
63	63.
+	63.
72	72.
+	135.
348	348.
=	483.

Hence

$$63 + 72 + 348 = 483$$

The rough estimate shows that the answer is sensible, but is it accurate?

Any answer produced by a calculator must be carefully checked. One way of checking the answer obtained in Example 7 is to input the numbers into the calculator in reverse order, i.e., $348 + 72 + 63$. If the same answer is obtained we can be confident that the answer is correct.

EXERCISE 1.4

Use a calculator to add the following sets of numbers:

1. 257 and 3258

2. 5496 and 229

3. 356, 489 and 2387

4. 58, 476, 3369 and 79

5. 609, 82, 3883 and 29

6. 54 382, 8578, 3 468 907 and 95

7. 6 328 236, 438 817, 16 763 and 9781

8. Find the value of $385 + 74 + 989 + 5378$.

9. Find the sum of 876, 98, 4329 and 85.

10. What is the total of 346 872, 28 432 and 974?

SUBTRACTION OF WHOLE NUMBERS

$-$ is the subtraction sign, meaning minus. Thus $8 - 3 = 5$ which is read as 'eight minus three equals five'.

The difference between two numbers is the larger number minus the smaller number.

Example 8

(a) Subtract 5 from 9.

$$9 - 5 = 4$$

(b) Take 3 from 7.

$$7 - 3 = 4$$

(c) Find the difference between 7 and 12.

$$\text{Difference} = 12 - 7 = 5$$

Example 9

Subtract 65 from 394.

$$
\begin{array}{r}
394 \\
65- \\
\hline
329
\end{array}
\qquad 394 - 65 = 329
$$

To check the subtraction the bottom two numbers when added will equal the top number if the subtraction is correct.

That is

$$
\begin{array}{r}
329 \\
65+ \\
\hline
394
\end{array}
$$

So we can be confident that

$$394 - 65 = 329$$

Most subtraction will be done using a calculator as shown in Example 10.

Example 10

Using a calculator subtract 763 from 2942.

Input	Display	
2942	2942.	
−	2942.	
763	763.	
=	2179.	(this is the answer)
+	2179.	
763	763.	
=	2942.	(this is the check)

Hence

$$2942 - 763 = 2179$$

If this answer is correct then

$$2179 + 763 = 2942$$

This check has been included in the above program.

The following questions should be tackled mentally.

1. Subtract 5 from 9.

2. Take 4 from 7.

3. Work out the difference between 3 and 9.

4. How many less than 7 is 2?

5. Subtract 8 from 17.

6. Work out 9 minus 5.

7. What is 7 minus 4?

8. Work out the value of $15 - 9$.

Use a calculator to find the answers to the following questions. Each answer should be carefully checked.

9. Take 598 from 995.

10. Calculate the difference between 89 and 4758.

11. Subtract 7546 from 19 132.

12. Take 29 847 from 359 978.

13. Work out the value of $1\,322\,673 - 98\,589$.

14. Find the difference between 9875 and 9892.

15. Find the value of 28 432 minus 16 998.

COMBINED ADDITION AND SUBTRACTION

Positive numbers are written with no sign in front of them or with a plus sign preceding them. *Negative* numbers are always written with a minus sign in front of them. So, in the expression

$$18 + 27 - 46 + 72 - 53$$

18, 27 and 72 are positive numbers whilst -46 and -53 are negative numbers.

When there are more than two numbers, some positive and some negative, we first add all the positive numbers together. Next we add all the negative numbers together. We are now left with two numbers, one positive and one negative. The answer is then found by ordinary subtraction.

Example 11

Find the value of $8 - 5 - 7 + 3 + 6 - 9 + 4 + 5 - 2$.

$8 - 5 - 7 + 3 + 6 - 9 + 4 + 5 - 2$

$\qquad = (8 + 3 + 6 + 4 + 5) - (5 + 7 + 9 + 2)$

$\qquad = 26 - 23$

$\qquad = 3$

When a calculator is used there is no need to add the positive and negative numbers separately. We can input the positive and negative numbers just as they occur as shown in Example 12.

Example 12

Use a calculator to work out the value of $72 - 43 - 59 + 34 + 112 - 89$.

Rough estimate $= 70 - 40 - 60 + 30 + 110 - 90$

$\qquad\qquad = (70 + 30 + 110) -$
$\qquad\qquad\qquad (40 + 60 + 90)$

$\qquad\qquad = 210 - 190$

$\qquad\qquad = 20$

Input	Display
72	72.
−	72.
43	43.
−	29.
59	59.
+	−30.
34	34.
+	4.
112	112.
−	116.
89	89.
=	27.

The rough estimate shows that the answer, which is 27, is sensible. To check the answer produced by the calculator, input the numbers in reverse as follows.

Input	Display
−	0.
89	89.
+	−89.
112	112.
+	23.
34	34.
−	57.
59	59.
−	−2.
43	43.
+	−45.
72	72.
=	27.

Since the same answer has been produced by two different methods we can be confident that

$$72 - 43 - 59 + 34 + 112 - 89 = 27$$

EXERCISE 1.6

Find the value of each of the following:

1. $8 - 6 + 7 + 5 + 9 - 2$

2. $9 - 7 - 6 - 5 + 8 + 3$

3. $11 - 7 - 5 + 9 + 6 - 8 - 3$

4. $10 - 6 + 5 + 4 + 3 + 2 - 12$

5. $16 - 9 - 8 - 7 - 6 + 18$

6. $21 + 32 - 63 - 58 + 79 + 32 - 11$

7. $152 - 78 - 81 + 43$

8. $27 + 45 + 9 + 7 - 15 - 23 - 41 - 8 + 17$

9. $256 - 318 - 56 - 98 + 179 + 52$

10. $489 + 78 - 526 - 819 - 75 + 362 + 625$

MULTIPLICATION OF WHOLE NUMBERS

$\times$ is the multiplication sign, meaning multiplied by, or times. Thus $6 \times 8 = 48$ which is read as six multiplied by 8 equals forty-eight or six times eight equals forty-eight.

Multiplication is a quick way of adding equal numbers.

$$7 + 7 + 7 + 7 + 7 = 35$$

$5 \times 7 = 35$ (i.e., five sevens equal thirty-five) 35 is called the product of 5 and 7.

The product of 4, 5 and 8 is $4 \times 5 \times 8 = 160$.

The order in which numbers are multiplied does not affect the product. Thus

$$3 \times 4 \times 6 = 6 \times 4 \times 3$$
$$= 4 \times 3 \times 6$$
$$= 72$$

This rule which is called the commutative law for multiplication may be used:

(1) To simplify multiplication when working mentally:

$$4 \times 9 \times 25 = (4 \times 25) \times 9$$
$$= 100 \times 9$$
$$= 900$$

(2) To check a product by interchanging numbers:

$$36 \times 97 = 3492$$
$$97 \times 36 = 3492$$

More often than not a calculator will be used for multiplying whole numbers.

Example 13

Use a calculator to find the product of 356 and 98.

For a rough estimate we will take

$$350 \times 100 = 35\,000$$

Input	Display
356	356.
$\times$	356.
98	98.
$=$	34888.

The rough estimate shows that the answer produced by the calculator is sensible. To check the accuracy of the answer we input the numbers in reverse order, i.e., 98×356.

EXERCISE 1.7

Working mentally answer the following questions:

1. Find the value of $3 \times 4 \times 5$.

2. Multiply 6 by 7.

3. Find the product of 3, 5 and 6.

4. Work out the value of $2 \times 3 \times 5 \times 8$.

5. Work out the product of 4, 2, 5 and 7.

8

Use a calculator to find the values of the following:

6. 53×74

7. 345×69

8. $19 \times 28 \times 36$

9. $9 \times 13 \times 16 \times 23$

10. $8 \times 12 \times 15 \times 17 \times 6$

DIVISION OF WHOLE NUMBERS

÷ is the division sign, meaning divided by. There are several ways of writing division problems. 6 divided by 3 may be written:

(1) $6 \div 3$ which reads six divided by three.

(2) $\frac{6}{3}$ which reads six over 3.

Division will usually be done using a calculator.

Example 14

Using a calculator divide 1554 by 42.

Rough estimate: $1600 \div 40 = 40$

Input	Display
1554	1554.
÷	1554.
42	42.
=	37.

Hence $1554 \div 42 = 37$ and the rough estimate shows that the answer is sensible.

The result of a division can always be checked by multiplying back. Thus if

$$1554 \div 42 = 37$$

then $42 \times 37 = 1554$.

We can check that this is so by using a calculator in the usual way.

EXERCISE 1.8

Use a calculator to answer the following questions:

1. Divide 623 by 7.

2. Work out $705 \div 5$.

3. Divide 1824 by 32.

4. Work out the value of $\frac{2816}{88}$.

5. Find the value of $\frac{11\,736}{36}$.

6. Work out $8773 \div 283$.

7. Divide $2\,264\,832$ by 768.

Remainders

Sometimes one number will not divide into another number a whole number of times. In such cases a remainder is left.

Example 15

Divide 22 by 5.

Since $4 \times 5 = 20$

$22 \div 5 = 4$ remainder 2

Remainders are often required when working with fractions (see Chapter 3).

9

EXERCISE 1.9

This exercise should be tackled mentally. Work out the answers to the following and write down the remainders:

1. $15 \div 2$ **4.** $13 \div 6$ **7.** $29 \div 9$

2. $25 \div 3$ **5.** $34 \div 5$ **8.** $43 \div 8$

3. $21 \div 4$ **6.** $47 \div 7$

THE ORDER OF ARITHMETIC OPERATIONS

In working out problems such as

$$3 \times (2 + 5)$$
$$16 - (8 - 3)$$
$$3 \times 5 + 2$$
$$3 \times 6 \div 2$$

a certain order of operations must be observed.

(1) First work out the contents of any brackets.

$$4 \times (3 + 5) = 4 \times 8 = 32$$
$$15 - (7 - 2) = 15 - 5 = 10$$

We get the same answer and sometimes make the work easier if we expand the brackets as follows:

$$8 \times (14 + 29) = 8 \times 14 + 8 \times 29$$
$$= 112 + 232$$
$$= 344$$

Sometimes the multiplication sign is omitted,

$$5(8 - 4) \text{ means } 5 \times (8 - 4)$$
$$= 5 \times 4$$
$$= 20$$

(2) Next multiply and/or divide before adding and/or subtracting.

$$3 \times 6 + 5 = 18 + 5 = 23$$
$$5 - 6 \div 3 = 5 - 2 = 3$$

Example 16

Find the value of $11 - 12 \div 4 + 3(6 - 2)$

$$11 - 12 \div 4 + 3(6 - 2) = 11 - 12 \div 4 + 3 \times 4$$
$$= 11 - 3 + 12$$
$$= 23 - 3$$
$$= 20$$

EXERCISE 1.10

Work out the value of each of the following:

1. $7 + 4 \times 5$

2. $3 \times 5 - 3$

3. $5 \times 4 - 2 \times 6 + 7$

4. $8 \times 5 - 30 \div 5 + 4$

5. $3 + 4 \times (8 - 6)$

6. $9 + 3(9 - 2)$

7. $15 \div (4 + 1) - 8 \times 3 + 7(2 + 3)$

8. $24 \div 4 - 24 \div 6$

9. $35 \div (30 - 25)$

10. $3(7 - 2) + 4$

11. $35 \div 7 - 3$

12. $3 - 12 \div 4 + 9$

13. $80 \div 8 + 72 \div 6$

14. $4(8 - 3) + 3(5 - 2)$

15. $48 \div 6 - 49 \div (5 + 2)$

SOME IMPORTANT FACTS

(1) When zero is added to any number the sum is the number. Thus

$$498 + 0 = 498 \quad \text{and} \quad 0 + 75 = 75$$

(2) When any number is multiplied by 1 the product is the number. Thus

$$6319 \times 1 = 6319 \quad \text{and} \quad 1 \times 97 = 97$$

(3) When a number is multiplied by zero the product is zero. Thus

$$764 \times 0 = 0 \quad \text{and} \quad 0 \times 9817 = 0$$

(4) It is impossible to divide a number by zero. The result has no meaning. Thus $53 \div 0$ has no meaning.

(5) If zero is divided by any number the result is zero. Thus

$$0 \div 97 = 0 \quad \text{and} \quad 0 \div 7893 = 0$$

EXERCISE 1.11

This exercise should be tackled mentally. Work out the value of each of the following:

1. $892 + 0$
2. 8716×1
3. 0×70
4. $0 \times 4 + 7$
5. $3 \times 6 \times 1$
6. $8 \times 0 \times 7$
7. $16 - 9 \times 0 + 3$
8. $12 - 24 \div 6 + 0 \times (7 - 5)$
9. $0 \div 57$
10. $(7 - 7) \times 7$
11. $7(9 - 3) + 0 \div 5$
12. $28 \times 0 + 3(9 - 9) + 6$

USING THE MEMORY KEYS ON A CALCULATOR

By using the memory keys on a calculator, quite difficult arithmetic problems can be solved.

Example 17

Using a calculator work out the value of $15 \times 19 + 32 \div 8 - 14 \times 7$.

Input	Display
15	15.
×	15.
19	19.
M+	285.
32	32.
÷	32.
8	8.
M+	4.
14	14.
×	14.
7	7.
M−	98.
MR	191.

$$15 \times 19 + 32 \div 8 - 14 \times 7 = 191$$

EXERCISE 1.12

Use a calculator to work out the values of each of the following:

1. $21 \times 32 + 25 \times 9$
2. $35 \times 19 - 16 \times 19$
3. $48 \div 6 - 54 \div 9$
4. $43 \times 33 + 55 \times 25 + 49 \times 11$
5. $45 \times 58 - 67 \times 13 - 15 \times 19$
6. $67 \times 139 - 96 \div 6 - 59 \times 27 + 64 \times 15$
7. $32(16 + 19) - 19(22 - 12)$
8. $59 \times (63 - 32) - 25 \times (17 + 19)$

SEQUENCES

A set of numbers connected by some definite law is called a sequence of numbers. Each of the numbers in the sequence is called a term of the sequence.

Example 18

(a) Find the next term of the sequence
1, 4, 7, 10, . . .

Each term in the sequence is formed by adding 3 to the previous term so the sequence is 1, 4, 7, 10, (10 + 3), . . .

That is 1, 4, 7, 10, 13, . . .

(b) Find the next two terms of the sequence 32, 28, 24, 20 . . .

Each term in the sequence is 4 less than the previous term. Therefore

5th term = 20 − 4 = 16

6th term = 16 − 4 = 12

(c) In the sequence 3, 6, 12, ?, 48, ?, write down the terms denoted by a question mark.

Each term is formed by multiplying the previous term by 2. Therefore

4th term = 12 × 2 = 24

6th term = 48 × 2 = 96

(d) Find the next two terms of the sequence 1, 2, 3, 5, 8, . . .

Each term is formed by adding the two previous terms. Hence

6th term = 5 + 8 = 13

7th term = 8 + 13 = 21

EXERCISE 1.13

Write down the next two terms of the following sequences:

1. 3, 15, 75, . . .

2. 1, 3, 5, 7, . . .

3. 5, 11, 17, 23, . . .

4. 256, 128, 64, . . .

5. 1, 3, 6, 10, . . .

6. 3, 8, 18, 38, . . .

7. 7, 9, 13, 21, . . .

8. 2, 6, 18, 54, . . .

9. 2, 3, 5, 8, . . .

10. 1, 1, 2, 3, 5, . . .

Write down the terms denoted by a question mark in the following sequences:

11. 1, 3, 5, ?, 9, ?

12. 32, 64, 128, ?, 512, ?

13. 1, 10, 19, ?, 37, ?

14. 1, 2, 3, 2, 3, 4, ?, ?, ?

15. 1, 3, 6, ?, 15, ?, 28, ?

12

PRACTICAL PROBLEMS INVOLVING WHOLE NUMBERS

The examples which follow are all of a practical nature. They all depend upon whole numbers for their solution.

Example 19

(a) Five resistors in an electrical circuit are connected in series. Their values are 837, 1356, 962, 258 and 739 ohms. Their total resistance is found by adding these five values. What is their total resistance?

$$\text{Total resistance} = 837 + 1356 + 962 + 258 + 739$$
$$= 4152 \text{ ohms}$$

(b) A farmer has a reel of wire containing 2397 metres. In making a fence he uses 398 metres. How much wire is left on the reel?

$$\text{Length remaining} = 2397 - 398$$
$$= 1999 \text{ metres}$$

(c) Seven people agree to share a bill of £203. How much will each person pay?

$$\text{Amount per person} = £203 \div 7$$
$$= £29$$

(d) A builder requires 81 pieces of wood each 13 metres long. What total length of wood does he require?

$$\text{Total length} = 81 \times 13 \text{ metres}$$
$$= 1053 \text{ metres}$$

EXERCISE 1.14

1. Figure 1.3 shows a shaft for an electrical machine. Work out the dimension marked x.

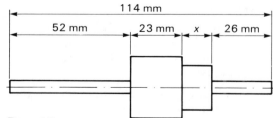

Figure 1.3

2. A tank holds 936 litres of oil. If 69 litres are used, how much oil remains in the tank?

3. A housewife bought some furniture. She spent £256 on a wardrobe, £987 on a three-piece suite, £198 on a bed and £357 on a table. How much money did the housewife spend on furniture?

4. On the first day of a county cricket match the attendance was 3857. On the second and third days the attendances were 2978 and 951 respectively.
   (a) What was the total attendance for the three days?
   (b) By how much did the attendance decrease on the second day?

5. A reel of ribbon originally contains 98 metres. 15 lengths each 6 metres long are cut from the reel. How much ribbon remains?

6. A plank of wood 432 centimetres long is cut into 27 equal parts. What is the length of each part?

7. A shopkeeper buys 1200 pens at a cost of 8400 pence. How much did he pay for each pen?

8. A Third World country has a debt of 876 million pounds. If it pays back 89 million pounds, how much will the country now owe?

9. A furniture shop orders 27 suites of furniture at £564 each and 76 beds at £128 each. What is the total cost of these purchases?

10. An approximate way of converting temperatures in degrees Celsius to temperatures in degrees Fahrenheit is to multiply the degrees Celsius by 2 and add 30. Using this rule, convert to degrees Fahrenheit:
   (a) 15 °C   (b) 24 °C   (c) 30 °C

MISCELLANEOUS EXERCISE 1

1. (a) Find the difference between 56 and 73.
   (b) What is the product of 7 and 9?
   (c) Work out the sum of 23, 47 and 298.
   (d) Find the value of 392 divided by 7.

2. Find the values of
   (a) $23 + 7 \times 3 - 5(6 - 2)$
   (b) $4(9 - 6) - 8$
   (c) $5 \times 3 + 6 \times 2 - 4 \times 4$
   (d) $(7 + 5) \div (8 - 2)$

3. Write down the terms denoted by a question mark in the following sequences of numbers:
   (a) 0, 3, 6, ?, ?, 15, ?
   (b) 42, 38, 34, ?, 26, ?, ?
   (c) 64, 32, 16, ?, ?, ?
   (d) 3, 7, 10, 17, ?, ?
   (e) 2, 5, 9, 14, ?, ?

4. Round off the following numbers:
   (a) 46 to the nearest number of tens
   (b) 850 to the nearest number of hundreds
   (c) 8359 to the nearest number of thousands.

5. The instructions for cooking a turkey are 'cook for 20 minutes per pound plus an additional 25 minutes'. Work out the time needed to cook a turkey weighing 17 pounds.

6. The temperature in a greenhouse was 3 degrees Celsius at 6 a.m. but at 11 a.m. it had risen to 15 degrees Celsius. What was the increase in temperature?

7. (a) Add twenty-one thousand to twenty-one million.
   (b) Subtract one hundred thousand from one million.

8. A motor car will travel 11 kilometres on 1 litre of petrol. How many litres will be needed for a journey of 297 kilometres?

9. Find the values of:
   (a) $(16 \div 4) \div 2$ (b) $16 \div (4 \div 2)$

10. The numbers 1, 2, 4, 7, 11, 16 form a sequence.
   (a) What is the next number in the sequence?
   (b) If each number can be used only once, which three numbers add up to 25?

MENTAL TEST 1

Try to write down the answers to the following questions without writing anything else.

1. Add 3, 6, 7 and 5.

2. Find the sum of 2, 5 and 8.

3. Work out the difference between 8 and 15.

4. Take 15 away from 24.

5. Multiply 16 by 5.

6. Work out the product of 6 and 9.

7. Divide 63 by 7.

8. Find the value of $3 \times 4 + 2$.

9. Work out the value of $15 - 3(7 - 2)$.

10. Find the value of $4 \times 5 - 12 \div 3$.

11. Find the value of $17 - 3$.

12. Work out the value of $16 - 9 - 5$.

13. Subtract 7 from 15.

14. Find the value of $8 \div 2 + 2$.

15. What is the product of 3, 4 and 5?

16. Work out $20 \div (7 + 3)$.

17. Find the value of $28 \div (5 + 2)$.

18. What is the next term in the sequence 2, 4, 8, . . .?

19. Find the next term of the sequence 3, 5, 7, . . .

20. What is the next term of the sequence 16, 13, 10 . . .?

Factors and Multiples

ODD AND EVEN NUMBERS

If we count in twos starting with 2 the sequence is 2, 4, 6, 8, 10, 12, 14, 16, 18, 20, . . . If we continue the sequence we discover that each number in it ends in 0, 2, 4, 6 or 8. These numbers are called *even numbers.* So 80, 192, 9754, 236 and 7398 are all even numbers.

If we now start at 1 and count in twos the sequence is 1, 3, 5, 7, 9, 11, 13, 15, 17, 19, . . . If we carry on the sequence we discover that each number in it ends in 1, 3, 5, 7 or 9. These numbers are called *odd numbers.* So 61, 83, 425, 3687 and 4869 are all odd numbers. Note that any number which when divided by 2 has a remainder of 1 is an odd number.

POWERS OF NUMBERS

The quantity $5 \times 5 \times 5 \times 5$ is often written as 5^4 which is called the fourth power of five. The number 4 which gives the number of fives to be multiplied together is called the *index* (plural indices).

$$2^5 = 2 \times 2 \times 2 \times 2 \times 2 = 32$$
$$9^2 = 9 \times 9 = 81$$

SQUARES OF NUMBERS

When a number is multiplied by itself the result is called the square of that number.

For example:

$$7 \text{ squared} = 7 \times 7 = 7^2 = 49$$
$$15 \text{ squared} = 15 \times 15 = 15^2 = 225$$
$$43 \text{ squared} = 43 \times 43 = 43^2 = 1849$$

The square of any number may be found by using a calculator in the way shown in Example 1.

Example 1

Using a calculator find the square of 31.

Input	Display
31	31.
×	31.
=	961.

Therefore

$$31 \text{ squared} = 31^2 = 961$$

CUBES OF NUMBERS

The cube of a number is that number raised to the power of 3. So

$$\text{cube of } 4 = 4^3 = 4 \times 4 \times 4 = 64$$

$$\text{cube of } 17 = 17^3 = 17 \times 17 \times 17 = 4913$$

The cube of any number can be found by using a calculator in the way shown in Example 2.

Example 2

Using a calculator find the cube of 19.

Input	Display
19	19.
××	19.
=	361.
=	6859.

Note carefully that the number of equals signs is one less than the power to which the number is raised (in this case there are only two equal signs).

Therefore

$$19^3 = 19 \times 19 \times 19 = 6859$$

By using a calculator in the way shown in Example 3 we can raise a number to any power.

Example 3

Using a calculator find the value of 8^5. The program is as shown below. Note carefully that because we want to calculate the fifth power of 8 we need only four equal signs.

Input	Display
8	8.
××	8.
=	64.
=	512.
=	4096.
=	32768.

Therefore

$$8^5 = 8 \times 8 \times 8 \times 8 \times 8 = 32\,768$$

SQUARE ROOTS OF NUMBERS

The square root of a number is the number whose square equals the given number.

$\sqrt{}$ is the square root sign and means 'the square root of'.

$$\text{The square of } 5 = 5 \times 5 = 25$$

So

$$\sqrt{25} = 5$$

$$\text{The square of } 12 = 12 \times 12 = 144$$

So

$$\sqrt{144} = 12$$

The square root of any number can be found by using a calculator.

Example 4

Using a calculator find $\sqrt{289}$.

Input	Display
289	289.
$\sqrt{}$	17.

Therefore $\sqrt{289} = 17$

To find the square root of numbers which are multiplied together we proceed as shown in Example 5.

Example 5

(a) Find the square root of 4×9.

$$\sqrt{4 \times 9} = \sqrt{4} \times \sqrt{9} = 2 \times 3 = 6$$

(b) Find the square root of $16 \times 25 \times 49$.

$$\sqrt{16 \times 25 \times 49} = \sqrt{16} \times \sqrt{25} \times \sqrt{49}$$

$$= 4 \times 5 \times 7$$

$$= 140$$

EXERCISE 2.1

State whether each of the numbers shown below is an even number or an odd number.

1. 75   **3.** 752   **5.** 4829   **7.** 9386

2. 824   **4.** 623   **6.** 7778   **8.** 59751

Find the square roots of:

9. 36   **14.** 25×36

10. 64   **15.** 49×64

11. 169   **16.** $9 \times 16 \times 25$

12. 256   **17.** $81 \times 100 \times 144$

13. 625

Find the squares of the following numbers:

18. 7   **22.** 44   **25.** 123

19. 8   **23.** 55   **26.** 543

20. 13   **24.** 89   **27.** 356

21. 27

Find the cubes of the following numbers:

28. 3   **31.** 38   **33.** 132

29. 7   **32.** 59   **34.** 206

30. 17

Work out the values of the following:

35. 2^6 **38.** 8^4 **40.** 28^3

36. 3^4 **39.** 15^4 **41.** 9^6

37. 5^6

TESTS FOR DIVISIBILITY

(1) If a number is even then 2 will divide into it without leaving a remainder. Numbers which are divisible by 2 are called *multiples of 2*. So 14, 78 and 194 are all multiples of 2.

(2) A number is divisible by 3 if the sum of its digits is divisible by 3. The number 3156 is divisible by 3 because $3 + 1 + 5 + 6 = 15$ which is divisible by 3. Numbers which are divisible by 3 are called *multiples of 3*.

(3) A number is divisible by 4 if its last two digits are divisible by 4. The number 3024 is divisible by 4 because $24 \div 4 = 6$. Numbers which are divisible by 4 are called *multiples of 4*.

(4) A number is divisible by 5 if its last digit is 0 or 5. So 890 and 7345 are both divisible by 5. Numbers which are divisible by 5 are called *multiples of 5*.

(5) A number is divisible by 10 if its last digit is 0. So 80 and 7960 are both divisible by 10. Numbers which are divisible by 10 are called *multiples of 10*.

Example 6

Write down all the multiples of 3 between 13 and 25.

The multiples are 15, 18, 21 and 24 because each of these numbers is divisible by 3.

FACTORS

A number is a *factor* of a second number if it divides into that second number without leaving a remainder.

6 is a factor of 42 because it divides into 42 exactly.

42 is also divisible by 7 and so 7 is also a factor of 42.

42 has other factors, namely 1, 2, 3, 14, 21 and 42 as well as 6 and 7.

1. Which of the following numbers are multiples of 2: 3, 7, 11, 29, 36 and 47?

2. Which of the following numbers are multiples of 3: 6, 8, 12, 26, 30, 33 and 54?

3. Which of the following numbers are multiples of 4: 8, 10, 12, 14, 18, 24, 36 and 44?

4. Which of the following numbers are multiples of 5: 15, 20, 23, 28, 30, 35, 42 and 55?

5. Which of the following numbers are multiples of 10: 15, 20, 60, 90, 95, 120 and 240?

6. Write down all the multiples of 7 between 15 and 36.

7. Write down all the multiples of 9 between 10 and 37.

8. Which of the following numbers are factors of 63: 2, 3, 4, 5, 6, 9 and 21?

9. Which of the following numbers are factors of 72: 1, 2, 3, 4, 5, 6, 7, 8, 9, 10, 11, 12, 13 and 14?

10. Write down all the factors of 20.

PRIME NUMBERS

Every number has itself and 1 as factors. If it has no other factors it is said to be a *prime number*. It is useful to learn all the prime numbers up to 100. They are

2, 3, 5, 7, 11, 13, 17, 19, 23, 29, 31, 37, 41, 43, 47, 53, 59, 61, 67, 71, 73, 79, 83, 89, 97

Note that with the exception of 2 all the prime numbers are odd. Also note that although 1 is a factor of all other numbers it is not regarded as being a prime number.

PRIME FACTORS

A factor which is a prime number is called a *prime factor*. In the statement $42 = 6 \times 7$, 7 is a prime factor but 6 is not because it equals 2×3.

Example 7

Find all the factors of 80.

Note that 1 and 80 are regarded as factors of 80. If we pair off the factors from each end as shown above and multiply them together we get:

$$1 \times 80 = 80 \qquad 2 \times 40 = 80$$
$$4 \times 20 = 80 \qquad 5 \times 16 = 80$$
$$8 \times 10 = 80$$

We see that each pair gives a product of 80. We can always check that we have found all the factors of a number by this method of pairing.

Example 8

Find all the factors of 64.

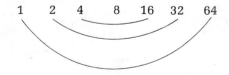

In this case there is an odd number of factors and there is no factor which pairs with 8. If a number is a perfect square (i.e., its square root is a whole number) the odd factor is the square root of the number, in this case $\sqrt{64} = 8$.

Write down all the factors of the following numbers and check by pairing.

1. 36	**3.** 100	**5.** 60	**7.** 70
2. 56	**4.** 84	**6.** 105	**8.** 96

LOWEST COMMON MULTIPLE (LCM)

The multiples of 3 are 3, 6, 9, 12, 15, 18, 21, 24, 27, 30, 33, 36, 39, . . .

The multiples of 4 are 4, 8, 12, 16, 20, 24, 28, 32, 36, 40, . . .

We see that 12, 24 and 36 are multiples of both 3 and 4. The lowest of these multiples is 12 and we say that the LCM of 3 and 4 is 12. We mean that 12 is the lowest number into which 3 and 4 will divide exactly.

Thus the LCM of a set of numbers is the smallest number into which each of the numbers in the set will divide exactly.

The LCM of many sets of numbers can be found by just looking at them but sometimes the method of Example 9(c) has to be used.

Example 9

(a) Find the LCM of 2, 3 and 4.

The LCM of 2, 3 and 4 is 12 because $12 \div 2 = 6$, $12 \div 3 = 4$ and $12 \div 4 = 3$

(b) Find the LCM of 5, 10 and 20.

The LCM of 5, 10 and 20 is 20 because $20 \div 5 = 4$, $20 \div 10 = 2$ and $20 \div 20 = 1$

(c) Find the LCM of 4, 5 and 6.

The prime factors of the three numbers are:

$4 = 1 \times 2^2$, $5 = 1 \times 5$ and $6 = 1 \times 2 \times 3$

The LCM is the product of the highest power of each prime number. Hence

LCM of 4, 5 and $6 = 1 \times 2^2 \times 3 \times 5 = 60$

Find the LCM of the following sets of numbers:

1. 2 and 3	**6.** 6 and 15
2. 4 and 8	**7.** 3, 5 and 6
3. 4 and 5	**8.** 12 and 16
4. 6 and 9	**9.** 3, 5 and 10
5. 2, 3 and 5	**10.** 2, 3, 4 and 9

1. Given the numbers 2, 3, 4, 5, 6, 7, 8 and 9, write down:
   (a) all the even numbers,
   (b) the multiples of 3,
   (c) all the prime numbers.

2. Given the numbers 47, 55, 60, 63, 81 and 122:
   (a) Write down the multiples of 5.
   (b) Find the sum of the multiples of 3.
   (c) One of the numbers has a square root which is a whole number. Write down the square root of this number.

3. Three prime numbers are 11, 13 and 37:
   (a) Add them up. Is the sum a prime number?
   (b) Multiply them together. Is the product a prime number?

4. Consider the numbers 13, 24, 31, 65, 75 and 125.
   (a) Two of these numbers are prime. Which are they?
   (b) Three of the numbers have a common factor. What is it?

5. List the following numbers:
   (a) Multiples of 8 which are less than 48.
   (b) The next three prime numbers greater than 23.

6. Find the LCM of 3, 4, 6 and 9.

7. Find the value of $13^2 - 12^2$.

8. Find the square root of 16×49.

9. Find the value of 7^4.

10. A baker wants to bake a batch of cakes which can be packed either in threes only, in fives only or in tens only. He wants to pack the cakes he bakes into all three types of packet. What is the smallest number of cakes that he needs to bake to do this?

11. What is the difference between the cube of 2 and the square of 3?

12. List all the factors of 120.

MENTAL TEST 2 _____

Try to answer the following questions without writing anything down except the answer.

1. Is 128 an even number?

2. Is 347 divisible by 3?

3. What is the square of 7?

4. Find the value of 2 raised to the power of 4.

5. Is 529 an even number?

6. Find the square root of 64.

7. Find the square root of 36×49.

8. Is the number 425 divisible by 5?

9. Write down all the factors of 24.

10. Write down all the multiples of 4 up to 33.

11. Write down the prime factors of 18.

12. What is the LCM of 2 and 5?

13. Find the sum of all of the prime numbers in the following set of numbers: 3, 6, 8, 9, 11, 15 and 19.

CHAPTER 3

Fractions

INTRODUCTION

In a fraction the top number is called the *numerator* and the bottom number is called the *denominator*. In the fraction $\frac{5}{8}$, 5 is the numerator and 8 is the denominator.

The denominator shows the number of equal parts into which the whole has been divided whilst the numerator tells how many of these equal parts are taken. In the fraction $\frac{9}{11}$, the whole has been divided into 11 equal parts and 9 of these equal parts have been taken.

TYPES OF FRACTION

In a *proper fraction* the top number (the numerator) is less than the bottom number (the denominator). Thus $\frac{3}{7}$ and $\frac{24}{37}$ are both proper fractions.

In an *improper fraction* the top number is larger than the bottom number. Thus $\frac{15}{2}$ and $\frac{29}{7}$ are both improper fractions.

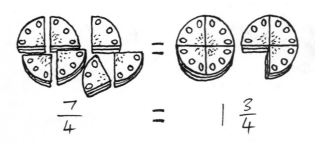

$$\frac{7}{4} = 1\frac{3}{4}$$

A *mixed number* is the sum of a whole number and a proper fraction. Thus $5 + \frac{7}{8}$ (usually written $5\frac{7}{8}$) is a mixed number.

A mixed number can be converted into an improper fraction and vice versa.

Example 1

(a) Convert $8\frac{2}{3}$ into an improper fraction.

$$8\frac{2}{3} = \frac{(8 \times 3) + 2}{3}$$

$$= \frac{26}{3}$$

(b) Express $\frac{27}{4}$ as a mixed number.

$\frac{27}{4} = 6\frac{3}{4}$ (since $27 \div 4 = 6$ remainder 3)

EQUIVALENT FRACTIONS

Two fractions are *equivalent* if they have the same value.

The value of a fraction remains the same if both its numerator and its denominator are multiplied or divided by the same number provided that the number is not zero.

$\frac{5}{8}$ is equivalent to $\dfrac{5 \times 3}{8 \times 3} = \dfrac{15}{24}$

$\frac{12}{18}$ is equivalent to $\dfrac{12 \div 6}{18 \div 6} = \dfrac{2}{3}$

LOWEST TERMS

A fraction is said to be in its *lowest terms* when it is impossible to find a number which will divide exactly into both its numerator and denominator.

The fractions $\frac{5}{7}$ and $\frac{11}{19}$ are both in their lowest terms but the fraction $\frac{6}{10}$ is not in its lowest terms because it can be reduced to $\frac{3}{5}$ by dividing top and bottom numbers by 2.

Example 2

Reduce $\frac{21}{35}$ to its lowest terms.

$\frac{21}{35}$ is equivalent to $\dfrac{21 \div 7}{35 \div 7} = \dfrac{3}{5}$

EXERCISE 3.1

Express each of the following as mixed numbers:

1. $\frac{9}{2}$ 3. $\frac{23}{5}$ 5. $\frac{39}{8}$

2. $\frac{11}{3}$ 4. $\frac{19}{7}$

Express each of the following as improper fractions:

6. $3\frac{1}{4}$ 8. $5\frac{7}{8}$ 10. $5\frac{1}{8}$

7. $2\frac{3}{5}$ 9. $3\frac{7}{20}$

Reduce each of the following fractions to its lowest terms:

11. $\frac{6}{15}$ 13. $\frac{6}{18}$ 15. $\frac{25}{30}$

12. $\frac{15}{20}$ 14. $\frac{18}{30}$

COMPARING THE SIZE OF FRACTIONS

When the values of two or more fractions are to be compared, express each of the fractions with the same denominator. This common denominator should be the LCM of the denominators of the fractions to be compared. It is sometimes called the *lowest common denominator.*

Example 3

Arrange the fractions $\frac{5}{6}$, $\frac{8}{9}$, $\frac{7}{8}$ and $\frac{11}{12}$ in order of size beginning with the smallest.

The LCM of the denominators 6, 8, 9 and 12 is 72, i.e. the lowest common denominator is 72.

$\frac{5}{6}$ is equivalent to $\dfrac{5 \times 12}{6 \times 12} = \dfrac{60}{72}$

$\frac{8}{9}$ is equivalent to $\dfrac{8 \times 8}{9 \times 8} = \dfrac{64}{72}$

$\frac{7}{8}$ is equivalent to $\dfrac{7 \times 9}{8 \times 9} = \dfrac{63}{72}$

$\frac{11}{12}$ is equivalent to $\dfrac{11 \times 6}{12 \times 6} = \dfrac{66}{72}$

Because all the fractions have been expressed with the same denominator all that we have to do is to compare the numerators. Therefore the order of size is

$\frac{60}{72}, \frac{63}{72}, \frac{64}{72}$ and $\frac{66}{72}$ or $\frac{5}{6}, \frac{7}{8}, \frac{8}{9}$ and $\frac{11}{12}$

ADDING AND SUBTRACTING FRACTIONS

Two fractions which have the same denominator can be added together by adding their numerators. Thus

$$\frac{3}{11} + \frac{5}{11} = \frac{3 + 5}{11}$$
$$= \frac{8}{11}$$

When two fractions have different denominators they cannot be added together directly. However, if we express the fractions with the same denominator they can be added.

Example 4

Add $\frac{2}{5}$ and $\frac{3}{7}$.

The lowest common denominator of 5 and 7 is 35.

$\frac{2}{5}$ is equivalent to $\dfrac{2 \times 7}{5 \times 7} = \dfrac{14}{35}$

$\frac{3}{7}$ is equivalent to $\dfrac{3 \times 5}{7 \times 5} = \dfrac{15}{35}$

$$\frac{2}{5} + \frac{3}{7} = \frac{14}{35} + \frac{15}{35}$$

$$= \frac{14 + 15}{35}$$

$$= \frac{29}{35}$$

If desired, the work may be set out as follows:

$$\frac{2}{5} + \frac{3}{7} = \frac{(2 \times 7) + (3 \times 5)}{35}$$

$$= \frac{14 + 15}{35}$$

$$= \frac{29}{35}$$

When mixed numbers are to be added together, the whole numbers and the fractions are added separately.

Example 5

Add $4\frac{2}{3}$ and $2\frac{3}{5}$

$$4\frac{2}{3} + 2\frac{3}{5} = 6 + \frac{2}{3} + \frac{3}{5}$$

$$= 6 + \frac{10}{15} + \frac{9}{15}$$

$$= 6 + \frac{19}{15}$$

$$= 6 + 1\frac{4}{15}$$

$$= 6 + 1 + \frac{4}{15}$$

$$= 7\frac{4}{15}$$

Two fractions which have the same denominator can be subtracted by finding the difference of their numerators.

$$\frac{7}{9} - \frac{2}{9} = \frac{7 - 2}{9}$$

$$= \frac{5}{9}$$

When the fractions to be subtracted do not have the same denominator a method similar to that for addition is used.

Example 6

Subtract $\frac{3}{4}$ from $\frac{5}{6}$.

The lowest common denominator is 12.

$\frac{3}{4}$ is equivalent to $\dfrac{3 \times 3}{12} = \dfrac{9}{12}$

$\frac{5}{6}$ is equivalent to $\dfrac{5 \times 2}{12} = \dfrac{10}{12}$

$$\frac{5}{6} - \frac{3}{4} = \frac{10}{12} - \frac{9}{12}$$

$$= \frac{10 - 9}{12}$$

$$= \frac{1}{12}$$

If desired the work may be set out as follows:

$$\frac{5}{6} - \frac{3}{4} = \frac{(5 \times 2) - (3 \times 3)}{12}$$

$$= \frac{10 - 9}{12}$$

$$= \frac{1}{12}$$

When mixed numbers are involved first subtract the whole numbers and then deal with the fractional parts.

24

Example 7

Subtract $4\frac{1}{3}$ from $6\frac{3}{4}$.

$$6\tfrac{3}{4} - 4\tfrac{1}{3} = 2 + \tfrac{3}{4} - \tfrac{1}{3}$$
$$= 2 + \tfrac{9}{12} - \tfrac{4}{12}$$
$$= 2 + \tfrac{5}{12}$$
$$= 2\tfrac{5}{12}$$

Example 8

Take $3\frac{3}{5}$ from $7\frac{1}{2}$.

$$7\tfrac{1}{2} - 3\tfrac{3}{5} = 4 + \tfrac{1}{2} - \tfrac{3}{5}$$
$$= 4 + \frac{5 - 6}{10}$$
$$= 4 - \tfrac{1}{10}$$
$$= 3 + 1 - \tfrac{1}{10}$$
$$= 3 + \tfrac{9}{10}$$
$$= 3\tfrac{9}{10}$$

EXERCISE 3.2

Arrange the following fractions in order of size beginning with the smallest:

1. $\frac{2}{5}, \frac{3}{7}$ and $\frac{1}{3}$ **3.** $\frac{3}{4}, \frac{11}{16}, \frac{7}{8}$ and $\frac{21}{32}$

2. $\frac{7}{10}, \frac{2}{3}$ and $\frac{3}{4}$ **4.** $\frac{4}{5}, \frac{13}{20}, \frac{7}{10}$ and $\frac{3}{4}$

Add together:

5. $\frac{2}{3} + \frac{1}{5}$ **10.** $2\frac{5}{8} + 3\frac{1}{4}$

6. $\frac{1}{4} + \frac{3}{8}$ **11.** $3\frac{2}{3} + 4\frac{3}{5}$

7. $\frac{5}{8} + \frac{1}{9}$ **12.** $2\frac{3}{8} + 4\frac{2}{7} + 1\frac{3}{4}$

8. $\frac{1}{2} + \frac{2}{3} + \frac{3}{4}$ **13.** $5\frac{1}{2} + 4\frac{1}{3} + 3\frac{1}{5}$

9. $\frac{3}{8} + \frac{2}{5} + \frac{1}{3}$ **14.** $2\frac{5}{8} + 4\frac{1}{4} + \frac{9}{10} + 5\frac{1}{2}$

Subtract the following:

15. $\frac{2}{3} - \frac{1}{4}$ **19.** $5\frac{7}{16} - 3\frac{1}{3}$

16. $\frac{5}{8} - \frac{1}{3}$ **20.** $2\frac{3}{8} - \frac{9}{16}$

17. $\frac{3}{4} - \frac{2}{5}$ **21.** $5\frac{1}{3} - 2\frac{3}{4}$

18. $3\frac{3}{4} - 2\frac{3}{8}$ **22.** $7\frac{2}{5} - 6\frac{5}{8}$

MULTIPLICATION OF FRACTIONS

To multiply fractions first multiply their numerators and then multiply their denominators.

Example 9

Multiply $\frac{3}{8}$ by $\frac{5}{7}$.

$$\frac{3}{8} \times \frac{5}{7} = \frac{3 \times 5}{8 \times 7}$$
$$= \frac{15}{56}$$

If any factors are common to a numerator and a denominator they should be cancelled before multiplying.

Example 10

Find the value of $\frac{2}{3} \times \frac{5}{7} \times \frac{21}{32}$

$$\frac{\overset{1}{2}}{\underset{1}{3}} \times \frac{5}{\underset{1}{7}} \times \frac{\overset{3\,\,1}{21}}{\underset{16}{32}} = \frac{1 \times 5 \times 1}{1 \times 1 \times 16}$$
$$= \frac{5}{16}$$

Mixed numbers must be converted into improper fractions before multiplying.

25

Example 11

Multiply $1\frac{3}{8}$ by $2\frac{1}{3}$.

$$1\frac{3}{8} \times 2\frac{1}{3} = \frac{11}{8} \times \frac{7}{3}$$

$$= \frac{11 \times 7}{3 \times 8}$$

$$= \frac{77}{24}$$

$$= 3\frac{5}{24}$$

In problems with fractions the word 'of' is frequently used. It should always be taken as meaning 'multiply'.

Example 12

Find $\frac{2}{3}$ of $\frac{4}{5}$.

$$\frac{2}{3} \text{ of } \frac{4}{5} = \frac{2}{3} \times \frac{4}{5}$$

$$= \frac{2 \times 4}{3 \times 5}$$

$$= \frac{8}{15}$$

DIVISION OF FRACTIONS

To divide by a fraction, invert it and multiply.

Example 13

Divide $\frac{3}{5}$ by $\frac{7}{8}$.

$$\frac{3}{5} \div \frac{7}{8} = \frac{3}{5} \times \frac{8}{7}$$

$$= \frac{3 \times 8}{5 \times 7}$$

$$= \frac{24}{35}$$

Multiply the following:

1. $\frac{5}{8} \times \frac{4}{7}$ 5. $\frac{2}{5} \times \frac{10}{11} \times \frac{3}{4}$

2. $\frac{1}{4} \times \frac{3}{5}$ 6. $2\frac{1}{4} \times \frac{8}{27} \times \frac{5}{7}$

3. $\frac{5}{9} \times 2\frac{2}{3}$ 7. $3\frac{2}{3} \times 3\frac{3}{5} \times 1\frac{1}{6}$

4. $1\frac{3}{4} \times \frac{5}{8}$ 8. $3\frac{1}{3} \times 4\frac{1}{2} \times 7\frac{1}{5}$

Find the values of:

9. $\frac{2}{3}$ of 27   12. $\frac{1}{2}$ of $\frac{2}{5}$

10. $\frac{3}{5}$ of 120   13. $\frac{2}{3}$ of $\frac{27}{64}$

11. $\frac{3}{4}$ of 16

Divide each of the following:

14. $\frac{5}{6} \div \frac{2}{3}$ 18. $\frac{3}{8} \div 2\frac{1}{4}$

15. $\frac{7}{8} \div \frac{3}{4}$ 19. $1\frac{1}{2} \div 2\frac{1}{4}$

16. $1\frac{1}{8} \div \frac{3}{4}$ 20. $1\frac{2}{3} \div 2\frac{2}{9}$

17. $2\frac{2}{5} \div \frac{3}{10}$

OPERATIONS WITH FRACTIONS

The sequence of operations when dealing with fractions is the same as that used when dealing with whole numbers.

(1) First work out the contents of any brackets.

(2) Multiply and/or divide.

(3) Add and/or subtract.

Example 14

Simplify $(2\frac{1}{2} - 1\frac{1}{3}) \div 1\frac{5}{9}$.

$$(2\frac{1}{2} - 1\frac{1}{3}) \div 1\frac{5}{9} = (\frac{5}{2} - \frac{4}{3}) \div \frac{14}{9}$$

$$= \frac{5 \times 3 - 4 \times 2}{6} \div \frac{14}{9}$$

$$= \frac{7}{6} \div \frac{14}{9}$$

$$= \frac{\cancel{7}^{1}}{\cancel{6}_{2}} \times \frac{\cancel{9}^{3}}{\cancel{14}_{2}}$$

$$= \frac{1 \times 3}{2 \times 2}$$

$$= \frac{3}{4}$$

EXERCISE 3.4

Work out:

1. $\frac{1}{4} \div (1\frac{1}{8} \times \frac{2}{5})$

2. $1\frac{2}{3} \div (\frac{3}{5} \div \frac{9}{10})$

3. $(1\frac{7}{8} \times 2\frac{2}{5}) - 3\frac{2}{3}$

4. $(2\frac{2}{3} + 1\frac{1}{5}) \div 5\frac{4}{5}$

5. $3\frac{2}{3} \div (\frac{2}{3} + \frac{4}{5})$

6. $\frac{2}{5} \times (\frac{2}{3} - \frac{1}{4}) + \frac{1}{2}$

7. $2\frac{8}{9} \div (1\frac{2}{3} + \frac{1}{2})$

8. $(2\frac{1}{2} - 1\frac{3}{8}) \times 1\frac{1}{3}$

PRACTICAL APPLICATIONS OF FRACTIONS

The examples which follow are all of a practical nature. They depend upon fractions for their solution.

Example 15

(a) A girl spends $\frac{3}{4}$ of her pocket money and has 90 p left. How much did she have to start with?

The whole amount of her pocket money is represented by 1, so the amount left is represented by

$$1 - \frac{3}{4} = \frac{1}{4}$$

$\frac{1}{4}$ represents 90 p

1 represents 4×90 p $= 360$ p

The girl had £3.60 to start with.

(b) A group of school children went to a hamburger bar. $\frac{2}{5}$ of them bought hamburgers only, $\frac{1}{4}$ bought chips only, and the remainder bought drinks only.
   (i) What fraction bought food?
   (ii) What fraction bought drinks?

(i) Fraction who bought food

$$= \frac{2}{5} + \frac{1}{4}$$

$$= \frac{8 + 5}{20}$$

$$= \frac{13}{20}$$

(ii) The whole group of school children is a whole unit, i.e. 1. Therefore

Fraction who bought drinks

$$= 1 - \frac{13}{20}$$

$$= \frac{20 - 13}{20}$$

$$= \frac{7}{20}$$

EXERCISE 3.5

1. Calculate $\frac{3}{16}$ of £800.

2. Jane takes $5\frac{3}{4}$ minutes to iron a blouse. How many blouses can she iron in 23 minutes?

3. At a youth club $\frac{2}{5}$ of those present were playing darts and $\frac{1}{4}$ were playing other games.

   (a) What fraction were playing games?
   (b) What fraction were not playing games?

4. A watering can holds $12\frac{1}{2}$ litres. It is filled 11 times from a tank containing 400 litres. How much water is left in the tank?

5. A school has 600 pupils, $\frac{1}{5}$ are in the upper school, $\frac{1}{4}$ in the middle school and the remainder in the lower school. How many pupils are in the lower school?

6. A boy spends $\frac{5}{8}$ of his pocket money and has 60 p left. How much money did he have to start with?

7. During 'bob a job week' a boy scout decided to earn money by cleaning shoes. It takes him $2\frac{1}{2}$ minutes to clean one pair. At one house he was given 12 pairs to clean. How long did it take him to complete the task?

8. The profits of a business are £29 000. It is shared between two partners A and B. If A receives $\frac{9}{20}$ of the profits, how much money does B receive?

POWERS OF FRACTIONS

To raise a fraction to a power we raise both the numerator and the denominator to that power. Thus

$$\left(\tfrac{2}{5}\right)^3 = \frac{2^3}{5^3}$$

$$= \tfrac{8}{125}$$

SQUARE ROOTS OF FRACTIONS

To find the square root of a fraction we find the square roots of the numerator and denominator separately. Thus

$$\sqrt{\frac{16}{81}} = \frac{\sqrt{16}}{\sqrt{81}}$$

$$= \frac{4}{9}$$

EXERCISE 3.6

Find values for each of the following:

1. $\left(\tfrac{1}{2}\right)^4$ **6.** $\left(2\tfrac{2}{5}\right)^2$

2. $\left(\tfrac{3}{4}\right)^2$ **7.** $\left(\tfrac{3}{4}\right)^3$

3. $\left(\tfrac{3}{7}\right)^2$ **8.** $\left(\tfrac{5}{6}\right)^2$

4. $\left(\tfrac{2}{3}\right)^3$ **9.** $2 \times \left(\tfrac{4}{5}\right)^2$

5. $\left(1\tfrac{1}{3}\right)^2$ **10.** $\tfrac{3}{4} \times \left(\tfrac{2}{3}\right)^3$

Find the square roots of the following:

11. $\tfrac{4}{9}$ **15.** $\tfrac{1}{36}$

12. $\tfrac{81}{100}$ **16.** $(25 + 144)$

13. $\tfrac{25}{49}$ **17.** $(169 - 25)$

14. $\tfrac{100}{256}$ **18.** $(25 - 16)$

19. What is the value of $9 \times \sqrt{1\tfrac{7}{9}}$?

20. Work out the value of $2\tfrac{1}{2} \times \sqrt{\tfrac{16}{25}}$.

MISCELLANEOUS EXERCISE 3

1. Consider the fractions $\frac{3}{5}, \frac{3}{4}, \frac{7}{10}$ and $\frac{13}{20}$.

   (a) What fraction is the largest?
   (b) What is the difference between the largest and smallest fractions?
   (c) Calculate the product of $\frac{3}{5}$ and $\frac{3}{4}$.
   (d) Divide $\frac{3}{5}$ by $\frac{13}{20}$.

2. Give the answers to the following in their lowest terms:

    (a) $\frac{3}{5} \times \frac{10}{21}$ (b) $\frac{5}{8} \div 2\frac{3}{4}$

    (c) $\frac{7}{8} - \frac{2}{3}$ (d) $1\frac{1}{3} + 2\frac{3}{4}$

3. Find $\frac{3}{4}$ of $\frac{2}{3}$.

4. Find the next three terms in the sequence $2\frac{1}{4}, 2\frac{5}{8}, 3, \ldots$

5. Find $\frac{5}{8}$ of 32.

6. Write down the next fraction in the sequence $\frac{3}{4}, \frac{9}{16}, \frac{3}{8}, \ldots$

7. Express $\frac{1}{2} - \frac{3}{4} + \frac{5}{8} - \frac{7}{16} + \frac{19}{32}$ as a single fraction.

8. Express as a single fraction $(2\frac{1}{2} + 1\frac{1}{4}) \div 2\frac{1}{2}$.

9. A man left $\frac{3}{8}$ of his money to his wife and half the remainder to his son. If he left £8000, how much did his son receive?

10. Find $\frac{3}{4}$ of $7\frac{1}{3}$.

11. Work out $\dfrac{\frac{1}{4} + \frac{1}{3}}{\frac{1}{2} \times \frac{1}{3}}$.

12. Find $\frac{5}{9}$ of £1350.

13. $\frac{5}{8}$ of a fence has been built. If there is still 40 ft to be built, how long will the fence be?

14. Three people A, B and C share a sum of money. A takes one sixth of it, B takes one-fifth of the remainder and C takes what is left. If the amount of money to be divided is £1200, how much does each person receive?

15. Express as a single fraction in its lowest terms $(3\frac{1}{2} + 2\frac{1}{4}) \div 2\frac{1}{2}$.

16. Next year a woman will receive a rise amounting to one-eighth of her weekly wage. Her weekly wage will then be £180. What is her present weekly wage?

17. A man left three-eighths of his money to his wife and half the remainder to his son. The rest was divided equally between his five daughters. Find what fraction of the money each daughter received.

18. A man sells his car for £1620 and, as a result, loses one-tenth of the price he paid for it. What price did he pay for it?

MENTAL TEST 3

Try to write down the answers to the following without writing anything else.

1. Fill in the missing number in $\frac{2}{3} = \frac{?}{9}$.

2. Reduce $\frac{3}{12}$ to its lowest terms.

3. Change $\frac{5}{4}$ to a mixed number.

4. Change $3\frac{1}{2}$ to an improper fraction.

5. Is $\frac{2}{3}$ larger than $\frac{3}{4}$?

6. Work out the value of $\frac{1}{4} + \frac{1}{2}$.

7. What is the value of $1 - \frac{1}{3}$?

8. What is $\frac{1}{4}$ of 20?

9. What is $6 \times \frac{1}{3}$?

10. What is $3 - \frac{1}{2}$?

29

CHAPTER 4

The Decimal System

PLACE VALUE

The number 4945 means four thousand nine hundred and forty-five. Each figure in the number has a place value because it is so many thousands, hundreds, tens or units according to its place in the number.

Notice that in the number 4945, the first four has a value of 4 thousand, i.e., 4000 whilst the second four has a value of 4 tens, i.e., 40.

The number 4945 means:

$$4 \times 1000 + 9 \times 100 + 4 \times 10 + 5 \times 1$$

Money is usually written in decimal form. For instance £39.03 means thirty-nine pounds and three pence. The dot, called the decimal point, separates the pounds from the pence.

Now £39.03 is an amount of money between £39 and £40.

The 3 pence is a part of a whole pound, that is it is a fraction of a whole pound. Because there are 100 pence in a whole pound then three pence is three-hundredths of a pound.

Pounds		Pence
39	.	03

Now consider the number 39.03. By comparing it with £39.03 we see that it means thirty-nine and three hundredths.

Tens	Units		Tenths	Hundredths
3	9	.	0	3

We see that figures to the left of the decimal point are whole numbers whilst those to the right of the decimal point are fractions of a whole number.

The number 39.03 means

$$3 \times 10 + 9 \times 1 + 3 \times \frac{1}{100}$$

Note that the zero in the first column of the table after the decimal point keeps the place for the missing tenths.

Next consider the number 7.38.

Units		Tenths	Hundredths
7	.	3	8

It means:

$$7 + \frac{3}{10} + \frac{8}{100}$$

We see that:
The first place after the decimal point represents tenths.
The second place after the decimal point represents hundredths.

30

This can be extended to show:

The third place after the decimal point represents thousandths.

The fourth place after the decimal point represents ten-thousandths and so on.

Note carefully that one-tenth is ten times greater than one-hundredth and that one-hundredth is ten times greater than one-thousandth and so on. Each figure in the table below is ten times greater than the figure which follows it.

Units		Tenths	Hundredths	Thousandths
3	.	3	3	3

The number 3.333 means:

$$3 + \frac{3}{10} + \frac{3}{100} + \frac{3}{1000}$$

We can write three-tenths as .3 or $\frac{3}{10}$.

When there are no whole numbers it is usual to put a nought in front of the decimal point so that .3 becomes 0.3.

$\frac{47}{100}$ in decimal form is written 0.47.

Numbers such as 0.3, 8.59 and 736.28 are called *decimal numbers*.

Example 1

(a) Write down the place value of the figure 3 in the number 42.43.

Because the 3 occurs in the second column after the decimal point, its value is three-hundredths.

(b) Find the difference between the actual values of the two sevens in the number 7074.

The first seven has a value of 7000.
The second seven has a value of 70.
The difference between the actual values of the two sevens is $7000 - 70 = 6930$.

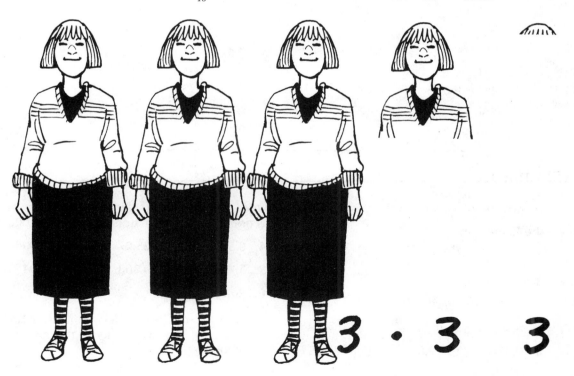

3 · 3 3

WRITING FRACTIONS AS DECIMALS

Example 2

Write the following fractions as decimals:

(a) $\dfrac{4}{10}$ (b) $\dfrac{7}{100}$ (c) $\dfrac{19}{100}$ (d) $\dfrac{9}{1000}$ (e) $\dfrac{29}{1000}$ (f) $\dfrac{287}{1000}$

(g) $5\dfrac{9}{10}$ (h) $8\dfrac{96}{1000}$

Fractional	Units	.	Tenths	Hundredths	Thousandths
(a) $\dfrac{4}{10}$	0	.	4		
(b) $\dfrac{7}{100}$	0	.	0	7	
(c) $\dfrac{19}{100}$	0	.	1	9	
(d) $\dfrac{9}{1000}$	0	.	0	0	9
(e) $\dfrac{29}{1000}$	0	.	0	2	9
(f) $\dfrac{287}{1000}$	0	.	2	8	7
(g) $5\dfrac{9}{10}$	5	.	9		
(h) $8\dfrac{96}{1000}$	8	.	0	9	6

EXERCISE 4.1

Write down the place value of:

1. The figure 7 in
   (a) 21.67   (b) 2.567   (c) 274.34

2. The figure 5 in
   (a) 569.08   (b) 0.058   (c) 19.765

3. The figure 8 in
   (a) 0.378   (b) 2.874   (c) 2834.5

Write the following decimal numbers as fractions with denominators of 10, 100 or 1000:

4. 0.3   7. 25.27   9. 60.009

5. 3.7   8. 0.308   10. 0.004

6. 20.08

11. Find the difference between the actual values of the two eights in the number 8058.

12. Write down the figure which is
    (a) in the tenths place of 4.523,
    (b) in the thousandths place of 189.2365,
    (c) in the hundredths place of 36.782.

13. Write down the following fractions in decimal form:
    (a) $\dfrac{9}{100}$ (b) $\dfrac{273}{1000}$ (c) $\dfrac{45}{100}$

14. Express as fractions in their lowest terms
    (a) 0.4   (b) 0.35   (c) 0.875

ADDING AND SUBTRACTING DECIMALS

When adding or subtracting decimal numbers the decimal points must be placed underneath each other.

It is often helpful to add zeros so that the same number of figures follow the decimal point.

Example 3

(a) Find the sum of 127.35, 28, 0.37 and 19.6.

28.00 is the same as 28 and 19.60 is the same as 19.6.

$$
\begin{array}{r}
127.35 \\
28.00 \\
0.37 \\
19.60+ \\
\hline
175.32 \\
\end{array}
$$

To do the addition add upwards. To check the answer add downwards.

(b) Subtract 38.192 from 93.2.

93.200 is the same as 93.2.

$$
\begin{array}{r}
93.200 \\
38.192- \\
\hline
55.008 \\
\end{array}
$$

The answer can be checked by adding the bottom two lines (38.192 + 55.008).

If the calculation is correct their sum will equal the top line (i.e., 93.2).

MULTIPLICATION OF DECIMAL NUMBERS

To multiply two decimal numbers:

(1) Multiply the two numbers disregarding the decimal point, i.e., treat them as though they were whole numbers.

(2) Next add the number of decimal places (the number of figures that follow the decimal point) in the first number to the number of decimal places in the second number.

(3) Place the decimal point in the answer so that this has the same number of decimal places as the sum found in (2).

Example 4

Find the product of 2.34 and 5.6.

$$
\begin{array}{r}
2.34 \quad \text{two decimal places} \\
\times\ 5.6 \quad \text{one decimal place} \\
\hline
13.104 \quad \text{three decimal places} \\
\end{array}
$$

$2 + 1 = 3$

DIVISION OF DECIMAL NUMBERS

To divide one decimal number by another:

(1) Move the decimal point in the number we want to divide by until it is a whole number.

(2) Compensate for (1) by moving the decimal point in the number to be divided by exactly the same number of places.

Example 5

Divide 0.012 by 0.4.

Because we have to divide by 0.4 we make this into a whole number by moving the decimal point 1 place to the right. The number to be divided is 0.012 and to compensate we move the decimal point in this number one place to the right so that it becomes 0.12.

Therefore

$$0.012 \div 0.4 = 0.12 \div 4$$

$$4 \overline{)0.12}$$
$$0.03$$

Hence $0.012 \div 0.4 = 0.03$.

A division can always be checked by multiplying back.

In Example 5 the check is:

$$0.4 \times 0.03 = 0.012$$

A calculator will usually be used to add, subtract, multiply and divide. However the rules given above are very useful when doing mental arithmetic.

Example 6

Use a calculator to divide 3.62 by 0.25.

Input	Display	
3.62	3.62	
÷	3.62	
0.25	0.25	
=	14.48	(This is the answer)
×	14.48	
0.25	0.25	
=	3.62	(This is the check)

EXERCISE 4.2

Without using a calculator work out each of the following:

1. $2.3 + 5.6$

2. $8.72 + 9.37$

3. $5.6 + 7.4$

4. $4.652 + 9.638 + 15.748$

5. $27.6 - 5.32$

6. $769.078 - 85.981$

7. $0.7 - 0.59$

8. $11.03 - 1.698$

Work out each of the following by using mental arithmetic:

9. 0.4×5

10. 0.3×6

11. 0.5×3

12. 0.04×0.3

13. 0.1×0.1

14. 0.003×0.04

15. 8×0.002

16. $3.6 \div 4$

17. $2.5 \div 5$

18. $4.6 \div 2$

19. $7.2 \div 9$

20. $0.4 \div 0.2$

21. $0.09 \div 0.3$

22. $90 \div 0.03$

23. $0.56 \div 0.008$

24. $8.4 \div 0.7$

25. $4.8 \div 0.08$

Using a calculator work out each of the following:

26. $3.462 + 0.794 + 25.6$

27. $0.689 + 0.088 + 0.007 + 1.362$

34

28. $27.6 - 5.32$

29. $758.085 - 85.983$

30. 509.1×8

31. 58.23×0.46

32. $3.362 \times 0.075 \times 15.16$

33. $33.12 \div 24$

34. $1.0116 \div 0.009$

35. $0.0034 \div 2.5$

MULTIPLYING BY POWERS OF 10

When a number is multiplied by 10^n all the figures are moved n places to the left.

Example 7

(a) Multiply 93.587 by 10
$$93.587 \times 10 = 93.587 \times 10^1$$
$$= 935.87 \text{ (figures moved 1 place to the left)}$$

(b) $93.587 \times 100 = 93.587 \times 10^2$
$$= 9358.7 \text{ (figures moved 2 places to the left)}$$

(c) $93.587 \times 1000 = 93.587 \times 10^3$
$$= 93\,587 \text{ (figures moved 3 places to the left)}$$

DIVIDING BY POWERS OF 10

When a number is divided by 10^n all the figures are moved n places to the right.

Example 8

(a) $18.2 \div 10 = 18.2 \div 10^1$
$$= 1.82 \text{ (figures moved 1 place to the right)}$$

(b) $18.2 \div 100 = 18.2 \div 10^2$
$$= 0.182 \text{ (figures moved 2 places to the right)}$$

(c) $18.2 \div 1000 = 18.2 \div 10^3$
$$= 0.0182 \text{ (figures moved 3 places to the right)}$$

EXERCISE 4.3

This exercise should be done mentally. Multiply each of the following numbers by (a) 10, (b) 100 and (c) 1000:

1. 0.35	4. 98.2345	7. 0.000 58
2. 5.983	5. 8.1624	8. 0.009
3. 0.038	6. 0.046	

Divide each of the following numbers by (a) 10, (b) 100 and (c) 1000:

9. 189	12. 0.03	14. 0.0028
10. 18.13	13. 0.325	15. 5.62
11. 527.31		

DECIMAL PLACES

The number of decimal places in a decimal number is the number of figures which follow the decimal point. Thus 18.36 has two decimal places and 0.0046 has four decimal places.

Example 9

Divide 15.187 by 3.57.

Using an eight digit calculator

$$15.187 \div 3.57 = 4.2540616$$

This is the limit of accuracy of the calculator but it is probably not the correct answer. It is the answer correct to 7 decimal places because this is the number of figures following the decimal point.

For most purposes in arithmetic, numbers can be approximated by stating them correct to so many decimal places (d.p. for short).

To correct a number to so many decimal places, if the first figure to be discarded is 5 or more, the previous figure is increased by 1.

Example 10

(a) 93.7254 = 93.725   correct to 3 d.p.

       = 93.73   correct to 2 d.p.

       = 93.7   correct to 1 d.p.

(b) 0.007 362 = 0.007 36   correct to 5 d.p.

       = 0.0074   correct to 4 d.p.

       = 0.01   correct to 2 d.p.

(c) 7.601 = 7.60   correct to 2 d.p.

       = 7.6   correct to 1 d.p.

Note carefully how zeros must be kept to show the position of the decimal point or to indicate that it is one of the decimal places as shown in Example 10(c).

SIGNIFICANT FIGURES

A second way of approximating a number is to use significant figures. In the number 2179, the figure 2 is the most significant because it has the greatest value. The figure 1 is the next significant figure whilst 9 is the least significant figure because it has the least value. The rules regarding significant figures (s.f. for short) are as follows:

(1) If the first figure to be discarded is 5 or more, the previous figure is increased by 1.

7.192 53 = 7.1925   correct to 5 s.f.

       = 7.193   correct to 4 s.f.

       = 7.19   correct to 3 s.f.

       = 7.2   correct to 2 s.f.

(2) Zeros must be kept to show the position of the decimal point or to indicate that zero is a significant figure.

35 291 = 35 290   correct to 4 s.f.

       = 35 300   correct to 3 s.f.

       = 35 000   correct to 2 s.f.

       = 40 000   correct to 1 s.f.

0.0739 = 0.074   correct to 2 s.f.

       = 0.07   correct to 1 s.f.

18.403 = 18.40   correct to 4 s.f.

       = 18.4   correct to 3 s.f.

NECESSARY AND UNNECESSARY ZEROS

A possible source of confusion is deciding which zeros are necessary and which are not.

(1) Zeros are not needed after the last non-zero figure in a number unless it is a significant figure.

$$6.3000 = 6.3$$
$$4.70 = 4.7$$
$$7.364\,50 = 7.3645$$

The number half-way between 5.4 and 5.8 is 5.6. The number half-way between 5.9 and 6.1 is 6.0.

In this case the zero is a significant figure and should be kept.

(2) Zeros are needed to keep the place for any missing hundreds, tens, units, tenths, hundredths, thousandths, etc. In the following numbers the zeros are needed:

70; 7.205; 0.004; 9.005; 5000

(3) One zero is usually written before the decimal point if the number has no whole numbers but this is not essential. Thus

.837 is usually written 0.837
.058 is usually written 0.058

(4) Sometimes zeros are written in front of whole numbers. For instance the early pages of a document are often written 001, 002, 003, ... 036, 037, ... whilst James Bond is also known as 007.

CORRECTING ANSWERS

The answer to a calculation should not have more significant figures than the least number of significant figures used amongst the given numbers.

Example 11

Work out the product of 1.384, 7.23 and 1.246.

The least number of significant figures amongst the given numbers is three (for the number 7.23).

Hence the answer should only be stated correct to 3 s.f.

Using a calculator:

$$1.384 \times 7.23 \times 1.246 = 12.467\,874$$
$$= 12.5 \text{ correct to 3 s.f.}$$

EXERCISE 4.4

Write down the following numbers correct to the number of decimal places stated:

1. 19.372
   (a) 2 d.p.   (b) 1 d.p.

2. 0.007 519
   (a) 5 d.p.   (b) 3 d.p.   (c) 2 d.p.

3. 4.9703
   (a) 3 d.p.   (b) 2 d.p.

4. 153.2617
   (a) 3 d.p.   (b) 2 d.p.   (c) 1 d.p.

Use a calculator to work out:

5. 18.89 + 14.2 correct to 1 d.p.

6. 0.0396 ÷ 2.51 correct to 3 d.p.

7. 7.217 × 3.26 correct to 2 d.p.

8. (184.3 × 0.000 116) ÷ (11.49 × 0.7362) correct to 4 d.p.

Write down each of the following numbers correct to the number of significant figures stated:

9. 24.935
   (a) 4 s.f.   (b) 2 s.f.

10. 0.007 326
    (a) 3 s.f.   (b) 2 s.f.   (c) 1 s.f.

11. 35.604

    (a) 4 s.f.   (b) 3 s.f.

12. 35 681

    (a) 4 s.f.   (b) 3 s.f.   (c) 2 s.f.

13. 13 359 285

    (a) 4 s.f.   (b) 3 s.f.   (c) 2 s.f.

14. Write down the following numbers without unnecessary zeros:

    (a) 48.90   (b) 4.000   (c) 0.5000
    (d) 600.00   (e) 0.007 30   (f) 108.070

Each number in the following is correct to the number of significant figures shown. Use a calculator to work out the answers to the correct number of significant figures.

15. 5.64×19.75

16. $14.6 \times 5.73 \times 2.68$

17. $13.96 \div 0.42$

18. $43.5 \times 0.87 \times 1.23$

19. $(15.76 \times 8.3) \div 9.725$

20. $(11.29 \times 3.2734) \div (77.23 \times 0.0068)$

ESTIMATION

Estimation is used to ensure that the answer to a calculation is sensible particularly if it has been produced by a calculator, see Rounding Numbers (p. 3).

In estimating an answer either rounding or significant figures may be used. Whatever method is used, try to choose numbers which are easy to add, subtract and multiply. If division is needed try to select numbers which will cancel or divide out exactly.

Example 12

(a) Multiply 32.7 by 0.259

For a rough estimate we will take

$$32 \times 0.25 = 32 \div 4 = 8$$

The accurate calculation gives:

$$32.7 \times 0.259 = 8.47 \text{ (correct to 3 s.f.)}$$

The rough estimate shows that the answer is sensible.

(b) Find the sum of 5.32, 0.925 and 17.81.

For a rough estimate we will take

$$5 + 1 + 18 = 24$$

The accurate calculation gives:

$$5.32 + 0.925 + 17.81 = 24.055$$

Again, the rough estimate shows that the answer produced is sensible.

(c) Work out $(47.5 \times 36.52) \div (11.3 \times 2.75)$

For a rough estimate we will take

$$\frac{50 \times 36}{10 \times 3} = 60$$

The accurate calculation gives:

$$\frac{47.5 \times 36.52}{11.3 \times 2.75} = 55.8$$

The rough estimate shows that the answer produced by the calculator is not wildly out.

EXERCISE 4.5

Make a rough estimate for each of the following and then, using a calculator, work out the answer correct to the required number of significant figures.

1. $18.25 + 39.3 + 429.8$

2. $76.815 - 57.23 - 9.63$

3. 22×0.57

4. 41.35×0.26

5. $0.732 \times 0.098 \times 2.17$

6. $92.17 \div 31.45$

7. $0.092 \div 0.035$

8. $(27.18 \times 29.19) \div 0.0532$

9. $(1.456 \times 0.0125) \div 0.0532$

10. $(29.92 \times 31.32) \div (10.89 \times 2.95)$

CONVERTING FRACTIONS INTO DECIMALS

The line separating the numerator and denominator of a fraction acts as a division sign. So

$$\tfrac{1}{4} \text{ is equivalent to } 1 \div 4$$

$$\tfrac{7}{8} \text{ is equivalent to } 7 \div 8$$

Example 13

(a) Convert $\tfrac{7}{8}$ into a decimal number.

$$\tfrac{7}{8} = 7 \div 8 = 0.875$$

(b) Convert $2\tfrac{9}{16}$ into a decimal number.

With mixed numbers we need only convert the fractional part to a decimal number. So

$$2\tfrac{9}{16} = 2 + \tfrac{9}{16}$$
$$= 2 + (9 \div 16)$$
$$= 2 + 0.5625$$
$$= 2.5625$$

RECURRING DECIMALS

Converting $\tfrac{3}{4}$ into a decimal number:

$$3 \div 4 = 0.75 \text{ exactly}$$

Converting $\tfrac{2}{3}$ into a decimal number by using a calculator gives:

$$2 \div 3 = 0.666\,666\,66$$

We see that we will continue to obtain sixes for evermore and we say that the 6 recurs.

Now converting $\tfrac{7}{11}$ to a decimal number

$$7 \div 11 = 0.636\,363\,63$$

we see that the 63 recurs.

Sometimes it is one figure which recurs and sometimes it is a group of figures. If one figure or a group of figures recurs we are said to have a *recurring decimal.*

To save writing so many figures the dot notation shown below is used:

$\tfrac{1}{3} = 1 \div 3 = 0.\dot{3}$ (meaning $0.333\,333\ldots$)

$\tfrac{1}{6} = 1 \div 6 = 0.1\dot{6}$ (meaning $0.166\,666\ldots$)

When two figures have dots over them the meaning is as follows:

$$0.3\dot{1}\dot{8} = 0.318\,181\ldots$$

$$0.4\dot{1}2\dot{7} = 0.412\,712\,712\ldots$$

For all practical purposes we do not need recurring decimals. What we need is a decimal number stated to so many decimal places or significant figures. Thus

$$\tfrac{2}{3} = 0.67 \text{ (correct to 2 s.f.)}$$

$$\tfrac{7}{11} = 0.636 \text{ (correct to 3 d.p.)}$$

CONVERTING DECIMALS INTO FRACTIONS

It will be recalled that decimals are fractions with denominators of 10, 100, 1000, etc. Thus

$$0.53 = \frac{53}{100}$$

$$0.625 = \frac{625}{1000} = \frac{5}{8}$$

Example 14

Subtract $2\frac{5}{16}$ from 2.3214.

$$2\frac{5}{16} = 2.3125$$

$$2.3214 - 2.3125 = 0.0089$$

EXERCISE 4.6 _____

1. Using a calculator convert the following fractions into decimal numbers:

   (a) $\frac{1}{4}$ (b) $\frac{7}{8}$

   (c) $2\frac{19}{32}$ (d) $3\frac{15}{64}$

2. Write the following recurring decimals correct to (i) 5 decimal places, (ii) correct to 6 significant figures:

   (a) $0.\dot{5}$ (b) $0.\dot{1}\dot{7}$ (c) $0.3\dot{5}$

   (d) $0.\dot{2}\dot{1}$ (e) $0.\dot{4}2\dot{8}$ (f) $0.5\dot{6}\dot{3}$

   (g) $0.56\dot{7}\dot{1}$ (h) $0.0\dot{3}\dot{2}$

3. Convert each of the following fractions to a recurring decimal:

   (a) $\frac{2}{9}$ (b) $\frac{5}{11}$ (c) $\frac{7}{15}$ (d) $\frac{9}{22}$

4. Convert the following decimal numbers into fractions in their lowest terms:

   (a) 0.3   (b) 0.65   (c) 0.375

   (d) 0.4375   (e) 1.75   (f) 7.36

5. Work out $\frac{3}{16} - 0.17$

6. What is 6.627 minus $5\frac{3}{8}$?

7. Find the sum of $2\frac{13}{16}$ and 1.782.

8. Find the difference between $\frac{43}{64}$ and 0.395.

RECIPROCALS

The reciprocal of a number is $\dfrac{1}{\text{number}}$.

So the reciprocal of 5 is $\frac{1}{5} = 0.2$

and the reciprocal of 8 is $\frac{1}{8} = 0.125$

Example 15

(a) The reciprocal of $0.362 = 1 \div 0.362$

$$= 2.762$$

(b) The reciprocal of $956.3 = 1 \div 956.3$

$$= 0.001\,05$$

Most calculators have a reciprocal key but if yours does not, a reciprocal can be found by dividing 1 by the number whose reciprocal we wish to find.

Example 16

Find, by using a calculator the value of

$$\frac{1}{9.6} + \frac{1}{8.7} \text{ correct to 4 s.f.}$$

To do this calculation we need to use the memory keys M+ and MR.

Input	Display
1	1.
÷	1.
9.6	9.6
M+	0.1041 . . .
1	1.
÷	1.
8.7	8.7
M+	0.1149 . . .
MR	0.2191 . . .

Therefore

$$\frac{1}{9.6} + \frac{1}{8.7} = 0.2191$$

EXERCISE 4.7

Using a calculator find the reciprocals of each of the following correct to 4 significant figures.

1. 8.19
2. 9.239
3. 89.2
4. 7149
5. 0.1537
6. 0.039 47
7. 0.001 56
8. 16 312
9. 0.1673

Work out the values of the following correct to 4 s.f.

10. $\dfrac{1}{15.28^2}$

11. $\dfrac{1}{0.1372^2}$

12. $\dfrac{1}{18.73}$

13. $\dfrac{1}{0.017\,98}$

14. $\dfrac{1}{8.2} + \dfrac{1}{9.9}$

15. $\dfrac{1}{0.7325} + \dfrac{1}{0.9817}$

PROBLEMS INVOLVING DECIMALS

The examples which follow are all of a practical nature. They all depend upon decimals for their solution.

Example 17

(a) A train consists of 35 trucks. 18 of them carry 15.4 tonnes each and the remainder carry 13.6 tonnes each. What is the total weight carried by the train?

Weight carried by 18 trucks

$$= (18 \times 15.4) \text{ tonnes}$$

$$= 277.2 \text{ tonnes}$$

Weight carried by remaining 17 trucks

$$= (17 \times 13.6) \text{ tonnes}$$

$$= 231.2 \text{ tonnes}$$

Total weight carried by the train

$$= (277.2 + 231.2) \text{ tonnes}$$

$$= 508.4 \text{ tonnes}$$

This problem may be solved by using a calculator as follows:

Input	Display
18	18.
X	18.
15.4	15.4
M+	277.2
17	17.
X	17.
13.6	13.6
M+	231.2
MR	508.4

(b) Flour is packed in bags of 2.27 kilograms capacity. Find the amount of flour needed to fill 432 (3 gross) bags.

Amount needed $= (432 \times 2.27)$ kilograms

$$= 980.64 \text{ kilograms}$$

EXERCISE 4.8

1. A lorry weighs 2.7 tonnes when empty. It is loaded with 52 steel bars each weighing 0.038 tonnes. What is the total weight of the loaded lorry?

2. A herd of 34 cows yields 622.2 litres of milk on a certain morning. How much milk, on average, does each cow yield?

3. A car travels 76.5 kilometres on 6 litres of petrol. How far does it travel per litre of petrol?

4. A consignment of pills weighs 1410 grams. If each pill has a weight of 0.6 grams, how many pills are there in the consignment?

5. A lady has £21.36 in her bank account. On separate occasions she deposits £87.53 and £39.84. On a third visit she withdraws £109.35. How much money is left in her account?

41

6. Find the total weight of 50 boxes if 29 of them weigh 18.4 kilograms each and the remainder weigh 21.3 kilograms each.

7. An operator in a factory takes 0.83 minutes to make a soldered joint. How long will it take the operator to make 348 such joints.

8. A drum contains 510 kilograms of a certain chemical. How many packets each weighing 0.15 kilograms can be obtained from the drum?

9. An oil tank contains 1750 litres. How many tins each containing 0.6 litres can be filled from the tank?

10. Jane takes 5.75 minutes to iron a blouse. How long will it take her to iron 32 blouses?

MISCELLANEOUS EXERCISE 4

1. An eight-digit calculator gives the value of $\sqrt{11}$ as 3.3166248. Write down the value of $\sqrt{11}$ correct to:
   (a) 3 decimal places,
   (b) 3 significant figures.

2. Express as fractions in their lowest terms
   (a) 0.88   (b) 0.026.

3. (a) Write down $0.1\dot{7}$ correct to 4 d.p.
   (b) Write down $0.\dot{2}1\dot{5}$ correct to 5 s.f.

4. (a) Reduce $\frac{20}{24}$ to its lowest terms.
   (b) Convert this fraction to a decimal number correct to 3 s.f.

5. By rounding off the numbers to the nearest number of tens obtain the best estimate for:
$$\frac{27.5 \times 60.52}{11.3 \times 20.51}$$

6. Find the difference between $3\frac{7}{20}$ and 3.37.

7. What is the sum of 3.98, 0.745 and 52.7?

8. Find the exact value of $\dfrac{45}{0.09} + \dfrac{6.6}{0.55}$.

9. Express $27 \div 81$ as
   (a) a fraction in its lowest terms,
   (b) a decimal number correct to 3 d.p.

10. Find the square root of 86.32 correct to 4 s.f.

MENTAL TEST 4

Try to answer the following questions without writing anything down except the answer.

1. Add 1.3 and 2.7.

2. What is the sum of 0.2 and 0.05?

3. Subtract 0.7 from 1.2.

4. Multiply 2.1 by 5.

5. Find the product of 0.2 and 0.3.

6. Read off the number 0.6 as a fraction in its lowest terms.

7. Read off $\frac{53}{100}$ as a decimal number.

8. Which number has the greatest value: 0.6 or 0.008?

9. Multiply 0.93 by 10.

10. Find the product of 0.457×1000.

11. Divide 47.38 by 100.

12. Write the number 5.687 correct to 2 decimal places.

13. Write the number 38.685 correct to 3 significant figures.

14. Write the number 27.503 correct to 4 significant figures.

15. Round off the number 49.783 to the nearest tenth.

43

CHAPTER 5

Measurement

MEASUREMENT OF LENGTH

In the metric system the standard unit of length is the metre (abbreviation: m). For some purposes the metre is too large a unit and so it is split up into smaller units as follows:

$$1 \text{ metre (m)} = 10 \text{ decimetres (dm)}$$
$$= 100 \text{ centimetres (cm)}$$
$$= 1000 \text{ millimetres (mm)}$$

In dealing with long distances the kilometre is used.

$$1 \text{ kilometre (km)} = 1000 \text{ metres (m)}$$

Because the metric system is essentially a decimal system it is easy to convert from one unit to another by multiplying or dividing by 10, 100 and 1000. The decimetre is rarely used but the other units are frequently used.

Example 1

(a) Convert 15 m into millimetres.

$$15 \text{ m} = (15 \times 1000) \text{ mm} = 15\,000 \text{ mm}$$

(b) Change 900 cm into metres.

$$900 \text{ cm} = (900 \div 100) \text{ m} = 9 \text{ m}$$

(c) Change 850 mm into centimetres.

$$850 \text{ mm} = (850 \div 10) \text{ cm} = 85 \text{ cm}$$

(d) Change 72 000 m into kilometres.

$$72\,000 \text{ m} = (72\,000 \div 1000) \text{ km} = 72 \text{ km}$$

EXERCISE 5.1

This exercise should be done mentally.

1. Change to millimetres:
   (a) 3 cm (b) 28 cm (c) 134 cm
   (d) 5 m (e) 63 m (f) 4.6 m

2. Change to centimetres:
   (a) 60 mm (b) 240 mm (c) 720 mm
   (d) 4 m (e) 56 m (f) 3.74 m

3. Change to metres:
   (a) 5000 mm (b) 700 cm
   (c) 890 cm (d) 5643 mm
   (e) 5 km (f) 6.42 km

4. Change to kilometres:
   (a) 7000 m (b) 6340 m (c) 8325 m

In the imperial system small lengths are measured in inches whilst longer lengths are measured in feet and yards. Very long lengths are measured in miles.

$$12 \text{ inches (in)} = 1 \text{ foot (ft)}$$
$$3 \text{ feet (ft)} = 1 \text{ yard (yd)}$$
$$1760 \text{ yards (yd)} = 1 \text{ mile}$$

44

Example 2

(a) Change 48 in into feet.

$$48 \text{ in} = (48 \div 12) \text{ ft} = 4 \text{ ft}$$

(b) Change 24 ft into yards.

$$24 \text{ ft} = (24 \div 3) \text{ yd} = 8 \text{ yd}$$

(c) Change 12 320 yd into miles.

$$12\,320 \text{ yd} = (12\,320 \div 1760) \text{ miles} = 7 \text{ miles}$$

Example 3

(a) Change 8000 g into kilograms.

$$8000 \text{ g} = (8000 \div 1000) \text{ kg} = 8 \text{ kg}$$

(b) Change 5 kg into grams.

$$5 \text{ kg} = (5 \times 1000) \text{ g} = 5000 \text{ g}$$

(c) Change 18 000 mg into grams.

$$18\,000 \text{ mg} = (18\,000 \div 1000) \text{ g} = 18 \text{ g}$$

EXERCISE 5.2 _____

Use a calculator for this exercise.

1. Change to feet:
   (a) 24 in   (b) 60 in   (c) 144 in
   (d) 5 yd   (e) 80 yd

2. Change to yards:
   (a) 6 ft   (b) 72 ft   (c) 900 ft
   (d) 2 miles   (e) 28 miles

3. Change to inches:
   (a) 5 ft   (b) 20 ft   (c) 34 ft
   (d) 3 yd   (e) 15 yd

4. Change to miles:
   (a) 5280 yd   (b) 15 840 yd
   (c) 35 200 yd

EXERCISE 5.3 _____

This exercise should be done mentally.

1. Change to grams:
   (a) 8 kg   (b) 19 kg   (c) 15 kg
   (d) 12 000 mg   (e) 27 000 mg

2. Change to kilograms:
   (a) 5000 g   (b) 18 000 g
   (c) 3 t   (d) 18 t

3. Change to milligrams:
   (a) 7 g   (b) 24 g   (c) 0.5 g

4. Change to tonnes:
   (a) 8000 kg   (b) 427 000 kg
   (c) 600 kg

WEIGHT

In the metric system, light objects are weighed in milligrams or grams. Heavier objects are weighed in kilograms but very heavy objects are weighed in tonnes.

$$1 \text{ gram (g)} = 1000 \text{ milligrams (mg)}$$

$$1 \text{ kilogram (kg)} = 1000 \text{ grams (g)}$$

$$1 \text{ tonne (t)} = 1000 \text{ kilograms (kg)}$$

In the imperial system light objects are weighed in ounces. Heavier objects are measured in pounds whilst very heavy objects are measured in hundredweights or tons.

$$16 \text{ ounces (oz)} = 1 \text{ pound (lb)}$$

$$112 \text{ pounds} = 1 \text{ hundredweight (cwt)}$$

$$1 \text{ ton} = 20 \text{ hundredweight (cwt)}$$
$$= 2240 \text{ lb}$$

Example 4

(a) How many ounces are there in 2 lb?

$$2 \text{ lb} = (2 \times 16) \text{ oz} = 32 \text{ oz}$$

(b) Change 386 oz to pounds

$$368 \text{ oz} = (368 \div 16) \text{ lb} = 23 \text{ lb}$$

(c) Change 672 lb into hundredweight.

$$672 \text{ lb} = (672 \div 112) \text{ cwt} = 6 \text{ cwt}$$

(d) How many pounds are there in 4 tons?

$$4 \text{ tons} = (4 \times 2240) \text{ lb} = 8960 \text{ lb}$$

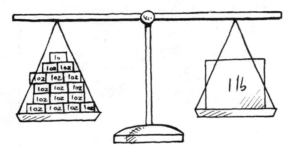

EXERCISE 5.4

A calculator should be used for this exercise.

1. Change to ounces:
   (a) $\frac{1}{4}$ lb   (b) $\frac{1}{2}$ lb   (c) $4\frac{1}{2}$ lb
   (d) 5 lb   (e) 8 lb

2. Change to pounds:
   (a) 12 oz   (b) 48 oz   (c) 8 oz
   (d) 96 oz   (e) 5 cwt   (f) 3 tons

3. Change to hundredweight:
   (a) 5 tons   (b) 8 tons   (c) 560 lb

4. Change to tons:
   (a) 60 cwt   (b) 6720 lb   (c) 17 092 lb

CAPACITY

Fluids of various kinds are usually stored in tins, bottles or tanks. The amount of fluid that a container will hold is called its capacity. In the metric system capacities are measured in millilitres, centilitres and litres.

$$\begin{aligned} 1 \text{ litre (l)} &= 100 \text{ centilitres (cl)} \\ &= 1000 \text{ millilitres (ml)} \end{aligned}$$

Example 5

(a) How many centilitres are there in 4 litres?

$$4 \text{ l} = (4 \times 100) \text{ cl} = 400 \text{ cl}$$

(b) Change 23 000 ml into litres.

$$23\,000 \text{ ml} = (23\,000 \div 1000) \text{ l} = 23 \text{ l}$$

In the imperial system capacities are measured in fluid ounces, pints and gallons.

$$\begin{aligned} 20 \text{ fluid ounces (fl oz)} &= 1 \text{ pint (pt)} \\ 8 \text{ pints (pt)} &= 1 \text{ gallon (gal)} \end{aligned}$$

Example 6

(a) How many pints are there in 5 gal?

$$5 \text{ gal} = (5 \times 8) \text{ pt} = 40 \text{ pt}$$

(b) How many fluid ounces are there in 3 pt?

$$3 \text{ pt} = (3 \times 20) \text{ fl oz} = 60 \text{ fl oz}$$

EXERCISE 5.5

This exercise should be done mentally.

1. Change to centilitres:
   (a) 70 ml   (b) 560 ml   (c) 6 l

2. Change to millilitres:
   (a) 5 cl   (b) 26 cl   (c) 8 l

3. Change to litres:

    (a) 600 cl   **(b)** 50 cl   **(c)** 3000 ml

4. Change to fluid ounces:

    (a) 3 pt   **(b)** $\frac{1}{2}$ pt   **(c)** 2 gal

5. Change to pints:

    (a) 40 fl oz **(b)** 120 fl oz **(c)** 6 gal

6. Change to gallons:

    (a) 16 pt   **(b)** 64 pt

CONVERSION OF METRIC AND IMPERIAL UNITS

Approximate imperial/metric conversions are:

1 inch is slightly more than $2\frac{1}{2}$ cm
(i.e., 2 in is about 5 cm)

1 foot is about 30 cm

1 yard is slightly less than 1 metre

1 kilometre is about $\frac{5}{8}$ mile
(i.e., 5 miles is about 8 km)

1 kilogram is about $2\frac{1}{4}$ lb
(i.e., 4 kg is about 9 lb)

1 fluid ounce is about 30 ml

1 litre is about $1\frac{3}{4}$ pt
(i.e., 4 litres is about 7 pints)

1 gallon is about $4\frac{1}{2}$ litres
(i.e., 2 gallons is about 9 litres)

Example 7

(a) Find in pounds the approximate weight of 20 kg of potatoes.

$$20 \text{ kg} = (20 \times 2\tfrac{1}{4}) \text{ lb} = (20 \times \tfrac{9}{4}) \text{ lb}$$
$$= 45 \text{ lb approx.}$$

(b) The distance between Calais and Lille is 96 km. How many miles is this?

$$96 \text{ km} = (96 \times \tfrac{5}{8}) \text{ miles} = 60 \text{ miles approx.}$$

EXERCISE 5.6

Use the approximate conversions given above to answer the following questions.

  1. Convert 64 kg into pounds.

  2. Convert 5 ft into centimetres.

  3. Change 90 cm into feet.

  4. How many yards are approximately equivalent to 200 m?

  5. Change 18 lb into kilograms.

  6. In Great Britain the speed limit on motorways is 70 miles per hour. How many kilometres per hour is this?

  7. How many millilitres are there in 5 fluid ounces?

  8. Convert 21 pints into litres.

  9. Change 12 litres into pints.

10. How many gallons are equivalent to 27 litres?

THE ARITHMETIC OF METRIC QUANTITIES

Metric quantities are added, subtracted, multiplied and divided in the same way as decimal numbers. It is important that all the quantities used are in the same units. For instance we cannot add millimetres and centimetres directly but if we change the millimetres to centimetres then we can add the two quantities.

47

Example 8

(a) Add 15.2 m, 39 cm and 140 mm giving the answer in metres.

$$\begin{array}{r} 15.2 \text{ m} \\ 39 \text{ cm} = 0.39 \text{ m} \\ 140 \text{ mm} = 0.14 \text{ m} + \\ \hline 15.73 \text{ m} \\ \hline \end{array}$$

(b) A bottle contains 3 litres of water. 90 centilitres are poured out of the bottle. How much water remains?

$$\begin{array}{r} 3.00 \text{ l} \\ 90 \text{ cl} = 0.90 \text{ l} - \\ \hline 2.10 \text{ l} \\ \hline \end{array}$$

2.10 litres of water remain in the bottle.

(c) 57 lengths of wood each 95 cm long are needed by a builder. Assuming no waste in cutting the wood, calculate, in metres, the total length of wood needed.

Total length needed $= (57 \times 95)$ cm

$= (57 \times 0.95)$ m

$= 54.15$ m

(d) Frozen peas are packed in bags containing 450 grams. How many full bags can be filled from 2 tonnes of peas?

2 tonnes $= 2000$ kg $= 2\,000\,000$ g

Number of bags filled $= 2\,000\,000 \div 450$

$= 4444$

EXERCISE 5.7

A calculator should be used for this exercise.

1. Add 50 cm, 5.8 m and 400 mm giving your answer in metres.

2. Subtract 80 mm from 27 cm giving the answer in centimetres.

3. A reel contains 24 metres of ribbon. Lengths of 30 cm and 700 mm are cut from it. What length, in metres, of ribbon remains?

4. A bottle contains 75 centilitres of medicine. How many 5 millilitre doses can be obtained from it?

5. A bottle of lemonade contains 2 litres. 15 centilitres are poured from the bottle. How much lemonade, in litres, remains?

6. 95 lengths of steel bar each 127 mm long are required by a toy manufacturer. Work out, in metres, the total length of steel bar needed.

7. 209 lengths of cloth each 135 cm long are required by a clothing manufacturer. What total length of cloth, in metres, is required?

8. Garlic salt is packed in jars containing 32 g. How many jars can be filled from 15 kg of garlic salt?

9. How many lengths of string 50 cm long can be cut from a ball containing 3.5 metres?

10. A tablet has a weight of 40 milligrams. How many of these tablets make up a weight of 60 grams?

MISCELLANEOUS EXERCISE 5

1. Express each of the following in metres:
   (a) 4 km
   (b) 3 km 56 m
   (c) 893 cm
   (d) 28 400 mm

2. How many 5 millilitre doses can be obtained from a bottle of medicine containing 2 litres?

3. How many lengths of tape each 75 cm long can be cut from a reel 15 m long?

4. Express 55 cm as a fraction of 2 m. State the fraction in its lowest terms.

5. Put in order of size, smallest first, 90 g, 0.9 kg, 90 mg and 0.9 g.

6. Four packets have weights of 4 kg, 800 g, 3.06 kg and 4500 mg. Work out the total weight of these four packets giving the answer in grams.

7. What is the difference, in grams, between 2 kg and 2900 g?

8. The distance between Tours and Limoges (in France) is 192 km. If 1 km $= \frac{5}{8}$ mile, what is this distance in miles?

MENTAL TEST 5

Try to answer the following questions without writing anything down except the answer. Convert each of the following:

1. 4 m into centimetres.

2. 7 m into millimetres.

3. 8000 m into kilometres.

4. 7.3 km into metres.

5. 20 mm into centimetres.

6. 9 cm into millimetres.

7. 48 inches into feet.

8. 1 mile into feet.

9. 72 inches into yards.

10. 8000 g into kilograms.

11. 6 kg into grams.

12. 7000 mg into grams.

13. 6.5 g into milligrams.

14. 3 lb into ounces.

15. 2 cwt into pounds.

16. 40 fl oz into pints.

17. 4 litres into centilitres.

18. 3 litres into millilitres.

19. 800 centilitres into litres.

20. 5 centilitres into millilitres.

21. Add 400 cm and 6 m giving the answer in metres.

22. Add 6 cm and 40 mm giving the answer in millimetres.

23. Subtract 40 cm from 3 m giving the answer in metres.

24. How many 5 millilitre doses can be obtained from 1 litre of liquid?

25. If 1 fluid ounce = 30 millilitres, calculate the number of fluid ounces in 60 millilitres.

CHAPTER 6

Money

THE BRITISH SYSTEM

The British system of currency uses the pound sterling as the basic unit. The only sub-unit used is pence.

$$100 \text{ pence (p)} = £1$$

A decimal point (or sometimes a dash) is used to separate the pounds and the pence. For instance £3.58 or £3-58 means three pounds and fifty-eight pence.

There are two ways of writing amounts less than £1. For instance 74 pence can be written 74 p or £0.74. 5 pence may be written as 5 p or as £0.05.

The addition, subtraction, multiplication and division of sums of money are performed in exactly the same way as for decimal numbers.

Example 1

(a) Add £7.84, £3.48 and 87 p.

When amounts are given in pence it is best to convert these to pounds before attempting to add.

$$
\begin{array}{r}
£7.84 \\
3.48 \\
0.87+ \\
\hline
12.19 \\
\hline
\end{array}
$$

(b) A man buys groceries which cost £8.53. How much change should he get from a £10 note?

Amount of change $= £10.00 − £8.53 = £1.47$

(c) Find the cost of 42 articles if each costs 93 p.

Since 93 p $= £0.93$

Cost of 42 articles $= 42 × £0.93 = £39.06$

(d) If 37 similar articles cost £34.78, how much does each article cost?

Cost of each article $= £34.78 ÷ 37 = £0.94$

EXERCISE 6.1

1. Add £12.63, £2.98 and £5.61.

2. Add £7.36, £1.68 and 76 p.

3. Add 28 p, 96 p, 73 p and £2.36.

4. Subtract £3.59 from £8.37.

5. Subtract 87 p from £2.05.

6. A woman spends amounts of £43.64, £59.76, and £87.49 in a departmental store. How much did she spend altogether?

7. A man has £635 in his bank account but withdraws amounts of £128.36, £74.93 and £302.95. How much money is left in his account?

8. Jane had two ten pound notes. She spent £1.36, £2.50 and £12.68. How much money has she left?

9. Find the cost of 15 articles if each article costs 18 p.

10. Find the total cost of 93 articles if each costs £2.36.

11. Bread rolls cost 8 p each. 160 of these rolls are needed for a party. How much do the rolls cost?

12. 18 similar articles cost £5.58. How much does each cost?

13. 784 similar articles cost £721.28. How much does each article cost?

14. A shop assistant can give change in a variety of ways using coins of value 1 p, 2 p, 5 p, 10 p, 20 p and 50 p. A girl buys sweets costing 23 p. If the girl tenders a £1 coin work out a way in which the shop assistant can give the change, without using each type of coin more than once.

15. In a snack bar I buy a sandwich costing 65 p, a cup of tea costing 36 p and a cake costing 48 p. To pay for these items I tender a five pound note. How much change should I get?

BALANCING

When dealing with the addition and subtraction of sums of money it is impossible to be too careful. Whenever possible checks should be made. One way of doing this is the method of balancing.

Example 2

Add separately each column and each row and check by obtaining the overall totals for each.

	Grocery	Toys	Children's wear	Women's wear	Men's wear
Week 1	£2087.58	£976.43	£875.34	£1794.69	£1068.89
Week 2	£2165.42	£758.58	£918.89	£1689.73	£1265.98
Week 3	£2200.31	£834.67	£812.89	£2178.98	£1358.90
Week 4	£2178.95	£768.50	£805.12	£2334.42	£1234.56
Week 5	£2317.78	£812.34	£798.03	£3217.87	£1178.92
Week 6	£2412.67	£913.42	£821.76	£2816.33	£1245.89

	Grocery	Toys	Children's wear	Women's wear	Men's wear	Totals
Week 1	£2087.58	£976.43	£875.34	£1794.69	£1068.89	£6802.93
Week 2	£2165.42	£758.58	£918.89	£1689.73	£1265.98	£6798.60
Week 3	£2200.31	£834.67	£812.89	£2178.98	£1358.90	£7385.75
Week 4	£2178.95	£768.50	£805.12	£2334.42	£1234.56	£7321.55
Week 5	£2317.78	£812.34	£798.03	£3217.87	£1178.92	£8324.94
Week 6	£2412.67	£913.42	£821.76	£2816.33	£1245.89	£8210.07
Totals	£13 362.71	£5063.94	£5032.03	£14 032.02	£7353.14	£44 843.84

The overall total is shown within the box. All the additions are correct if the overall total obtained by adding the vertical total column equals the overall total obtained by adding the horizontal total row.

51

EXERCISE 6.2

1. The table below shows the weekly petty cash expenditure of a business for four successive weeks. Find the total expenditure for each week and also the total expenditure for each item for the four weeks. Finally add together the vertical and horizontal totals to obtain the final total for the four weeks.

	Postage	Office tea	Stationery	Cleaner's pay	Sundries	Totals
Week 1	£44.50	£6.32	£9.60	£30.00	£4.05	
Week 2	£39.25	£5.02	£12.48	£30.00	£2.34	
Week 3	£46.80	£9.96	£11.34	£30.00	£1.68	
Week 4	£43.15	£4.26	£15.18	£30.00	£3.75	
Totals						

2. The following table shows the tax paid by 5 men during the month of July. Work out the vertical and horizontal totals as shown and by finding the overall total perform a balance.

	Man A	Man B	Man C	Man D	Man E	Totals
Week 1	£45.76	£39.88	£51.63	£87.62	£49.88	
Week 2	£42.89	£43.67	£54.68	£78.90	£51.27	
Week 3	£52.78	£64.68	£53.22	£80.81	£48.69	
Week 4	£77.83	£49.73	£50.00	£71.42	£36.25	
Totals						

3. The table below shows income tax deductions made from a woman's earnings during six months of a tax year. Calculate the weekly and monthly totals and perform a balance.

	Week 1	Week 2	Week 3	Week 4	Week 5	Totals
April	—	£47.49	£42.80	£39.81	—	
May	£40.37	£41.63	£40.85	£42.70	—	
June	£37.93	£38.93	£43.37	£37.89	—	
July	£41.65	£41.20	£41.35	£43.37	£38.80	
August	£37.71	£62.35	£40.89	£37.73	—	
September	£39.90	£44.30	£40.05	£37.92	—	
Totals						

FINANCIAL STATEMENTS

It is important that you should be able to understand a financial statement. The one which is shown below is a statement for a club dance.

	Income			*Expenditure*	
Date	Particulars	Receipts	Date	Particulars	Payments
8/6	Sale of 400 tickets @ £4	1600.00	11/6	Hire of hall	150.00
			17/6	Printing of tickets	62.50
20/6	Sale of 250 tickets @ £4	1000.00	23/6	Cost of band	350.00
23/6	Sale of tickets at door. 120 @ £5	600.00	23/6	Cost of buffet @ £2 per head	1540.00
					2102.50
				Balance carried down	1097.50
	Total	£3200.00			£3200.00

The statement shows clearly how much money has been received and how much has been spent. The balance carried down is the profit made on the dance and it is found by subtracting the total payments (£2102.50) from the total receipts (£3200.00). This balance is added to the total payments and both sides of the book, i.e., income and expenditure should be the same.

The accounts for business transactions are kept in a book called the ledger which is usually ruled as shown in Example 3. The general rule for entering up ledger accounts is:
  debit — the amounts of money placed in the account
  credit — the amounts of money flowing out of the account

Example 3

Enter the following transactions in a cash account. Balance the account and bring down the balance.

1/5	Cash in hand £58.73		12/5	Bought goods for cash £15.74
8/5	Paid telephone bill £33.40		15/5	Cash sales £89.70
10/5	Received cash from L. Thomas £29.00		18/5	Paid into bank £75.00

Dr			Cash a/c		Cr
		£			£
May 1	To balance b/d	58.73	May 8	By telephone	33.40
May 10	To L. Thomas	29.00	May 12	By purchases	15.74
May 15	To sales	89.70	May 18	By bank	75.00
		177.43	May 20	By balance c/d	53.29
May 22	To balance	53.29			177.43

The following points should be carefully noted:

(1) The name of the account is Cash a/c (a/c stands for account).

(2) Left hand side: Dr = debit. Right hand side: Cr = credit.

(3) c/d stands for carried down. b/d stands for brought down.

(4) For the entries receipts are entered under Dr and payments are entered under Cr.

(5) On the debit side all entries are prefixed 'to' and the name of the account from which the money is received is stated.

(6) On the credit side all entries are prefixed 'by' and the name of the account into which the money is paid is stated.

(7) The opening balance is the amount left in the account from the previous period.

(8) The closing balance is the amount necessary for the account to balance. On the credit side the payments made amount to £33.40 + £15.74 + £75.00 = £124.14. The closing balance is found by subtracting this from the total receipts of £177.43 giving a closing balance of £53.29. Thus the account shows that we have a balance of £53.29 in our cash account on May 22nd.

EXERCISE 6.3

Draw up financial statements to show the following transactions taking care to balance the receipts and payments columns.

1. Hockey club accounts:

   1/9 Annual subscriptions 32 members @ £9.50 each

   10/9 Match fees (received from players) for game v. Old Manorians £16.50

   10/9 Cost of teas for game v. Old Manorians £18.70

   10/9 Umpire's expenses £3.50

   17/9 Match fees (received from players) for mixed game v. Moorpark £14.30

   17/9 Cost of teas £19.80

   17/9 Umpire's expenses £3.00

2. Annual outing of Youth Club:

   5/7 Received £2.95 from each of 70 members

   7/7 Received subsidy of £75 from General Committee

   9/7 Hire of 2 coaches and drivers £172.50

   9/7 Cost of 72 teas at £1.20 each

3. Firm's annual sports day:

   3/6 Received subsidy from directors £100.00

   5/6 Received £62 from competitors

   8/6 Hire of tents £58

   8/6 Competitors prizes £146

   8/6 Cost of raffle tickets and prizes £17.20

   8/6 Sale of raffle tickets £54.60

4. Enter the following transactions in a Cash account. Balance the account and bring down the balance.

   1st Jan. Cash in hand £39.47

   5th Jan. Paid telephone account £37.89

   8th Jan. Received cash from P. Smith £62.00

   12th Jan. Bought goods for cash £53.25

   29th Jan. Cash sales £108.75

   31st Jan. Paid into bank £105.00

5. Enter the following transactions in a Cash account. Balance the account and bring down the balance.

   3rd March Cash in hand £97.57

   9th March Bought goods for cash £73.78

   16th March Cash sales £128.97

   18th March Received from T. Barnes £54.00

   28th March Banked £175.00

   30th March Bought postage stamps £3.40

PETTY CASH BOOK

Most offices keep a small amount of cash available for day to day running expenses such as cost of postage stamps, stationery, etc. This cash is called petty cash and it is important that an account be kept of how the money is spent. The account is kept in the petty cash book and it is prepared in much the same way as the financial statements previously discussed.

Receipts	Date	Particulars	Payments
24.00	1st Jan	Cash in hand	
	3rd Jan	Parcel post	1.70
	4th Jan	Letter post	2.52
	5th Jan	Window cleaner	3.60
	6th Jan	Stationery	4.05
		Total	11.87
11.87	7th Jan	Reimbursement	
		Balance carried down	24.00
35.87			35.87

Example 4

Enter the following transactions in a petty cash book.

1st Jan. Petty cash in hand £24.00
3rd Jan. Parcel post £1.70
4th Jan. Letter postage £2.52
5th Jan. Window cleaner £3.60
6th Jan. Purchase of stationery £4.05
7th Jan. Received reimbursement for the week's expenditure to keep balance in hand at £24.00

Sometimes it is desirable to know how much petty cash has been spent on the various items for a given period. For instance we might want to know how much has been spent on postage or on cleaning, etc. The method of entering the items shown in Example 4 is not very satisfactory in this respect because to obtain the information required means adding together several different entries. It is therefore better to set out the petty cash book in analysis columns as shown in Example 5.

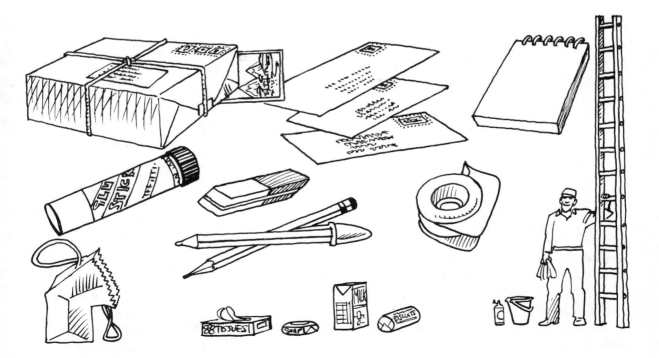

Example 5

A petty cash book has analysis columns for postage, stationery, travelling expenses, office expenses and cleaning. Enter the following transactions:

2nd July Received from cashier £30
3rd July Bus fares £1.28, postage 95 p
4th July Envelopes 65 p, string 24 p
5th July Parcel post £2.10, office teas 70 p
6th July Window cleaning £2.30, railway fares £6.25.
7th July Pencils 40 p, Cleaners wages £12.50
9th July Received reimbursement for the week's expenditure to keep balance in hand at £30.00

Receipts	Date	Particulars	Payments	Postage	Stationery	Travelling Expenses	Office Expenses	Cleaning
30.00	2nd July	Balance in hand						
	3rd July	Bus fares	1.28			1.28		
	3rd July	Postage	0.95	0.95				
	4th July	Envelopes	0.65		0.65			
	4th July	String	0.24		0.24			
	5th July	Parcel post	2.10	2.10				
	5th July	Office teas	0.70				0.70	
	6th July	Window cleaning	2.30					2.30
	6th July	Railway fares	6.25			6.25		
	7th July	Pencils	0.40		0.40			
	7th July	Cleaners wage	12.50					12.50
		Totals	27.37	3.05	1.29	7.53	0.70	14.80
27.37	9th July	Reimbursement						
		Balance carried down	30.00					
57.37			57.37					

BANK STATEMENTS

Bank statements are issued to people who have a current (or cheque) account with the bank. They give a record of payments (i.e., money drawn out of the account) and receipts (money deposited in the account). They are very similar to the financial statements already discussed. A typical bank statement is shown opposite.

On the first and third lines of the statement you will see 387.43DR and 382.43DR. This means that on these two occasions the account was overdrawn (i.e., the account holder owes the bank money).

Severn Bank plc
18 Southgate Street, Pellford

CHEQUE
Statement of Account
Account No. 50860805

M. Thomas
46 Spring Road
Pellford PL5 8KP

9 JUN 89

POST   1989/ 5

DETAILS		PAYMENTS	RECEIPTS	DATE	BALANCE
BALANCE FORWARD				9 MAY	387.43DR
	100088	50.00		13 MAY	
COUNTER CREDIT			55.00	13 MAY	382.43DR
FROM DEP A/C	TFR		500.00	16 MAY	117.57
	100089	25.00		20 MAY	92.57
	100091	12.99		2 JUN	79.58
	100090	27.98		5 JUN	51.60
FROM DEP A/C	TFR		200.00	6 JUN	251.60

DR indicates that the account is overdrawn, i.e., M. Thomas owes the bank money.

EXERCISE 6.4

1. Enter the following transactions in a petty cash book which has analysis columns for postage, stationery, travelling expenses, cleaning and office expenses:

   3rd Feb. Petty cash balance in hand £72
   4th Feb. Postage £5.64, Xerox copying £3.84
   5th Feb. Pencils £2.88, train fare £4.68, office teas £4.08
   6th Feb. Window cleaning £8.00, note-paper £4.80
   7th Feb. Parcel postage £5.02, type-writer ribbons £4.50
   8th Feb. Office teas £4.50, cleaner's wage £21
   10th Feb. Reimbursement to keep cash in hand at £72

2. Enter the following transactions in a petty cash book which has three analysis columns for postage, stationery and travelling expenses:

   5th June Balance in hand £96
   6th June Postage stamps £12, envelopes £3.78, bus fares £1.68
   7th June Notepaper £2.70, parcel post £5.88
   8th June Erasers £2.10, railway fares £2.76, ballpens £2.70
   9th June Envelopes £3.24, carbon paper £3.05
   13th June Reimbursement to keep cash in hand at £96

3. Enter the following transactions in a suitably ruled petty cash book:

8th Jan. Petty cash balance in hand £28.00
9th Jan. Postage 57 p
10th Jan. Parcel post £2.10
11th Jan. Window cleaner £5.00
12th Jan. Stationery £2.99
14th Jan. Cleaner's wages £12.00
15th Jan. Reimbursement to keep balance in hand at £28

4. Enter the following transactions on a bank statement:

8th Aug. Balance brought forward £1702.31
9th Aug. Payment of £79.42
10th Aug. Payment of £900.26
17th Aug. Payment of £1233.34
25th Aug. Receipt of £800.00

MISCELLANEOUS EXERCISE 6

1. **(a)** A cook buys $5\frac{1}{2}$ kg of raspberries, 2400 g of strawberries and 8 kg of sugar.
Work out the total weight of these items in kilograms.
(b) The raspberries cost £1.10 per kilogram, the strawberries cost 95 p per kilogram and the sugar costs 65 p per kilogram.
Work out the total cost of the purchases made by the cook.
(c) The cook makes jam using 5 kg of sugar and 5 kg of raspberries producing 10 kg of jam.
Calculate the cost of these ingredients in 1 kg of the jam.

2. How much change would I get from £20 when I buy 4 tins of coffee at £2.36 per tin, 5 cans of fruit at 42 p per tin and a pack of tea bags costing £3.49?

3. Work out the total cost of the following items:

2000 envelopes at 90 p per hundred
80 pencils at 7 p each
10 reams of typing paper at £3.65 per ream
11 packets of typing paper at 85 p per packet

4. The distance by rail between Manchester and London is 210 miles. If a return ticket costs £44.10, what is the cost per mile?

5. **(a)** What is the total cost of taking 34 children on an outing at £2.65 each?
(b) The owner of a toy shop buys 375 similar toys for £8013.75. How much does each toy cost?

6. Enter the following transactions on a bank statement:

9th Apr. Balance forward £3782.95
10th Apr. Receipt of £88.07
12th Apr. Payment of £34.87
14th Apr. Payment of £3000.00
20th Apr. Payment of £77.19
27th Apr. Receipt of £200.00

7. Enter the following transactions in a petty cash book:

4th Aug. Received from cashier £50.00
6th Aug. Postage stamps £5.40
8th Aug. Stationery £12.30, parcel post £3.69
11th Aug. Window cleaner £5.00, travelling expenses £3.69
15th Aug. Office cleaner £12.00, ballpoint pens £2.40
23rd Aug. Reimbursement £44.48

MENTAL TEST 6

1. Add £3.45 and 50 p.

2. Subtract 37 p from £1.50.

3. Find the cost of 10 items at £1.35 each.

4. 20 similar articles cost £10. How much does each cost?

5. 100 similar articles cost £12.00. How much does each cost?

6. 25 articles cost £5. How much does each cost?

7. What is the total cost of 30 articles if each costs 20 p?

8. Find the cost of 5 articles if each costs 99 p.

9. Sheets cost £4.75 each. What is the cost of 20 sheets?

10. A shopkeeper buys 10 dolls for £39.80. How much does each doll cost?

CHAPTER 7

Ratio and Proportion

RATIO

Concrete is made by mixing sand and cement in the ratio 3:1 (three to one) and then adding water. You could put three sacks of sand to one sack of cement or three bucketfuls of sand to one bucketful of cement or three cups of sand to one cup of cement. These ratios are all 3:1.

As long as the sand and cement are kept in the same proportion when mixed with water they will make concrete. The actual amounts of sand and cement used only affects the amount of concrete made.

Example 1

A mortar mixture is made by mixing cement, sand and water in the ratio 1:2:4. If 80 kg of cement is used:

(a) What weight of sand and water is needed?
(b) What weight of concrete will be made?

(a)   Amount of cement used $= 80$ kg

Amount of sand needed $= (2 \times 80)$ kg
$= 160$ kg

Amount of water needed $= (4 \times 80)$ kg
$= 320$ kg

(b) Total amount of concrete made

$= (1 + 2 + 4) \times 80$ kg

$= (7 \times 80)$ kg

$= 560$ kg

SIMPLIFYING RATIOS

Problems are often made easier by putting the ratios into their *simplest terms.*

The ratios 1:3, 3:7 and 9:4 are in their simplest terms because there is no number which will divide exactly into both sides.

The ratio 6:8 is not in its simplest terms because 2 will divide into both sides. Thus
6:8 is equivalent to $6 \div 2 : 8 \div 2$
i.e., 6:8 is equivalent to 3:4

Example 2

Put the ratio 72:84 in its simplest terms.

12 divides exactly into 72 and 84.
72:84 is equivalent to $72 \div 12 : 84 \div 12$
i.e., 72:84 is equivalent to 6:7

Thus 6:7 is the same as 72:84 in its simplest terms.

EXERCISE 7.1

1. A mortar mixture is made of cement, sand and water in the ratio 1:3:5. If 40 kg of cement is used
   (a) What weight of sand and water is needed?
   (b) Work out what weight of mortar results.

2. Mr Jones, Mr Brown and Mr Smith are partners in a small business. They agree to share the profits of the business in the ratio 1:2:5. In 1986 Mr Jones was paid £3000.
   (a) How much did Mr Brown get?
   (b) How much did Mr Smith get?
   (c) What were the total profits for 1986?

3. Solder is made by mixing tin and lead in the ratio 3:1. If 5 kg of lead is used, work out:
   (a) the weight of tin required,
   (b) the total weight of solder made.

Express the following ratios in their simplest terms:

4. 5:20   7. 35:42   9. 20:30:45

5. 4:12   8. 64:56   10. 20:25:30:35

6. 42:49

EXERCISE 7.2

Express each of the following ratios as fractions in their lowest terms:

1. 9:7   5. 16:24   8. 15:18

2. 5:10   6. 80:100   9. 21:24

3. 14:7   7. 3:9   10. 45:81

4. 12:15

To simplify a ratio such as $1\frac{1}{4}:\frac{1}{3}$ we change the mixed number into a top-heavy fraction and then express each fraction with the same denominator. This common denominator should be the LCM of the original denominators.

$$1\frac{1}{4}:\frac{1}{3} \text{ is equivalent to } \frac{5}{4}:\frac{1}{3}$$

The LCM of 4 and 3 is 12. Expressing each fraction with a denominator of 12:

$$\frac{5}{4}:\frac{1}{3} \text{ is equivalent to } \frac{15}{12}:\frac{4}{12}$$

Multiplying each side by 12:

$$\frac{15}{12}:\frac{4}{12} \text{ is equivalent to } 15:4$$

This is the ratio $1\frac{1}{4}:\frac{1}{3}$ stated in its simplest terms.

Example 3

Express the ratio $1\frac{1}{3}:2\frac{1}{2}$ in its simplest terms.

$$1\frac{1}{3}:2\frac{1}{2} = \frac{4}{3}:\frac{5}{2} = \frac{8}{6}:\frac{15}{6} = 8:15$$

Exercise 7.1 should bring out the similarities between ratios and fractions. Compare, for instance

$$42:49 = 6:7 \text{ with } \frac{42}{49} = \frac{6}{7}$$
$$\text{and } 5:20 = 1:4 \text{ with } \frac{5}{20} = \frac{1}{4}$$

61

Simplifying Ratios with Units

The ratio 30 cm:80 cm can be simplified by first removing the units (because they are the same) and then dividing both sides by 10.

$$30 \text{ cm}:80 \text{ cm} \text{ is equivalent to } 3:8$$

The ratio 5 cm:2 m is simplified by first making the units the same on both sides and then removing them.

$$5 \text{ cm}:2 \text{ m} = 5 \text{ cm}:200 \text{ cm}$$
$$= 5:200$$
$$= 1:40$$

(by dividing both sides by 5)

EXERCISE 7.3

Simplify the following ratios:

1. $\frac{3}{4}:\frac{1}{3}$ 5. $2\frac{1}{4}:\frac{1}{4}$ 8. $2\frac{3}{4}:1\frac{1}{2}$

2. $\frac{2}{5}:\frac{3}{10}$ 6. $3\frac{1}{2}:1\frac{1}{2}$ 9. $1\frac{1}{3}:3\frac{1}{4}$

3. $\frac{1}{2}:\frac{3}{8}$ 7. $\frac{5}{6}:1\frac{2}{3}$ 10. $2\frac{2}{5}:5\frac{3}{20}$

4. $\frac{1}{6}:\frac{5}{12}$

By first removing the units simplify the following ratios:

11. 400 cm:100 cm   16. 400 mm:4 m

12. 500 cm:1 m   17. 2 km:500 m

13. 60 g:2 kg   18. 3 cm:9 mm

14. £1.50:50 p   19. £8.00:25 p

15. 5 kg:250 g   20. 3 kg:90 g

PROPORTIONAL PARTS

The line AB (Figure 7.1), whose length is 30 cm, has been divided into two parts in the ratio 2:3. As can be seen from the diagram the line has been divided into five parts in total. The length AC contains 2 of these parts and the length BC con-

tains 3 of them. Each part is $30 \text{ cm} \div 5 = 6 \text{ cm}$ long. Hence

$$AC = 2 \times 6 \text{ cm} = 12 \text{ cm}$$
$$BC = 3 \times 6 \text{ cm} = 18 \text{ cm}$$

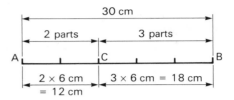

Figure 7.1

The problem of dividing the line AB into two parts in the ratio 2:3 could be tackled in this way:

Total number of parts $= 2 + 3 = 5$

Length of each part $= 30 \text{ cm} \div 5 = 6 \text{ cm}$

Length of AC $= (2 \times 6) \text{ cm} = 12 \text{ cm}$

Length of BC $= (3 \times 6) \text{ cm} = 18 \text{ cm}$

Example 4

(a) Divide £240 in the ratio 5:4:3.

Total number of parts $= 5 + 4 + 3 = 12$

Amount of each part $= £240 \div 12 = £20$

Amount of first part $= £20 \times 5 = £100$

Amount of second part $= £20 \times 4 = £80$

Amount of third part $= £20 \times 3 = £60$

(b) Three men A, B and C share the profits of a business in the ratio 1:3:7. Find the total profit in a year when B's share was £5700.

B's share represents 3 parts. Hence

Amount of each part $= £5700 \div 3 = £1900$

Total number of parts $= 1 + 3 + 7 = 11$

Total profit $= £1900 \times 11 = £20\,900$

EXERCISE 7.4

1. Divide £800 in the ratio 5:3.

2. Divide 160 kg in the ratio 7:3.

3. A piece of material is 120 m long. Divide it in the ratio 2:3:5.

4. A line 1.68 m long is to be divided into three parts in the ratio 2:7:11. Find, in centimetres, the length of each of the three parts.

5. The profits of a business are to be divided in the ratio 5:7. The smaller share amounts to £2000. Find the larger share.

6. An alloy consists of copper, zinc and tin in the ratio 2:3:5. Find the amount of each metal in 75 kg of the alloy.

7. A sum of money is shared into three parts in the ratio 2:4:5. If the largest share is £40, what is the total amount of money shared?

8. Four friends contribute sums of money to a charitable organisation in the ratio 2:4:5:7. The largest amount contributed is £4.20. Work out the total amount of money contributed by the four people.

DIRECT PROPORTION

Two quantities are said to be in *direct proportion* if they increase or decrease at the same rate. The quantity of petrol used and the distance travelled by a motor car are in direct proportion. Again, if 8 metres of stair carpet cost £40 then we expect to pay £20 for 4 metres. That is if we buy half the length we pay half the price. If we buy 16 metres then we expect to pay £80. That is if we buy twice the length we pay twice the price.

Example 5

A grocer buys 25 kg of butter for £38. How much would he pay for 8 kg?

Method 1 (the unitary method)

25 kg cost £38

1 kg costs £38 ÷ 25 = £1.52

8 kg costs £1.52 × 8 = £12.16

Method 2 (the fractional method)

25 kg cost £38

8 kg cost £38 × $\frac{8}{25}$ = £12.16

INVERSE PROPORTION

If an increase (or a decrease) in one quantity produces a decrease (or an increase) in a second quantity in the same ratio, the two quantities are said to be in *inverse proportion*.

Example 6

3 people can clean an office in 12 hours. How long would it take 9 people to clean the office?

3 people take 12 hours

1 person takes 3 × 12 = 36 hours
(1 person takes longer so multiply by 3)

9 people take 36 ÷ 9 = 4 hours
(9 people take less time so divide by 9)

Alternatively: 9 people take less time than 3 people so the time ratio is 3:9

Time taken by 9 people = $\frac{3}{9}$ × 12 = 4 hours

EXERCISE 7.5

1. If 74 exercise books cost £11.84, how much will 53 cost?

2. A car travels 205 km on 20 litres of petrol. How many litres of petrol will be needed for a journey of 369 km?

3. A train travels 200 km in 4 hours. If it travels at the same speed, how long will it take to complete a journey of 350 km?

4. Ingredients sufficient to make 12 small cakes are as follows: 150 grams each of butter, castor sugar and flour, 3 eggs and 120 grams of chocolate chips. What quantities would be needed to make 16 small cakes?

5. A machine makes 15 articles in half-an-hour. How many articles will it make in a shift of 4 hours?

6. 20 people working in a factory produce 3000 articles in 12 working days. How long would it take 15 people to make the articles?

7. A farmer employs 12 women to harvest his potato crop and they take 9 days to complete the work. If she had employed only 8 women, how long would it have taken them to harvest the crop?

8. A bag contains sweets. When divided amongst 8 children each child gets 9 sweets. If the sweets were divided amongst 12 children, how many sweets would each child get?

9. 7 women take 30 minutes to make 21 toys. How long would it take 20 women to make the 21 toys?

10. 8 men can do a piece of work in 60 hours. If the work is to be completed in 20 hours, how many men are needed?

11. 10 men can dig a row of carrots in 40 minutes. How long should it take 5 men?

12. 8 women take 5 hours to pick a row of raspberries. How long would it take 4 women to do the work?

BEST BUYS

I can buy 100 millilitres of shampoo for £1.40, 150 millilitres for £1.68 and 200 millilitres for £2.70. Which is the best buy?

The best buy is the one which costs the least per millilitre.

By using a calculator it is easy to work this out:
100 millilitres for £1.40 is equivalent to $(140 \div 100)$ p $= 1.40$ p
150 millilitres for £1.68 is equivalent to $(168 \div 150)$ p $= 1.12$ p
200 millilitres for £2.70 is equivalent to $(270 \div 200)$ p $= 1.35$ p

The best buy is therefore 150 millilitres for £1.68.

EXERCISE 7.6

Which are the best buys?

1. 20 grams for 60 p or 50 grams for £1.00.

2. 850 grams for £2.04 or 2500 grams for £7.00.

3. 250 grams of cornflour for 38 p or 300 grams for 50 p.

4. 250 gram packet of cornflakes for 55 p or a 750 gram packet for £1.12.

5. 100 millilitres for £1.50, 200 millilitres for £2.50 or 250 millilitres for £4.28.

MEASURES OF RATE

If a car travels 30 miles on 1 gallon of petrol we say that its fuel consumption is 30 miles per gallon. This is the rate at which the car uses petrol.

The flow of water from a pipe or a tap is often measured in litres per minute. This is the rate at which the water flows.

When a vehicle has a speed of 40 miles per hour this is the rate at which it is travelling, i.e., 40 miles in 1 hour.

Example 7

(a) A car has a fuel consumption of 7 km per litre of petrol. How much petrol will be needed for a journey of 105 km?

$$\text{Amount of fuel needed} = \frac{\text{length of journey}}{\text{fuel consumption}}$$

$$= \frac{105}{7} \text{ litres}$$

$$= 15 \text{ litres}$$

(b) The flow of water from a tap is 3 gallons per minute. How long will it take to fill a bucket with a capacity of 6 gallons?

$$\text{Time taken} = \frac{\text{capacity of the bucket}}{\text{rate of flow}}$$

$$= \frac{6}{3} \text{ min}$$

$$= 2 \text{ min}$$

EXERCISE 7.7

1. The rate of flow of water from a pipe is 12 litres per minute. Work out the time it will take to fill a container with a capacity of 120 litres.

2. A car has a fuel consumption of 40 miles per gallon. Work out the amount of fuel needed for a journey of 240 miles.

3. A schoolboy found that he walked 100 metres in 50 seconds.
   (a) What is his speed in metres per second?
   (b) If he keeps walking at the same speed, how long will it take him to walk 180 metres?

4. The density of aluminium is 2700 kilograms per cubic metre. How much does an ingot of aluminium with a volume of 3 cubic metres weigh?

5. Sheet metal weighs 5 lb per square foot.
   (a) How much will 12 square feet weigh?
   (b) A piece of this metal weighs 20 lb. What is its area?

RATE OF EXCHANGE

Every country has its own monetary system. If there is to be trade and travel between two countries there must be a rate at which money of one country can be converted into currency of the other country. This rate is called the *rate of exchange.*

Banks and bureaux de change usually give two rates of exchange one at which they buy and one at which they sell.

Foreign Exchange Rates at October 1988

Country	Buy	Sell	
Austria	22.20	21.00	schillings = £1
Belgium	68.80	65.30	francs = £1
Canada	2.18	2.07	dollars = £1
Eire	1.22	1.16	punt = £1
France	10.97	10.47	francs = £1
West Germany	3.24	3.06	marks = £1
Greece	267	252	drachmae = £1
Italy	2425	2295	lire = £1
Portugal	269	255	escudos = £1
Spain	213	202	pesetas = £1
Switzerland	2.76	2.60	francs = £1
USA	1.83	1.74	dollars = £1

Example 8

Using the rates of exchange on p. 65,

(a) Find the number of pesetas obtained by a tourist when he changes £300 into pesetas.
(b) At the end of a holiday he has 18 000 pesetas left which he changes into sterling. How much sterling will he get?

(a) £300 $= 300 \times 202 = 60\,600$ pesetas

(b) 18 000 pesetas $= £(18\,000 \div 213) = £84.51$

EXERCISE 7.8

Use a calculator and where necessary state the answers correct to 2 decimal places.
Using the exchange rates for Buy given on p. 65 find:

1. The number of German marks equivalent to £15.

2. The number of Spanish pesetas equivalent to £25.

3. The number of US dollars equivalent to £48.

Using the exchange rates for Sell given on p. 65 find:

4. The number of Belgian francs equivalent to £98.50.

5. The number of Italian lire equivalent to £60.

6. A tourist changes traveller's cheques for £100 into Greek currency at 252 drachmae to the £1. He spends 15 000 drachmae and the money he has left he changes into sterling at 267 drachmae to the £1. How much British money does he get?

7. A transistor radio costs £52.60 in London. An American visitor wishes to buy a set but he wants to pay in US dollars. If the exchange rate is $1.75 = £1, how much, in dollars, will he pay?

MISCELLANEOUS EXERCISE 7

1. A car travels 56 km on 7 litres of petrol. How far will it travel on 126 litres?

2. If a man walks 3 km in 40 minutes, how far will he have walked in 60 minutes if he keeps walking at the same rate?

3. Simplify the ratio 175:200.

4. At a certain time the rate of exchange between British and Spanish currency is £1 = 240 pesetas.
   (a) How many pounds are equivalent to 12 000 pesetas?
   (b) How many pesetas are equivalent to £40?
   (c) A family went on holiday to Spain. They paid £675 for the holiday (including flight and the hotel). They also spent 18 500 pesetas whilst on holiday. What was the total cost of the holiday in pounds?

5. Hyacinth bulbs cost 96 p for a pack of three. How much will a dozen bulbs cost?

6. The distance by rail between London and Gloucester is 102 miles. A return ticket costs £21.42.
   (a) What is the cost of rail travel per mile?
   (b) The distance between London and Cardiff is 155 miles. At the same rate, how much is the return fare for this journey?

7. The annual rent of a field amounts to £467.50 and it is shared by two farmers in the ratio 15:7. Find the difference in their shares.

8. If £1 is equivalent to $1.46, find how much 46 cents is worth, correct to the nearest number of pence.

9. 100 grams of cornflour can be bought for 35 p whilst 160 grams is priced at 60 p. Which is the better buy?

10. The model of an aeroplane is made to a scale of 1:78. If the wing span of the model is 35 cm, find, in metres, the wing span of the actual aeroplane.

11. If £1 = $1.80 and £1 = 2270 lire, find the number of lire which are equivalent to $1.

12. On returning from a business trip abroad an executive has remaining, 245 German marks and 378 French francs. If the exchange rates are: 3.24 marks = £1 and 10.97 francs = £1, how much British money will he receive for this currency?

13. Business partners A, B and C share the profits of a business in the ratio 1:4:7. Find the total profit in a certain year if B's share was £4800. Also calculate the amount of C's share in that year.

14. If two men can paint a fence in 6 hours, how long will it take four men to do the work?

15. A vending machine needs 15 litres of orangeade to fill 50 cups. How many litres are needed to fill 60 cups?

MENTAL TEST 7

Try to answer the following questions without writing anything down except the answer.

1. An alloy is made by mixing copper and zinc in the ratio 5:2. If 2 kg of zinc is used, how much copper is used?

2. Put the ratio 9:12 in its simplest form.

3. Express the ratio 16:20 as a fraction in its lowest terms.

4. Simplify the ratio £3:50 p.

5. Divide £100 in the ratio 7:3.

6. If 8 pens cost 80 p, how much do 5 cost?

7. 2 men digging a hole in a road take 8 days to complete the work. How long would 4 men take?

8. A tourist can buy francs at 10 to the £1. How many will he get for £5?

9. A bank sells German marks at 3 to the £1. How much in sterling will a customer get for 18 marks.

10. Divide 20 kg in the ratio 3:2.

11. A car has a fuel consumption of 30 miles per gallon. How many gallons of fuel are needed for a journey of 90 miles.

12. A vehicle has a speed of 50 kilometres per hour. How long will it take to complete a journey of 200 km?

CHAPTER 8

Percentages

INTRODUCTION

When comparing fractions it is often convenient to express them with a denominator of 100. Thus

$$\frac{1}{2} = \frac{50}{100} \quad \text{and} \quad \frac{2}{5} = \frac{40}{100}$$

Fractions with a denominator of 100 are called percentages.

$$\frac{1}{4} = \frac{25}{100} = 25 \text{ per cent}$$

$$\frac{3}{10} = \frac{30}{100} = 30 \text{ per cent}$$

The symbol % is often used instead of the words per cent. Thus

$$\frac{3}{20} = \frac{15}{100} = 15\%$$

CHANGING FRACTIONS INTO PERCENTAGES

To convert a fraction into a percentage multiply it by 100.

Example 1

(a) $\frac{17}{20} = \frac{17}{20} \times 100\% = 85\%$

(b) $0.3 = 0.3 \times 100\% = 30\%$

Not all percentages are whole numbers. For instance:

$$\frac{3}{8} = \frac{3}{8} \times 100\% = 37\frac{1}{2}\%$$

and $0.036 = 0.036 \times 100\% = 3.6\%$

Banks, finance houses and building societies frequently state their interest rates as mixed numbers or decimal numbers.

For instance, $7\frac{1}{4}\%$, $12\frac{1}{2}\%$ and 9.36%

CHANGING PERCENTAGES INTO FRACTIONS

To change a percentage into a fraction or a decimal divide it by 100.

Example 2

(a) $15\frac{1}{2}\% = 15\frac{1}{2} \div 100 = \frac{31}{200}$

(b) $9.2\% = 9.2 \div 100 = 0.092$

EXERCISE 8.1

The following table shows 12 numbers, each is expressed as either a fraction, a decimal or a percentage. Copy the table and write in the figures which should be placed in each of the spaces filled by a question mark. Express fractions in their lowest terms.

	Fraction	Decimal	Percentage
1.	$\frac{1}{4}$	?	?
2.	$\frac{11}{20}$	?	?
3.	$\frac{7}{8}$	?	?
4.	$\frac{2}{3}$	?	?
5.	?	0.08	?
6.	?	0.192	?
7.	?	?	15
8.	?	?	27
9.	?	?	62.5
10.	?	?	$8\frac{1}{4}$
11.	?	?	$9\frac{7}{8}$
12.	?	?	$6\frac{2}{3}$

PERCENTAGES OF A QUANTITY

To find the percentage of a quantity we first convert the percentage to a decimal number.

Example 3

(a) What is 10% of £60?

$$\text{Since } 10\% = 10 \div 100 = 0.1$$

$$10\% \text{ of } £60 = 0.1 \times £60 = £6$$

(b) Calculate $8\frac{1}{4}\%$ of 65 metres.

$$8\frac{1}{4}\% = 8.25\% = 8.25 \div 100 = 0.0825$$

$$8\frac{1}{4}\% \text{ of } 65 \text{ m} = (0.0825 \times 65) \text{ m}$$

$$= 5.3625 \text{ m}$$

(c) 22% of a certain length is 55 cm. What is the complete length?

The complete length is represented by 100%. Hence

$$\text{Complete length} = \left(\frac{100}{22} \times 55 \right) \text{ cm}$$

$$= 250 \text{ cm}$$

(d) What percentage is 37 of 264? State the answer correct to 5 significant figures.

$$\text{Percentage} = \frac{37}{264} = 14.015\%$$

EXERCISE 8.2

1. Calculate:
   (a) 20% of 50   (b) 30% of 80
   (c) 5% of 120   (d) 12% of 20
   (e) 20.3% of 105   (f) 3.7% of 68
   (g) $2\frac{1}{2}\%$ of 160   (h) $6\frac{1}{4}\%$ of 48

2. What percentage is:
   (a) 25 of 200?   (b) 30 of 150?
   (c) 24 of 150?   (d) 29 of 178?
   (e) 15 of 33?

   Where necessary state the percentage correct to 5 significant figures.

3. In a test a girl scores 36 marks out of 60.
   (a) What is her percentage mark?
   (b) The percentage needed to pass the test is 45%. What is the pass mark?

4. If 20% of a length is 23 cm, what is the complete length?

5. Given that 13.3 cm is 15% of a certain length, what is the complete length?

6. What is
   (a) 9% of £80?   **(b)** 12% of £110?
   (c) 75% of £250?

7. 27% of a consignment of fruit is bad. If the consignment weighs 800 kg, how much fruit is good?

8. In a certain county the average number of children eating lunches at school is 29 336, which represents 74% of the total number of children attending school. Calculate the total number of children attending school in the county.

PERCENTAGE CHANGE

An increase of 5% in a number means that if the number is represented by 100, the increase is 5 and the new number is 105. The ratio of the new number to the old number is 105 : 100.

Example 4

An increase of 10% in salaries makes the wage bill for a business £55 000 per week.

(a) What was the wage bill before the increase?
(b) What was the amount of the increase?

(a) If 100% represents the wage bill before the increase then 110% represents the wage bill after the increase.

$$\text{Old wage bill} = \frac{100}{110} \times £55\,000$$

$$= £50\,000$$

(b) Amount of increase $= 10\%$ of £50 000

$$= 0.1 \times £50\,000$$

$$= £5000$$

Example 5

When a sum of money is decreased by 20% it becomes £40. What was the original sum?

If 100% represents the original sum then the sum after the decrease of 20% is represented by 80%.

Therefore:

$$\text{Original sum} = \frac{100}{80} \times £40 = £50$$

EXERCISE 8.3

1. The duty on an article is 20% of its value. If the price of the article after the duty has been paid is £960, find the price before tax.

2. When a sum of money is decreased by 10% it becomes £18. What was the original sum?

3. A man sells his car for £850 thus losing 15% of what he paid for it. How much did the car cost him?

4. During an epidemic 40% of the people in a town in Africa died and 1200 were left. How many people died?

5. The value of a machine depreciates by 15% of its value at the beginning of the year. If its value at the end of the year was £1360, what was its value at the beginning of the year?

6. In a factory producing records, 25% of discs by a certain recording artist were badly damaged during pressing. If the remaining 1500 were playable, how many records were manufactured?

7. A man pays 20% of his salary in income tax. If his salary, after the tax had been paid, was £6400 per annum what was his salary before tax?

MISCELLANEOUS EXERCISE 8

1. Find 5% of £260.

2. Express $\frac{135}{150}$ as a percentage.

3. After prices have been raised by 8% the new price of an article is £70.47. Calculate the original price.

4. Next year a man will receive a wage increase of 12% and his weekly wage will then be £161.28. What is his present weekly wage?

5. The number of people working for a company at the end of 1987 was 1210. This was an increase of 10% on the number working for the company at the beginning of 1987. How many people worked for the company at the beginning of 1987?

6. The entry fee for an examination was £5.00 in 1987 and it rose to £6.40 in 1988. Express the increase in the fee as a percentage of the fee in 1987.

7. 8% of a sum of money is equal to £9.60.
   (a) What is the sum of money?
   (b) Calculate 92% of this sum of money.

8. A boy scores 66 marks out of 120 in an examination.
   (a) What is his percentage mark?
   (b) If the percentage required to pass the examination is 45%, how many marks are required for a pass?

9. In a class of 30 children 40% are boys.
   (a) How many boys are in the class?
   (b) What percentage of the class are girls?

10. 20% of a consignment of perishable goods was unsaleable. If 1500 kg was unsaleable, work out:
    (a) the total weight of the consignment,
    (b) the weight of saleable goods in the consignment.

MENTAL TEST 8

Try to answer the following questions without writing anything down except the answer.

1. Express $\frac{4}{5}$ as a percentage.

2. Convert 0.7 into a percentage.

3. Convert 30% to a decimal number.

4. Work out 30% of 80.

5. What is 8% of £40?

6. What percentage is 9 of 50?

7. Convert 37% into a decimal number.

8. 50% of a length is 30 cm. What is the whole length?

9. What is 9% of 200 mm?

10. Convert 60% into a fraction in its lowest terms.

CHAPTER 9

Wages and Salaries

INTRODUCTION

Everyone who works for an employer receives a wage or salary in return for their labour. The payment may be made in one of several different ways. Wages are usually paid weekly and salaries monthly.

PAYMENT BY THE HOUR

Many people are paid a certain amount of money for each hour that they work. They usually work a fixed number of hours per week which is called the *basic week*. It is this basic week which determines the hourly (or basic) rate of pay. The basic week and the basic rate of pay are often fixed by negotiation between the employer and the trade union which represents the workers.

Example 1

(a) A man works a basic week of 35 hours and his weekly wage is £140. Find his basic rate of pay.

$$\text{Basic rate of pay} = \frac{\text{Weekly wage}}{\text{Basic week}}$$

$$= £\frac{140}{35} = £4.00$$

So his basic rate of pay is £4.00 per hour.

(b) A woman works a basic week of 38 hours and her basic rate of pay is £3.50 per hour. Work out her weekly wage.

$$\text{Weekly wage} = \text{Basic week} \times \text{Basic rate of pay}$$

$$= £3.50 \times 38 = £133$$

OVERTIME

Hourly paid workers are usually paid extra for working more hours than the basic week requires. These extra hours of work are called overtime. Overtime is usually paid at one of the following rates:

Time-and-a-quarter: $1\frac{1}{4}$ times the basic rate.

Time-and-a-half: $1\frac{1}{2}$ times the basic rate.

Double time: twice the basic rate.

Example 2

A trainee is paid a basic rate of £2 per hour. Calculate the hourly rate of overtime when this is paid at (a) time-and-a-quarter, (b) time-and-a-half and (c) double time.

(a) Overtime rate at time-and-a-quarter

$$= 1\frac{1}{4} \times £2 = £2.50 \text{ per hour}$$

(b) Overtime rate at time-and-a-half

$$= 1\tfrac{1}{2} \times £2 = £3 \text{ per hour}$$

(c) Overtime rate at double time

$$= 2 \times £2 = £4 \text{ per hour}$$

Example 3

Peter Taylor works a 40 hour week for which he is paid £240. Overtime is paid at time-and-a-half. If he works 4 hours overtime, calculate his total wage for that week.

$$\text{Basic rate of pay} = £\frac{240}{40} = £6 \text{ per hour}$$

$$\text{Overtime rate} = 1\tfrac{1}{2} \times £6 = £9 \text{ per hour}$$

$$\text{Overtime payment} = £9 \times 4 = £36$$

$$\text{Total wage} = £240 + £36 = £276$$

EXERCISE 9.1

1. Copy and complete the table below:

	Basic week	Basic rate	Weekly wage
(a)	35	£3	?
(b)	40	£5	?
(c)	36	£4	?
(d)	32	?	£192
(e)	40	?	£200
(f)	38	?	£171

2. A man is paid a basic rate of £5 per hour. Work out his hourly overtime rate when this is paid at
   (a) time-and-a-quarter,
   (b) time-and-a-half,
   (c) double time.

3. A labourer is paid £120 for a basic 40-hour week. If overtime is paid at time-and-a-quarter, calculate:
   (a) his basic hourly rate of pay,
   (b) his hourly overtime rate of pay,
   (c) the amount paid in overtime when he puts in 5 hours overtime during one week,
   (d) his total wage for that week.

4. A woman's basic rate of pay is £5.36 per hour. She works a basic week of 35 hours from Monday to Friday. On Saturday and Sunday overtime is paid at double time.
   (a) How much will she earn per hour for working on Saturday or Sunday?
   (b) If she works 4 hours on Saturday and 7 hours on Sunday, how much will she be paid in overtime?
   (c) Calculate her total wage for that particular week.

PIECEWORK

Some workers are paid a certain amount for each article or piece of work that they produce. This is called piecework. Often if the worker makes more than a certain number of articles he or she will be paid a bonus.

Example 4

A woman is paid 5 p for each bag of sweets she packs up to a limit of 350 per day. After that she is paid a bonus of 1 p per bag. Work out the amount she earned during a day when she packed 420 bags of sweets.

$$\text{Money earned on first 350} = 350 \times 5\,\text{p} = £17.50$$

$$\text{Money earned on next 70} = 70 \times 6\,\text{p} = £4.20$$

$$\text{Total amount earned} = £17.50 + £4.20 = £21.70$$

EXERCISE 9.2

1. The basic rate for sewing a zip fastener onto men's trousers is 15 p up to a limit of 90 per day. How much will a woman earn if she just meets this target?

2. Work out the total amount earned for producing 180 items in each of the following cases:
   (a) 8 p each for the first 80 and a bonus of 3 p each above that target figure.
   (b) 12 p each for the first 100 and 16 p each for those made above that target figure.
   (c) 19 p for the first 110 made and a bonus of 3 p each for those above that target figure.

3. A man is paid 9 p for each spot weld that he makes up to 300 per day. After that he is paid a bonus of 2 p. If he makes 450 spot welds in a day, work out the amount he earns in that day.

4. Workers in a shirt factory are paid 50 p for each shirt that they complete up to a maximum of 25. After that they are paid 60 p for each completed shirt. If a worker completes 35 shirts in a day, how much will she earn?

COMMISSION

Shop assistants, salesmen and representatives are often paid commission with or without a basic wage for the job. Commission is calculated as a percentage (usually small) of the value of the goods that they have sold.

Example 5

(a) A sales executive is paid a commission of 2% on goods which she sells. Calculate her commission if she sells goods to the value of £6000.

Commission = 2% of £6000 = £120

(b) A shop assistant is paid a basic wage of £90 per week. In addition he is paid a commission of 3% on the value of his sales. During one week he sold goods to the value of £5000. Work out his total wage for that week.

Commission = 3% of £5000 = £150

Total wage = £90 + £150 = £240

EXERCISE 9.3

1. Find the commission at 5% on sales of:
   (a) £200   (b) £500
   (c) £800   (d) £300

2. A car salesman sells 4 cars during one week costing £4500, £3200, £7800 and £5600.
   On each sale he is paid a commission of 2%. Calculate his total commission for the week.

3. A trainee sales assistant is paid a basic wage of £50 per week. In addition she is paid a commission of 3% on the value of the sales that she makes.
   (a) If she sells goods to the value of £3500 during one week, how much is her commission?
   (b) Calculate her total wage for that week.

4. An agent selling agricultural machinery is paid a basic wage of £60 per week. In addition he is paid a commission of 2% on his sales. In one week he made sales to the value of £8500. Work out his gross wage for the week.

5. A door to door salesman selling encyclopaedias is paid only by commission at a rate of 15% of his total sales. During one week his daily sales amounted to £160, £150, £240, £100 and £170. Work out his earnings for that week.

SALARIES

People like teachers, civil servants, secretaries and company managers are usually paid a fixed salary each year. The money is generally paid in monthly instalments and they are not paid over-time or commission.

Example 6

A secretary is paid £9600 per annum. Work out her monthly salary.

$$\text{Monthly salary} = £9600 \div 12 = £800$$

EXERCISE 9.4

The following are the annual salaries of five people. Calculate, to the nearest pound, how much each is paid monthly.

1. £6000   **3.** £9380   **5.** £27 290

2. £8400   **4.** £11 863

DEDUCTIONS FROM EARNINGS

The wages and salaries so far discussed are not the actual amounts received by the workers. Certain deductions are made first. The most important of these are:

(1)   Income tax.

(2)   National insurance.

(3)   Pension fund payments.

Before these deductions the wage (or salary) is known as the *gross wage* (or *salary*). After the deductions have been made the wage (or salary) is known as the *net wage* (or *salary*). It is also called the *take-home pay*.

NATIONAL INSURANCE

At the present time most employees pay 9% of their gross pay in national insurance contributions. Men over 65, women over 60 and people earning less than £41 per week pay no national insurance.

The rates of national insurance are fixed by the Chancellor of the Exchequer and they may vary from year to year. National insurance contributions are used to pay for such things as sick pay, unemployment benefit, doctors, the cost of hospital treatment, etc.

Example 7

Jane earns a gross wage of £130 per week. Her deductions for national insurance are 9% of her gross wage. How much per week does she pay in national insurance?

$$\text{Amount of national insurance} = 9\% \text{ of } £130$$
$$= £11.70 \text{ per week}$$

PENSION FUND

Many firms operate their own private pension scheme to provide a pension in addition to the one provided by the state. Generally both the employer and the employee contribute to the scheme, the employee's share being of the order of 5% of the gross annual wage or salary.

The amount of pension received depends upon the length of service and earnings at the time of retirement.

Example 8

The firm of Wangate Cranes Ltd run a pension scheme for the benefit of their employees for which the employees pay 6% of their annual wage. Calculate the amount paid per annum by John Richards who earns £160 per week.

$$\text{Annual wage} = 52 \times £160$$
$$= £8320$$

$$\text{Annual contributions} = 6\% \text{ of } £8320$$
$$= £499.20$$

INCOME TAX

Taxes are levied by the Chancellor of the Exchequer to produce money to pay for such things as the armed forces, motorways, the Civil Service, etc. The largest producer of revenue is income tax. Every person who earns money above a certain amount pays income tax. Tax is not paid on the whole of the income. Certain allowances are made as follows:

(1) A personal allowance which depends upon whether the taxpayer is married or single. For the tax year 1988/9 these allowances were: single person £2605, married man £4095. For taxation purposes a wife's income is added to her husband's income and tax is paid on the joint income but the first £2605 of the wife's income is tax free.

(2) Expenses incurred with the taxpayers work.

(3) Pension fund contributions and special personal circumstances such as a dependent relative.

$$\text{Taxable income} = \text{Gross income} - \text{Allowances}$$

$$\text{Tax payable} = \text{Taxable income} \times \text{Tax rate}$$

Example 9

Jack Jones is a single man who earns an annual salary of £9000. For tax purposes his allowances are a single person's allowance of £2605 and

relief in full for pension fund payments of £450. If tax is levied at the basic rate of 25%, work out the annual tax to be paid by Jack Jones.

$$\text{Total allowances} = £2605 + £450 = £3055$$

$$\text{Taxable income} = £9000 - £3055 = £5945$$

$$\text{Tax payable} = 25\% \text{ of } £5945 = £1486.25$$

Most people pay income tax by a method known as *Pay-As-You-Earn* or *PAYE* for short. The tax is deducted from their wage or salary before they receive it. The taxpayer and the employer receive a notice of coding which gives the employee's allowances (based upon information given to the tax inspector) and sets a code number. The employer then knows from tax tables the amount of tax to deduct from the employee's wage or salary.

EXERCISE 9.5

1. At a time when national insurance contributions were fixed at 9% of gross income, John Carpenter & Sons Ltd ran a pension fund for their employees for which each employee paid 5% of their gross wage or salary. Below are given the gross wages of three employees: £7000, £9800 and £14 750. For each employee find:
   (a) the annual amount paid in national insurance,
   (b) the amount paid per annum into the pension fund.

2. A single woman has an annual income of £7000 per year. She is entitled only to a single person's allowance of £2605. Work out:
   (a) her taxable income,
   (b) the amount of tax payable if the basic rate of tax is 29%.

3. A married man earns £12000 per annum. His allowances to be set against income are married man's allowance of £4095 and pension fund payments of £720. Calculate:

   (a) his total allowances,
   (b) his taxable income,
   (c) the amount of tax payable per annum when the basic rate of tax is 25%.

4. A married man earns £8000 per annum and his wife earns £5000 per annum. The allowances are married man's allowance of £4095, wife's earned income allowance £2605 and pension fund payments of £400. Work out:

   (a) the total allowances,
   (b) the joint taxable income,
   (c) the amount of tax payable when the tax rate is 25% of taxable income.

MISCELLANEOUS EXERCISE 9

1. A woman's income is £9000 and she is allowed £3000 in tax free allowances.

   (a) Calculate her taxable income.
   (b) If tax is levied at 27%, find the amount of tax payable per annum.

2. A young man is paid £120 for a 40-hour week and overtime is paid at time-and-a-half.

   (a) Calculate the man's basic hourly rate of pay.
   (b) Calculate his hourly rate of overtime pay.
   (c) If he works 6 hours overtime in a certain week, work out his total wage for that week.

3. A salesman is paid a basic wage of £1100 per month. In addition he is paid a commission of 2% on the value of his sales. During one month he sold goods to the value of £15 000. Work out his total wage for the month.

4. A woman is paid 9 p for every article she produces up to a maximum of 160. After that she is paid a bonus of 2 p per article. During one day she produced 240 articles. how much did she earn on that day?

5. A secretary earns £9000 per annum. Deductions per annum amount to £810 for national insurance, £1800 for income tax and £540 for pension fund payments.

   (a) Calculate her total deductions for the year.
   (b) What is her net annual pay?
   (c) What is her monthly take-home pay?

6. A man has a taxable income of £25 000. Up to £17 200 tax is charged at 27%. After this the next £3000 is charged at 40% and the remainder, if any, at 50%. Calculate the amount of tax payable in a year.

7. A worker is paid £3.50 per hour for a 38-hour week.

   (a) Calculate his gross weekly wage.
   (b) He pays national insurance at a rate of 3.85% of his gross weekly wage. How much does he pay in national insurance per week?
   (c) If, in addition, he pays £17.30 per week in income tax, calculate his weekly take-home pay.

8. A man works a basic week of 40 hours at £5 per hour. Overtime is paid at time-and-a-quarter. Calculate his gross wage if he works 45 hours in a week.

Try to answer the following questions without writing anything down except the answer.

1. A man is paid £240 for a 40-hour week. What is his hourly rate of pay?

2. A man earns £5 per hour. How much will he earn for a 34-hour week?

3. A young woman is paid £2 per hour and overtime is paid at time-and-a-half. What is her overtime rate?

4. A jobbing gardener is paid £4 per hour. How much will she be paid for 5 hours work?

5. A man is paid 40 p for every article he produces. How much will he earn for a day in which he made 50 articles?

6. A woman has a taxable income of £300. If tax is levied at 25%, how much tax is payable?

7. National insurance is payable at 9% of gross salary. A man earns £6000 per annum. How much national insurance must he pay?

8. Commission is paid at 5% to an agent who sold £2000 of goods. How much commission did she earn?

CHAPTER 10

Money in Business and the Community

PROFIT AND LOSS

When a dealer buys or sells goods, the cost price is the price at which the goods are bought and the selling price is the price at which the goods are sold.

If a profit is made the selling price is greater than the cost price and

$$\text{Profit} = \text{Selling price} - \text{Cost price}$$

Example 1

A dealer buys a table for £120 and sells it for £170. Calculate the amount of profit made.

$$\text{Profit} = £170 - £120 = £50$$

The profit per cent is usually calculated on the cost price. That is:

$$\text{Profit \%} = \frac{\text{Profit}}{\text{Cost price}} \times \frac{100}{1}$$

Example 2

(a) A shopkeeper buys an article for £12 and sells it for £15. Calculate the percentage profit.

Selling price = £15

Cost price   = £12

Profit   = £15 − £12 = £3

$$\text{Profit \%} = \frac{3}{12} \times \frac{100}{1} = 25\%$$

(b) A shopkeeper buys 20 articles for a total cost of £40. She sells them for £3.60 each. Calculate:

 (i) The amount of the profit.

(ii) The percentage profit.

Cost price   = £40

Selling price = £3.60 × 20 = £72

(i) Profit = £72 − £40 = £32

(ii) Profit % $= \dfrac{32}{40} \times \dfrac{100}{1}$

$$= 80\%$$

If a loss is made, the cost price is greater than the selling price and

$$\text{Loss} = \text{Cost price} - \text{Selling price}$$

Example 3

A motor bike was bought for £300 and sold for £250. Work out the amount of the loss.

$$\text{Loss} = £300 - £250 = £50$$

As with percentage profit, the percentage loss is usually based upon the cost price.

$$\text{Loss \%} = \frac{\text{Loss}}{\text{Cost price}} \times \frac{100}{1}$$

Example 4

A woman buys a car for £6400 and sells it for £4800. Work out the percentage loss.

Cost price   = £6400

Selling price = £4800

Loss   = £6400 − £4800 = £1600

$$\text{Loss \%} = \frac{1600}{6400} \times \frac{100}{1} = 25\%$$

EXERCISE 10.1

1. A shopkeeper buys an article for £150 and sells it for £210. Work out the amount of his profit.

2. An article is bought for 30 p and sold for 45 p. Calculate the amount of the profit.

3. A greengrocer buys some grapes at 80 p per pound and sells them for £1 per pound. Calculate his percentage profit.

4. Calculate the percentage profit when:
   (a) cost price = £1.50 and selling price = £1.80.
   (b) cost price = 30 p and selling price = 35 p.

5. Calculate the loss per cent when:
   (a) cost price = 50 p and selling price = 40 p.
   (b) cost price = £80 and selling price = £60.

6. A retailer buys 30 ballpoint pens at 8 p each. Three of the pens are unsaleable but he sells the others for 10 p each. Work out his percentage profit.

7. A second-hand car is bought for £3000 and sold for £2500. Work out the percentage loss.

8. A shopkeeper buys a chair for £60 and sells it for £80.
   (a) What is the amount of his profit?
   (b) What is the percentage profit?

MARK UP

The mark up is the same as the percentage profit based on the cost price. That is

$$\text{Mark up} = \frac{\text{Profit}}{\text{Cost price}} \times \frac{100}{1}$$

Example 5

(a) A butcher buys a lamb weighing 15 kg for £30. He sells it at an average price of £2.60 per kilogram. Calculate the mark up.

Cost price   = £30 ÷ 15 = £2 per kilogram

Selling price = £2.60 per kilogram

Profit = £2.60 − £2.00 = £0.60 per kilogram

$$\text{Mark up} = \frac{0.60}{2.00} \times \frac{100}{1} = 30\%$$

(b) Calculate the price per kilogram at which potatoes should be sold if they are bought at £5 per 50 kg bag and the mark up is to be 30%.

In questions of this kind it is a good idea to set out the information in the form of a table as shown below:

	Cost price	Profit	Selling price
%	100	30	130
p	10	3	13

Note carefully that in problems on mark up, the cost price is always 100% and the selling price is the cost price plus the profit (in this case 100% + 30% = 130%). In the second row the cost price = 500 ÷ 50 = 10 p. The profit is 30% of 10 p = 3 p and the selling price is 10 p + 3 p = 13 p per kilogram.

(c) A furniture shop sells a table for £168. If the mark up is 40%, find the price the shop paid for the table.

	Cost price	Profit	Selling price
%	100	40	140
£			168

From the table we see that 140% is equivalent to £168. Since the cost price is represented by 100%:

$$\text{Cost price} = £\frac{100}{140} \times \frac{168}{1} = £120$$

EXERCISE 10.2

1. A carpet shop buys stair carpet at £6 per metre length and sells it for £7.20 per metre. Work out the mark up.

2. A greengrocer buys 200 grapefruit for £32. He sells them at 20 p each. Calculate his mark up.

3. A store buys dress material at £7.20 per metre length. The manager decides on a mark up of 25%. Work out the selling price of the material.

4. A department store buys washing machines for £270 each. Work out the selling price of the machines if the mark up is to be 30%.

5. A dealer buys 20 second-hand electric fires for £150. He wants a mark up of 50%. At what price should he sell each fire?

6. A furniture shop sells dining chairs for £40 each. If the mark up is 25%, work out the cost price of the chairs.

7. A carpet is sold to a customer for £98. If the mark up is 40%, calculate the cost price of the carpet.

8. A greengrocer sells oranges at 16 p each. If his mark up is 35%, find how much was paid for a box of 100 oranges.

9. A bakery has weekly takings of £4050. If the mark up is 20%, work out the amount of the weekly profit.

10. A book shop has monthly sales of £18 000. The mark up is 30%. Work out the amount of the monthly profit.

MARGIN

Although it is usual to calculate the percentage profit based upon the cost price it is much simpler for a retailer to calculate his percentage profit based upon the selling price. This is because the till shows the amount of the takings per day or per week and if the profit per cent is based upon the selling price it is easy to calculate the profit per cent. When the profit is stated as a percentage of the selling price it is called the *margin*.

Example 6

A retailer finds that a week's takings amount to £2400. His margin is 20%. Work out:

(a) the weekly profit,
(b) the cost price of the goods sold,
(c) the mark up.

Setting out the information in the form of a table we have:

	Cost price	Profit	Selling price
%	80	20	100
£			2400

In problems on margin it is the selling price which is represented by 100%.

$$\text{Since } 100\% = £2400$$

(a) $\text{Profit} = £\dfrac{20}{100} \times \dfrac{2400}{1} = £480$

(b) $\text{Cost price} = £2400 - £480 = £1920$

(c) $\text{Mark up} = \dfrac{\text{Profit}}{\text{Cost price}} \times \dfrac{100}{1}$

$$= \dfrac{480}{1920} \times \dfrac{100}{1}$$

$$= 25\%$$

RELATION BETWEEN MARGIN AND MARK UP

The method of dealing with margin and mark up is best illustrated by an example.

Example 7

A grocer marks up his goods by 30%. Work out his margin.

The easiest way is to assume that the grocer sells goods which cost him £100.

$\text{Profit} = 30\% \text{ of } £100 = £30$

$\text{Selling price} = £100 + £30 = £130$

$$\text{Margin} = \dfrac{\text{Profit}}{\text{Selling price}} \times \dfrac{100}{1}$$

$$= \dfrac{30}{130} \times \dfrac{100}{1}$$

$$= 23.08\%$$

EXERCISE 10.3

1. The weekly takings of a shop are £3000. If the margin is 20%, calculate the weekly profit.

2. A retailer has daily takings of £750. If his margin is 25%, calculate:
   (a) his profit,
   (b) the cost price of the goods sold,
   (c) the mark up.

3. A grocer works on a mark up of 40%. What is his margin?

4. A furniture store works on a margin of 20%. What is the mark up?

5. A firm works on a margin of 40%. During one month the firm made a profit of £2700. Work out the selling price of the goods sold.

6. A department store works on a margin of 35%.
   (a) Work out the mark up.
   (b) If its sales during one week are £53 000, work out the amount of the profit.

7. A grocer marks up the price of butter which he sells by 30%. Calculate his margin.

8. A butcher buys 60 kg of beef for £144. He sells it for an average price of £3 per kilogram. Calculate his margin.

(a) Gross profit = £350 000 − £220 000

   = £130 000

(b) Net profit = £130 000 − £70 000

   = £60 000

(c) Gross profit % = $\dfrac{130\,000}{350\,000} \times \dfrac{100}{1}$

   = 37.1%

(d) Net profit % = $\dfrac{60\,000}{350\,000} \times \dfrac{100}{1}$

   = 17.1%

GROSS AND NET PROFIT

We have seen that the profit is the difference between the cost price and the selling price. This gives us the *gross profit*.

However there are other expenses such as wages to pay assistants, transport costs, rates, etc. These extra expenses are called *overheads*.

To calculate the net profit we must subtract the overheads from the gross profit.

The total sales or takings are often called the *turnover*.

   Gross profit = Turnover − Cost price

   Net profit = Gross Profit − Overheads

Example 8

A turnover of a store during a certain year amounted to £350 000. The goods sold cost £220 000 and the overheads amounted to £70 000. Work out:

(a) the gross profit,
(b) the net profit,
(c) the gross profit as a percentage of the turnover,
(d) the net profit as a percentage of the turnover.

EXERCISE 10.4

1. The turnover of a small business totalled £38 000 during a certain year. If the goods sold cost £23 000 to buy and the overheads amounted to £7000, find:
   (a) the gross profit,
   (b) the net profit,
   (c) the gross profit expressed as a percentage of the turnover,
   (d) the net profit expressed as a percentage of the turnover.

2. A grocer's weekly takings are £5000 per week and he makes a gross profit of 25% on these sales. If the overheads amount to £400 per week, work out:
   (a) the gross profit per week,
   (b) the net profit per week,
   (c) the net profit per week expressed as a percentage of the weekly takings.

83

3. A grocer expects to make a net profit of £16 800 in a year's trading. During the year the cost price of the goods he sells amount to £72 000 and his overheads amount to £16 000.

   (a) Calculate the amount of his annual sales so that he can make the expected profit.

   (b) Express this expected net profit as a percentage of his annual sales.

4. The sales of a confectioner amount to £1400 per week and the cost price of the goods she sells amount to £880 per week. The shop costs £112 per week to rent and an assistant is paid £128 per week. Work out:

   (a) the net profit per week,

   (b) the net profit expressed as a percentage of the sales,

   (c) the net profit expressed as a percentage of the cost price of the goods sold.

5. A chemist has total sales of £110 000 per year and the cost price of the goods he sells amounted to £70 000 per year. The overheads consist of rates £1000 per year, salaries £10 000 per year, heating £1160 per year and lighting £600 per year. Calculate:

   (a) the gross profit,

   (b) the amount of the overheads,

   (c) the net profit,

   (d) the net profit expressed as a percentage of the turnover,

   (e) the net profit expressed as a percentage of the cost price.

DISCOUNT

When a customer buys goods from a retailer for cash (as opposed to hire-purchase) he or she will often ask the retailer for a *discount*. This discount which is a percentage of the selling price of the goods is the amount which the retailer will take off the selling price of the goods thus reducing the profit.

Example 9

A dining table is offered for sale at £350. A customer is offered a 10% discount for cash. Work out:

(a) the amount of the discount,
(b) the amount the customer actually pays.

(a) Amount of discount = 10% of £350 = £35

(b) Amount paid = £350 − £35 = £315

Alternatively:

Since a discount of 10% is given the customer pays only 90% of the selling price (i.e., 100% − 10%). So

Amount paid = 90% of £350 = £315

Sometimes discounts are quoted as so much in the pound, for instance 5 p in the £1. If it is remembered that 5 p in the £1 is the same as 5% then the calculation of discounts is the same as that shown in Example 9.

Example 10

A girl buys a dress priced at £12.50 but she is given a discount of 8 p in the £1. How much will she actually pay for the dress?

Because 8 p in the £1 is the same as a discount of 8%

Amount of discount = 8% of £12.50 = £1

Amount paid for the dress = £12.50 − £1
= £11.50

EXERCISE 10.5

1. A chair marked for sale at £28 is sold for cash at a discount of 10%. How much did the customer actually pay?

2. A tailor charges £60 for a suit of clothes but allows a discount of 5% for cash. How much is the cash price?

3. A furniture shop offers a $2\frac{1}{2}$% discount for all cash sales. How much will a customer pay for a wardrobe marked for sale at £400?

4. A clothing shop offers a discount of 5 p in the £1 on all sales. How much will a woman actually pay for a skirt marked for sale at £25?

5. During a sale a store offers a discount of 7 p in the £1 for all sales. A man buys a coat marked for sale at £90. How much will he actually pay for the coat?

INVOICES

An invoice is a document which states the quantity, description and prices of goods sold to a retailer by a manufacturer or a wholesaler. It also gives details of any discounts and it is sent to the purchaser when the goods are dispatched. Although it looks rather like a bill it is not a demand for payment.

A typical invoice is shown below.

INVOICE		
No. 93	Bought of	25 Great St
N. Green, Esq.	S. Brown	London W1
17 South St,		
Cheltenham		

30 pairs of shoes at £23.00 per pair	£690.00
20 pairs slippers at £8.80 per pair	176.00
40 pairs plimsoles at £7.20 per pair	288.00
	1154.00
Less 20% discount	230.80
	£923.20

VALUE ADDED TAX

Value added tax (or VAT for short) is a tax on goods and services which are purchased. Some services and goods bear no tax, for instance books, insurance premiums and food. The rate of tax varies from time to time but at the moment it is levied at 15%.

Example 11

(a) A man buys a lawn mower which is priced at £50 plus VAT. How much will he have to pay for the mower if VAT is levied at 15%?

Amount of VAT = 15% of £50 = £7.50
Total cost of mower = £50 + £7.50 = £57.50

(b) A housewife buys a dining table for £108 the price including VAT. If the rate of tax is 15%, what is the price of the table excluding VAT?

Let 100% be the price exclusive of VAT then 115% is the price inclusive of VAT
115% represents £108.

100% represents $£\dfrac{100}{115} \times \dfrac{108}{1} = £93.91$

So the price exclusive of VAT is £93.91

EXERCISE 10.6

1. Prepare an invoice for the following:

   50 pairs of double sheets at £16 per pair
   30 pairs of single sheets at £12 per pair
   80 pillowcases at £5 each
   20 duvets at £35 each

   A discount of 25% is allowed.

2. A housewife buys a washing machine whose price exclusive of VAT is £360. If VAT is charged at 15%, how much will the woman have to pay for the machine?

3. An armchair is priced at £108 inclusive of VAT which is levied at 15%. Find the price of the armchair exclusive of VAT.

4. A woman buys a refrigerator priced at £320 exclusive of VAT. If VAT is charged at 15%, find how much the woman pays altogether.

5. A telephone bill is £60 excluding VAT. How much is the bill when VAT at 15% is added on?

6. A radio costs £69 including VAT at 15%. What is the cost excluding VAT?

7. Work out the amount of VAT which is charged on a garage bill of £80 which includes VAT at 15%.

8. A carpet costs £460 including VAT. How much does it cost before VAT at 15% is added on?

RATES

Every property in a town or village is given a rateable value which is fixed by the District Valuer (an Inland Revenue official). This rateable value depends upon the size, condition and location of the property.

Each local authority calculates the amount of money it will need to raise through rates to pay for the services, such as education, police and libraries, which it provides. The rates are levied at so much in the £1 of rateable value, for example 129 p in the £1.

In addition, water rates are levied to pay for the cost of providing a water supply, sewerage and environmental services. The water rate is levied by the local water authority, for instance the Severn-Trent Water Authority.

Annual rates = Rateable value × Rate in the £1

Example 12

(a) The rateable value of a house is £220. If the rate is 125 p in the £1, how much must the householder pay in rates?

$$\text{Yearly rates} = 220 \times £1.25 = £275$$

(b) A householder pays £360 in rates on a property which has a rateable value of £300. What is the rate in the pound?

For a rateable value of £300 the rates payable are £360. For a rateable value of £1 the rates payable are

$$£\frac{360}{300} = £1.20$$

So the rates are levied at 120 p in the £1.

Most local authorities state, on their rate demand, the product of a penny rate. This is the amount that would be raised if the rate was levied at 1 p in the £1.

Example 13

(a) The total rateable value of a city is £93 350 000. Find the product of a penny rate.

$$\text{Product of penny rate} = £93 350 000 \times £0.01$$
$$= £933 500$$

(b) For a county council the total rateable value is £64 237 000. The cost of libraries and museums is estimated to be £17 220 000 per annum. What local rate should be levied to pay for this expenditure?

Product of penny rate $= £64\,327\,000 \times £0.01$

$$= £643\,270$$

Rate to be levied $= \dfrac{17\,220\,000}{643\,270}$ p

$$= 26.77 \text{ p}$$

Hence a rate of 26.77 p in the pound should be levied.

Example 14

A water authority levies a rate of 15.300 p in the £1 for water supply and 15.980 p in the £1 for sewerage and environmental services. A property has a rateable value of £320. How much, per annum, will the householder pay to the water authority?

Total rates payable $= (15.300 + 15.980)$
$$= 31.28 \text{ p}$$

Total amount payable $= 320 \times £0.3128$
$$= £100.10$$

EXERCISE 10.7

1. The rateable value of a house is £360. Calculate the yearly rates payable by the householder when the rates are levied at 140 p in the £1.

2. A householder pays £360 in rates when the rates are 150 p in the £1. What is the rateable value of the house?

3. A house has a rateable value of £270. The householder pays £324 in rates for the year. Work out the rate in the pound.

4. What rate should a local authority levy if they need to raise £100 000 from a total rateable value of £320 000?

5. Calculate the total income from the rates of a town having a rateable value of £2 150 000 when the rates are levied at 108 p in the £1.

6. A village having a rateable value of £772 000 needs to raise £70 400 from the rates. What rate in the £1 should they levy?

7. The total rateable value of all the property in a city is £85 000 000. Work out the product of a penny rate.

8. The total rateable value of a town is £8 796 000.
   (a) Work out the product of a penny rate.
   (b) What rate in the £1 should be levied if the total amount to be raised is £4 837 800.

9. The total rateable value of all the property in a small town is £2 550 000. Find the total annual cost of the public library if a rate of 4.6 p in the £1 must be levied for this purpose.

10. The expenditure of a town is £1 800 000 and its rates are levied at 174 p in the £1. The annual cost of its public park is £60 000. What rate in the £1 is needed for the upkeep of the park?

INSURANCE

Our future is something which is far from certain. We could become too ill to work or we could be badly injured or even killed in an accident. Our house could be burnt down or burgled. We could become involved in a motor accident in which we might be liable for injuries and damage. How do we take care of such eventualities? The answer is to take out insurance policies as a way of investing in the future that we are so uncertain about.

Insurance works like this. The insurance company charges the policy holders, each year, a sum of money known as the *premium*. Thousands of people pay these premiums and hence the insurance company collects a very large sum of money each year. It invests this money to earn interest and dividends which it uses to meet the claims of its policy holders.

Example 15

A householder values his house and its contents at £45 000. His insurance company charges a premium of £3 per annum per £1000 insured. How much is the annual premium?

$$\text{Annual premium} = £\frac{3 \times 45\,000}{1000} = £135$$

CAR INSURANCE

By law a vehicle must be insured and the owner of a vehicle can be prosecuted for not having third party insurance.

THIRD PARTY

There are two ways of insuring a vehicle. Third party insurance is taken out in case someone is injured or damage is caused which is the fault of the policy holder. Third party insurance covers only the other person: it does not cover the policy holder who will have to pay himself for any damage to his vehicle. A fully comprehensive policy is needed to cover damage to the policy holder's vehicle plus damage to other people and their property.

The size of the premium depends upon:

(1) The value of the policy holder's vehicle.

(2) The engine size.

(3) The area in which the policy holder lives.

(4) Special risks (sports cars and young drivers).

(5) The use to which the vehicle is put (taxi, private motoring, carrying of goods, etc.).

If a driver makes no claims during a year he or she will get a bonus (called a no-claims bonus) which means that he or she will pay a smaller premium the following year.

Example 16

A car owner is quoted a premium of £180 to insure his vehicle but he is allowed a no-claims bonus of 25%. How much does the car owner actually pay?

$$\text{No-claims bonus} = 25\% \text{ of } £180 = £45$$
$$\text{Insurance premium} = £180 - £45$$
$$= £135$$

COST OF RUNNING A CAR

Running a car can be expensive. The major expenses which will be incurred are as follows:

(1) Cost of petrol. This depends upon the petrol consumption (measured in kilometres per litre or miles per gallon). The greater the petrol consumption the greater the cost.

(2) Insurance premiums which have been discussed above.

(3) Road Fund Licence. Every motor vehicle requires this licence when it is first registered and the licence must be renewed periodically. In 1988 the licence fee for one year was £100.

(4) Depreciation. As a vehicle ages it loses value.

(5) Cost of maintenance and repairs including tyre wear. The cost of repairs depends upon the amount of work you do yourself.

Example 17

A car has an average petrol consumption of 40 miles per gallon. If petrol costs £1.74 per gallon and the yearly mileage was 11 000 miles, work out the yearly expenditure on petrol.

Amount of petrol used = (11 000 ÷ 40) gallons

$$= 275 \text{ gallons}$$

Cost of petrol = £1.74 × 275

$$= 478.50$$

Example 18

A car is bought for £4600 and used for one year. It is then sold for £3500. During this year the car did 20 000 km and averaged 12 km per litre of petrol which cost 45 p per litre. Insurance cost £187, tax £100 and repairs and maintenance £450. Work out

(a) the cost of petrol used during the year,
(b) the total cost of a year's motoring,
(c) the cost per kilometre.

(a) Amount of petrol used = (20 000 ÷ 12) litres

$$= 1667 \text{ litres}$$

Cost of petrol = £0.45 × 1667

$$= £750$$

(b)

	£
Depreciation	= 1100
Insurance	= 187
Tax	= 100
Repairs and maintenance	= 450
Cost of petrol	= 750
Total cost for the year	= 2587

(c) Cost per kilometre = £2587 ÷ 20 000 = £0.13 or 13 p

LIFE ASSURANCE

With this type of assurance a sum of money, depending upon the size of the premium, etc., is paid to the dependants (wife or husband and children) of the policy holder upon his or her death. The amount of the premiums depend upon:

(1) The age of the person (the younger the policy holder is the less he or she pays in premiums because there is less chance of him or her dying soon).

(2) The amount of money the policy holder wants the dependants to receive (the larger the amount the greater the premiums).

Example 19

A man aged 35 years wishes to assure his life for £7000. The insurance company quotes an annual premium of £13.90 per £1000 assured. Calculate the amount of the monthly premium.

$$\text{Annual premium} = £13.90 \times \frac{7000}{1000} = £97.30$$

$$\text{Monthly premium} = 97.30 \div 12 = £8.11$$

ENDOWMENT ASSURANCE

This is very similar to life assurance but the policy holder can decide for how long she is going to pay the premium. At the end of the chosen period a lump sum is paid to the policy holder. If, however, the policy holder dies before the end of the chosen period, the assured sum of money is paid to his or her dependants. Some endowment and whole life policies are 'with profits'. This means that a bonus based upon the profits that the insurance company makes will be paid in addition to the sum assured.

Example 20

A woman aged 35 wishes to take out a 'with profits' endowment assurance policy. She is quoted a monthly premium of £14.95 for a 15 year term. The guaranteed death benefit is £20 000. Calculate the monthly premium if she wishes to insure herself for £50 000.

$$\text{Monthly premium} = £14.95 \times \frac{50\,000}{20\,000} = £37.38$$

EXERCISE 10.8

1. A householder wishes to insure his house against fire for £40 000. His insurance company charge an annual premium of £1.60 per £1000 insured.

   (a) Work out the amount of the annual premium.
   (b) What is the monthly premium?

2. The insurance premium on a car is £110 but a 40% no-claims bonus is allowed. How much is the annual premium?

3. A car is bought for £6500 and sold, one year later, for £5600. During this year it used petrol costing £950. Insurance cost £130, road tax £100 and maintenance £240. Work out the cost of running the car for the year.

4. During one year a motorist travelled 15 000 miles. The fuel consumption of his car was 30 miles per gallon.

   (a) Work out the number of gallons of petrol used during the year.
   (b) If petrol cost £1.75 per gallon, calculate the cost of petrol.

5. After one year's use the depreciation on a motor cycle was £200. The owner travelled 10 000 miles on it during that year and fuel consumption was, on average, 80 miles per gallon. If petrol cost £1.90 per gallon, road tax £60 and insurance £85, work out:

   (a) the cost of petrol for the year,
   (b) the total cost of a year's motorcycling,
   (c) the cost per mile of motorcycling.

6. A man aged 40 years takes out a 'with profits' endowment policy for which the monthly premium is £10.95. He is guaranteed £8000 at the end of 15 years but the insurance company states that the maturity value of the policy is likely to be £10 000.

   (a) Calculate how much the man will pay in premiums over the 15 year period.
   (b) Work out the amount of the profit he is likely to make on the policy.

7. A man wishes to assure his life for £20 000. The insurance company quotes an annual premium of £12.80 per £1000 assured. Calculate the amount of the monthly premium.

MISCELLANEOUS EXERCISE 10

1. The premium for insuring a car is £180 but the owner is allowed a no-claims bonus of 30%. How much does the owner actually pay for the insurance?

2. Mrs Smith insures her jewellery for £3000. The premium is 30 pence per £100 insured. What is the total premium?

3. A home computer costs £1200 plus VAT at 15%. Work out the amount a customer will have to pay for the computer.

4. An electric fire is offered for sale at £90. For cash, a customer will be allowed a discount of 5%. How much will a customer actually pay for the fire?

5. A dealer buys an armchair for £600 and sells it for £720. Work out his percentage profit.

6. The rateable value of a house is £400. How much will be paid annually in rates when these are levied at £1.20 in the £1?

7. The costs involved in running a car for one year are: depreciation £350, petrol and oil £820, maintenance £250 and insurance and road tax £340.
(a) Work out the cost of running a car for the year.
(b) If the owner travelled 8000 miles during the year, what was the cost per mile?

8. A motor cycle was bought for £400 and sold for £350. Work out the percentage loss.

MENTAL TEST 10

1. The total cost of running a car for a year was £4000. If it travelled 50 000 km, how much did it cost per kilometre?

2. VAT is charged at 15%. How much VAT is payable on goods priced at £300?

3. The rateable value of a house is £500. Rates are levied at £2 in the £1. How much must the householder pay in rates for a year?

4. A shopkeeper made a profit of £20 on an article which he bought for £200. What was his percentage profit?

5. An article is priced at £500 but a discount of 10% is allowed for cash. How much will a cash-paying customer actually pay?

6. A car owner suffered a loss of £100 in selling his car which he bought for £1000. What was his percentage loss?

7. A car is insured for £100 but a no-claims bonus of 25% is allowed. How much does the owner have to pay?

8. A house is insured for £40 000. The annual premium is £5 per £1000 of insurance. How much is the annual premium?

91

CHAPTER 11

Household Finance

CREDIT

Several forms of credit are available.

Hire Purchase

When goods are purchased and paid for by instalments they are said to be bought on *hire-purchase.* Usually the purchaser pays a deposit and the remainder of the purchase price (called the balance) plus interest is repaid by a number of instalments.

Example 1

A woman buys a microwave oven for £220. She pays a deposit of 20% and interest of 10% is paid on the outstanding balance. She repays the balance plus interest in 12 monthly instalments. Calculate the amount of each instalment.

Deposit = 20% of £220 = £44

Balance = £220 − £44 = £176

Interest = 10% of £176 = £17.60

Total to be repaid = £176 + £17.60 = £193.60

Monthly repayments = £193.60 ÷ 12 = £16.13

In Example 1, 10% would only be the true rate of interest if all the outstanding balance was paid at the end of the year. However, as each instalment is paid the amount outstanding is reduced and hence a larger proportion of each successive payment is interest. The true rate of interest, called the *annual percentage rate,* or APR for short, is in fact about 19%.

Credit Cards

Goods and services may also be purchased by means of credit cards. These cards are issued by banks and other credit agencies. When buying goods the card is handed to the shop assistant who takes a note of its number and issues the purchaser with a form which gives details of the purchase. A copy of this form is sent to the credit card company which sends a monthly statement to the purchaser, listing the purchases made and total amount owed. If the purchaser pays off this amount within a set period, (say, within four weeks of the statement date) no interest is payable. However, if desired the purchaser can pay the bill by instalments. Interest will be charged but note that no deposit need be paid; however, the credit card company does impose a limit on the amount of credit it will allow.

Example 2

A customer buys goods to the value of £500 in a departmental store and pays on a credit scheme at an interest rate of 26.8%. If the bill plus interest is to be paid in ten equal instalments work out the amount of each instalment.

Interest = 26.8% of £500 = £134

Total to be repaid = £500 + £134 = £634

Amount of instalment = £634 ÷ 10 = £63.40

Example 3

A credit card company charges a nominal interest rate of 12% for credit. A woman buys an armchair for £128 and pays back the cost of the chair plus interest in four equal instalments. Work out the true rate of interest (i.e., the APR).

Interest = 12% of £128 = £15.36

Total to be paid = £128 + £15.36 = £143.36

Amount of each instalment = £143.36 ÷ 4
= £35.84

Interest payable every three months = £15.36
÷ 4 = £3.84

£128 is the balance outstanding for the first three months

£(128 − 32) = £96 is the balance for the next three months

£(96 − 32) = £64 is the balance for the next three months

£32 is the balance for the final three months

Note that in calculating the outstanding balances we have said that the amount actually paid off the balance every three months is

$$£35.84 - £3.84 = £32.$$

Average amount of the loan for the entire year

$$= £(128 + 96 + 64 + 32) \div 4 = £80$$

As £15.36 is the interest paid on an actual loan of £80, the true rate of interest may be calculated by using the simple interest formula:

$$R = \frac{100I}{PT} = \frac{100 \times 15.36}{80 \times 1} = 19.2\%$$

Thus APR = 19.2%

Personal Loans

Banks and finance houses often make personal loans. They charge interest for this service and in this way they make a profit. The borrower pays back the loan plus interest (calculated by using the APR) which is repaid in a number of equal monthly instalments.

A typical repayment table giving monthly repayments over various periods is shown below.

Personal loan (18.8% APR)				
	3 years	5 years	10 years	15 years
£1000	35.85	25.07	17.63	15.67
£2000	71.70	50.14	35.27	31.35
£5000	179.26	125.34	88.17	78.37
£10 000	358.52	250.68	176.34	156.74
£20 000	717.04	501.36	352.68	313.49

Example 4

Use the monthly repayment table above to find the monthly repayments on a loan of £5000 taken out for a period of 3 years.

Monthly repayments for 5 years = £179.26

EXERCISE 11.1

1. The following items are available from a mail-order catalogue. Work out (i) the total cost when paying by instalments, (ii) the difference between the cash price and the instalment price.
   (a) A blouson, cash price £129.00 or £6.97 for 20 weeks.
   (b) A ladies leather suit, cash price £199.00 or £2.45 for 100 weeks.
   (c) A wardrobe, cash price £160 or £4.67 for 38 weeks.

2. A credit card company put out the following table showing the monthly repayments for various loans over different periods.

	12 months	24 months	36 months
Amount of loan	Monthly payments	Monthly payments	Monthly payments
£300	£27.52	£14.99	£10.86
£500	£45.86	£24.99	£18.10
£800	£73.38	£39.98	£28.96
£1000	£91.73	£49.98	£36.21

(a) Work out the total amount payable for loans of (i) £300 over 12 months, (ii) £800 over 36 months and (iii) £1000 over 24 months.

(b) Calculate the total amount payable on a loan of £500 over 24 months and find how much of this is interest.

3. (a) A man buys a washing machine for £300. He pays a deposit of 20%. Work out the amount of the deposit.
   (b) How much is the outstanding balance?
   (c) Interest of £47.28 is added to the outstanding balance. Find the total amount to be repaid.
   (d) If the balance plus interest is repayable by 12 equal monthly instalments, find the amount of each instalment.

4. The cash price of a dining room table is £400. To buy it on hire purchase a deposit of £100 plus ten equal monthly payments of £42 is required.
   (a) Calculate the amount paid for the table if it is bought on hire purchase.
   (b) What is the difference between the hire purchase price and the cash price?

5. A woman buys a suite of furniture for £750. A deposit of 25% is paid and interest on the outstanding balance amounts to £112.50. Work out
   (a) the amount of the deposit,
   (b) the outstanding balance,

(c) the total amount to be repaid,
(d) the amount of each instalment if four quarterly repayments are to be made.

6. A man borrows £500 from his bank and interest amounts to £100. He repays the loan plus interest in ten equal monthly payments. Calculate the amount of each payment.

7. A woman buys a washing machine priced at £150. She pays a deposit of £30. If the APR is 20% and the balance plus interest is to be repaid in 10 equal monthly instalments,
   (a) how much is the outstanding balance?
   (b) work out the amount of interest payable
   (c) calculate the outstanding balance plus interest
   (d) how much is each instalment?

8. A man buys a motor cycle for £640. He pays a deposit of 20% and the APR is 12%. The balance plus interest is to be repaid in 4 equal quarterly instalments.
   (a) Work out the amount of the deposit.
   (b) How much is the outstanding balance?
   (c) Calculate the amount of interest payable.
   (d) How much is the total amount to be repaid?
   (e) How much is each quarterly instalment?

9. A man buys a refrigerator for £240. He uses a credit card to pay and hence pays no deposit. He is charged interest at a nominal 10% for the whole period of the loan. The loan plus interest is to be repaid in 4 equal quarterly instalments. Find:
   (a) the amount of interest payable
   (b) the total amount to be repaid
   (c) the amount of each quarterly instalment
   (d) the average amount of the loan for the entire year
   (e) the true rate of interest (i.e., the APR).

10. A woman pays for a chest of drawers priced at £100 by means of a credit card. She agrees to pay the £100 plus interest at 20% over the complete period of the loan. If she pays two half-yearly instalments, find the amount of each and calculate the APR.

RENT

Rent is a charge for accommodation and it is generally paid weekly or monthly to the landlord who owns the property. The biggest owners of rented property are local councils.

The landlord may include rates in the charge for accommodation but if he or she does not it is the tenant's responsibility to see that these are paid.

Example 5

A landlord charges £17 per week rent for a flat. If the rates are £101.40 per annum calculate the weekly cost of rent and rates.

Rates per week = £101.40 ÷ 52 = £1.95

Cost of rent and rates = £17.00 + £1.95

= £18.95 per week

MORTGAGES

People who want to buy their own house generally borrow the money they need from a bank, a building society or a local council. Such loans are called *mortgages.*

The lenders, whoever they are, will usually demand a deposit of 5, 10 or 20% although sometimes 100% mortgages are available. Today there are several different kinds of mortgages, to suit a variety of personal financial circumstances.

Repayment Mortgages

With this type of mortgage the money borrowed is repaid over an agreed number of years by means of monthly instalments. Each monthly instalment includes interest plus some of the original capital. Although adding the two amounts together can produce a total monthly outlay (before tax relief is taken into account) which is the same throughout the mortgage, in the early years the amount paid each month is mainly taken up in interest payments and consequently the amounts paid in capital are lowest. The cost of life assurance or other protection (to repay the mortgage should the borrower die unexpectedly) must be added to capital and interest payments.

Endowment Mortgages

With this type of mortgage interest is paid on the money borrowed along with premiums on a life assurance policy. This policy ensures that the mortgage is paid off should the borrower die unexpectedly, whilst building up capital out of which the loan will finally be repaid. Often a tax-free, cash surplus remains. A 'with profits' endowment mortgage is more expensive but the tax-free cash surplus will be much greater and for young people the cost of the insurance is often low enough for the with profits endowment mortgage to prove competitive with the repayment type mortgage.

MIRAS

Tax relief is given only on the interest paid; it does not apply to repayments of the original capital. This tax relief, known as Mortgage Interest Relief At Source (MIRAS) plays a major part in bringing down the cost of borrowing money to buy your home. In most cases this tax relief is given automatically. The rules are set by the Inland Revenue but the work is done by the banks, building societies and others who lend the money. Relief at the basic rate of income tax (at present 25%) is deducted from the interest that borrowers are asked to pay. Basic rate taxpayers have no more to do but if tax is paid at the higher rate (at present 40%) the borrower must ask the tax office to change his tax code to claim full relief. Tax relief is only given on mortgages up to a maximum of £30 000 on the property irrespective of the number of borrowers.

The Mortgage Rate

Interest is charged at a nominal rate (at present 13%) which may vary from time to time at the discretion of the bank or building society who lend the money. However it is the APR figure which shows the true cost of mortgage borrowing. It is this rate which should be used to make any cost comparisons between lenders, as well as comparing the actual monthly repayments.

The following tables show mortgage repayment information and are typical of those produced by banks and building societies.

ENDOWMENT AND PENSION MORTGAGES
Mortgage term: 25 years

AMOUNT OF MORTGAGE		£20,000	£50,000
APR		13.7%	13.6%
Typical gross quarterly interest charge		£650.00	£1,625.00
Typical net quarterly interest charge		£487.50	£1,381.25
Total amount payable gross[1]		£85,157.82	£212,757.06
Total amount payable net[1]		£68,896.88	£188,365.96

REPAYMENT MORTGAGE
Mortgage term: 25 years

AMOUNT OF MORTGAGE		£20,000	£50,000
APR		13.7%	13.7%
Gross repayments	Monthly repayment	£223.58	£558.95
	Total amount payable[1]	£67,191.17	£167.840.70
Annually revised net monthly repayments	First year	£170.08	£477.70
	Final year	£219.34	£549.29
	Total amount payable net[1]	£55,516.84	£146,488.56
Constant net monthly repayments	Monthly repayment	£177.20	£480.45
	Total amount payable net[1]	£53,281.05	£144,289.40

[1] Includes interest, capital and an estimate of expenses, but not life assurance cover or a pension plan.
[2] The net interest and the total amount payable figures shown are after the deduction of mortgage interest relief at the basic rate of income tax only (currently 25%) and are subject to the present mortgage interest relief limit of £30 000.
[3] The APR may vary from time to time.
[4] No account has been taken of any higher rate tax relief.

Example 6

(a) A man wishes to buy a house costing £32 000. He pays a 10% deposit. How much mortgage will he require?

Method 1

Deposit $= 10\%$ of £32 000 $=$ £3200

Mortgage required $=$ £32 000 $-$ £3200

$= $ £28 800

Method 2

Since a deposit of 10% is paid the mortgage required is 90% of the purchase price.

Mortgage required $= 90\%$ of £32 000

$= $ £28 000

(b) A building society quotes the repayments on a mortgage as being £98.80 per month per £10 000 borrowed over a period of 20 years. Work out the monthly repayments on a mortgage of £35 000 over 20 years.

Monthly repayments $=$ £$\dfrac{35\,000}{10\,000} \times 98.80$

$= $ £345.80

Example 7

A man wants to borrow £50 000 to buy a house. The loan is to be covered by an endowment policy for a 20-year period which costs £3.88 per £1000 assured per annum. A bank quotes the quarterly interest charges as £1406.25. Taking a quarter as being three months, work out the total monthly cost of the arrangement.

Monthly interest payments $=$ £1406.25 $\div$ 3

$= $ £468.75

Monthly endowment premiums $=$ £$\dfrac{50\,000}{1000} \times 3.88$

$= $ £194

Total monthly payments $=$ £468.75 $+$ £194.00

$= $ £662.75

EXERCISE 11.2

1. Calculate the weekly rent of flats or houses when the annual rent is as follows:
   (a) £988   (b) £1222   (c) £1846

2. A house is rented for £45.32 per week and the rates are £247 per annum. Work out the cost per week of rent and rates.

3. A house is rented for £49.36 per week. Its rateable value is £228 and the rates are levied at £1.36 in the £1.
   (a) Work out the annual cost of the rates.
   (b) Calculate the cost per week for rent and rates.

4. The table below shows the monthly repayments payable on a building society mortgage of £10 000.

Period	Monthly repayments
15 years	£88.79
20 years	£78.33
25 years	£72.75

Find the monthly repayments for the following mortgages:
   (a) £20 000 for 20 years,
   (b) £50 000 for 15 years,
   (c) £35 000 for 25 years.

5. A woman borrows £36 000 from a building society to buy a house. The loan is covered by an endowment policy for the ten-year term of the loan, the premiums being £7.95 per annum per £1000 assured. The building society charges £1012.50 per quarter (3 months). Work out the woman's total monthly repayments.

6. Calculate the monthly cost of owning a house if the outgoings are as follows: mortgage repayments £168.64 per month, insurances £354 per annum and rates £163 per half-year.

BUDGET ACCOUNTS

Most banks now operate budget accounts. The customer tells the bank the amounts he or she expects to pay out during next year. The bank then transfers one-twelfth of the year's total from the customer's current account each month to a special budget account. The bills are then paid out of that account.

Example 8

A family wish to open a budget account for bills which they think will occur next year. They want to budget for:

Life assurance premiums of £8.76 per month
Mortgage repayments of £128.83 per month
Gas bills of £46 per quarter
Electricity bills of £52 per quarter
Telephone bills of £42 per quarter

(a) Work out the amount which should be placed in the budget account per month.
(b) The bank makes a charge for this service which is £80 per £2000 paid out plus £1 for each additional £50 or part of £50. Work out the bank charges for this budget account.

(a) The costs per annum are:

Life assurance	= £8.76 × 12	= £105.12
Mortgage	= £128.83 × 12	= £1545.96
Gas	= £46 × 4	= £184.00
Electricity	= £52 × 4	= £208.00
Telephone	= £42 × 4	= £168.00

Total annual cost = £2211.08

Cost per month = £2211.08 ÷ 12 = £184.26

(b) Residue over £2000 = £211.08

Therefore the additional charge is £5 and the total bank charges are £85.

GAS BILLS

Gas is charged according to the number of therms used (for natural gas 1 therm = 103.5 cubic feet). In addition a standing charge is also made.

$$\text{Cost of gas used} = \text{Standing Charge} + \text{Therms used} \times \text{Cost per therm}$$

Example 9

A customer uses 85 therms of gas in a quarter. She is charged 36.3 p per therm plus a standing charge of £8.30 per quarter. How much is her gas bill?

Cost of gas £0.363 × 85 + £8.30

= £30.86 + £8.30

= £39.16

Reading a Gas Meter

The amount of gas used is usually measured by using a meter calibrated in hundreds of cubic feet. In the ordinary way the gas meter in your home will be read at regular intervals. However, there may be times when you wish to check the meter yourself. The dials on a gas meter usually look like those shown in Figure 11.1. It is only the bottom four dials which need to be read. Where the hand stands between two figures take the lower figure but when the hand lies between 9 and 0 take 9 as the reading. The dials in the diagram show 7519.

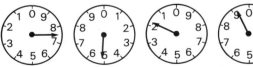

Dial 1 pointer has passed 7, reading is 7   Dial 2 pointer has passed 5, reading is 5   Dial 3 pointer has passed 1, reading is 1   Dial 4 pointer has passed 9, reading is 9

Figure 11.1

Some gas meter displays are digital and look like the one shown in Figure 11.2. These meters are much easier to read than the meters with dials.

Figure 11.2

Having read the meter:

Number of therms used = Meter reading × 1.035

Example 10

A gas meter calibrated in hundreds of cubic feet gave a reading of 1119 at the end of a quarter. The reading at the end of the previous quarter was 798. Calculate the number of therms used in the quarter.

$$\text{Therms used} = (1119 - 798) \times 1.035$$
$$= 321 \times 1.035$$
$$= 332$$

ELECTRICITY BILLS

Electricity is charged according to the number of units used (1 unit = 1 kilowatt hour). In addition there is usually a standing charge.

Cost of electricity = Standing charge
+ Number of units used
× Cost per unit

Example 11

(a) A user of electricity uses 1987 units of electricity in a quarter. If the standing charge is £6.40 and the cost per unit is 5.52 p, find the cost of electricity for the quarter.

Cost of electricity = £6.40 + £0.0552 × 1987
= £6.40 + £109.68
= £116.08

(b) An electric fire is rated at 2 kilowatts. During one day in the winter the fire was used for 9 hours.
  (i) Work out the number of units used during that day.
  (ii) If each unit used costs 5.87 p calculate the cost of using the fire.

(i) Because 1 unit of electricity is 1 kilowatt hour an appliance rated at 1 kilowatt will use 1 unit in 1 hour. Therefore
Number of units used by the fire = 2 × 9 = 18

(ii) Cost of using fire = 18 × 5.87 p
= 106 p

Electricity boards allow an economy tariff which means that the user gets cheaper electricity during the night.

Example 12

An economy tariff charges for electricity as follows: day rate 5.73 p per unit; night rate 2.42 p per unit. During one quarter a water heater used 65 units during the day and 780 units at night. Work out the cost per quarter of heating water.

Cost of day-time heating = £0.0573 × 65
= £3.73

Cost of night-time heating = £0.0242 × 780
= £18.88

Total cost of water heating = £3.73 + £18.88
= £22.61

Reading an Electric Meter

An electric meter (Figure 11.3) is read in a similar way to a gas meter. The meter shown in the diagram reads 56 378 units.

Figure 11.3

99

EXERCISE 11.3

1. A housewife decides to open a budget account with her bank. She wishes to include the following items:

   Car insurance   £95 per annum
   Car tax   £100 per annum
   Life assurance   £43 per month
   Gas bill   £127 per quarter
   Electricity bill   £86 per quarter

   (a) Work out the total annual cost of these items.
   (b) For this service the bank charges £75 for the first £1000 paid out plus £8 for each additional £100 or part of £100. Work out the bank charge.
   (c) By adding the bank charges to the total from part (a), calculate the monthly amount which the house-wife needs to put in the budget account.
   (d) In working out the bills for next year the housewife assumes that inflation will be 4%. Work out how much the housewife should put in the budget account per month next year.

2. Copy and complete the following table:

Charge per therm (p)	Number of therms used	Cost of gas used in pence	in pounds
38	110		
43	215		
36.2	87		
39.8	108		

3. A family estimates that 1 200 therms of gas will be used per year for full central heating, cooking and hot water. If gas costs 36.3 p per therm and the standing charge is £8.60 per quarter, work out the total cost per year for gas.

4. At the end of a quarter the gas meter reading was 1238, the reading at the end of the previous quarter was 793. The meter is calibrated in hundreds of cubic feet.

   (a) How many hundreds of cubic feet have been used?
   (b) How many therms have been used? (Use a factor of 1.035)
   (c) Gas is charged at 40.3 p per therm plus a standing charge of £8.85 per quarter. How much will the gas bill be for this quarter?

5. Figure 11.4 shows the dials of a gas meter. Copy these and put in hands to show:

   (a) 1700   (b) 7674   (c) 3561

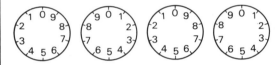

Figure 11.4

6. Write down the readings on the gas meter dials shown in Figure 11.5.

Figure 11.5

100

7. Copy and complete the table below:

Charge per unit (p)	Number of units used	Cost of electricity in pence in pounds	
4.65	200		
5.20	120		
4.93	206		
5.91	569		

8. A householder uses 1980 units of electricity in a quarter. It is charged at 5.86 p per unit plus a standing charge of £9.50 per quarter. Work out the cost of the electricity used.

9. An economy tariff charges for electricity as follows: day rate 6.08 p per unit; night rate 2.35 p per unit. A family have five storage heaters for their central heating system. In one week each heater uses 60 units at the night-time rate and 5 units at the day-time rate. Work out the weekly cost of central heating.

10. Copy the electricity meter dials shown in Figure 11.6 and draw hands to show readings of:

(a) 71 483   (b) 36 425   (c) 83 452

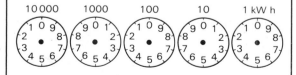

Figure 11.6

11. Read the electricity meter dials shown in Figure 11.7.

Figure 11.7

12. The wattage of all the lights in a house is 900. If they burn for 8 hours per day for a week

(a) How many units of electricity do they use?
(b) If the electricity costs 5.12 pence per unit, work out the cost of lighting per week.

13. A householder receives an electricity bill for £77.60. If electricity is charged at 5.70 p per unit and the standing charge is £9.20, work out the number of units used by the household.

HOLIDAYS

Holidays whether at home or abroad can prove quite costly and some provision out of weekly or monthly income must be made to cover the cost. The main costs are accommodation (hotel, guest-house, or self-catering), travel (whether by car, rail or coach), and miscellaneous expenses such as drinks, souvenirs, etc. People now buy package holidays which consist of accommodation and the cost of travelling.

Example 13

A family consisting of two adults and three children (all under 11 years of age) plan to book a week's seaside holiday. The cost of the guest house is £40 per week for each adult and £22 per week for each child under 11. The rail fare is £24 per adult and half-price for children. Miscellaneous expenses are expected to be £150.

(a) Work out the total cost of the holiday.

(b) The parents reckon they need to save for 40 weeks to provide for the cost. How much per week do they need to save?

(a) Cost of accommodation $= £(2 \times 40 + 3 \times 22)$

$$= £146$$

Rail fare $= £(2 \times 24 + 3 \times 12)$

$$= £84$$

Miscellaneous expenses $= \underline{£150}$

$$\underline{£380}$$

(b) Weekly savings needed $= £380 \div 40$

$$= £9.50$$

Example 14

The table below shows the charges made for a summer holiday in Tenerife by the Island Holiday Company. The prices shown are in pounds per person for a self-catering holiday.

Date of Departure	6th July	13th July	20th July	27th July	4th Aug.
	169	179	184	195	209

The prices quoted are for a stay of 7 nights. Extra weeks are charged at £60 per week. The first child, if under 11 years of age, is given a free holiday but second and subsequent children are given a 10% reduction on the above prices.

(a) A family consisting of two adults and two children under 11, wish to depart on 13th July for 4 weeks. How much will the holiday cost them?

(b) How much will the family save if they decide to depart on 6th July instead of 13th July?

(a) Cost per adult $= £179 + 3 \times £60$

$$= £359$$

Cost of 2nd child $= 90\%$ of £359

$$= £323$$

Total cost $= 2 \times £359 + £323$

$$= £718 + £323$$

$$= £1041$$

(b) The safest way is to work out the cost of the holiday as in part (a) but departing on 6th July.

Cost per adult $= £169 + 3 \times £60$

$$= £349$$

Cost of 2nd child $= 90\%$ of £349

$$= £314$$

Total cost $= 2 \times £349 + £314$

$$= £698 + £314$$

$$= £1012$$

Amount saved $= £1041 - £1012$

$$= £29$$

A quicker way is as follows:

Amount saved per adult $= £179 - £169$

$$= £10$$

Amount saved for child $= 90\%$ of £10

$$= £9$$

Total amount saved $= 2 \times £10 + £9$

$$= £29 \text{ (as before)}$$

TELEPHONE BILLS

The amount of a telephone bill depends on the number of units used and the charge made for the rental of the telephone itself. At the time of going to press each unit costs 4.4 pence excluding VAT. The time allowed for each unit depends upon the destination of the call, the time of day and the length of the call. The table below shows the time allowance (in seconds) for each unit.

Destination	Cheap rate	Standard rate	Peak rate
Local	360	90	60
Up to 56 km	100	34	26
Over 56 km	45	24	18
Eire	12	8	8

The cheap rate applies to calls made between 6 p.m. and 8 a.m. Monday to Friday and Saturday and Sunday all day.
The standard rate applies from 8 a.m. to 9 a.m. and from 1 p.m. to 6 p.m. Monday to Friday.
The peak rate applies from 9 a.m. to 1 p.m. Monday to Friday.

Note that parts of a unit are regarded as whole units when pricing a call.

Telephone bills are paid quarterly and VAT at 15% is charged.

Example 15

(a) A telephone subscriber one day makes the following local calls: a cheap rate call lasting 8 minutes, a standard rate call lasting 4 minutes and a peak rate call lasting 3 minutes. Work out the number of units used.

Units used at cheap rate call
$$= 480 \div 360 = 2 \text{ units}$$

Units used at standard rate call
$$= 240 \div 90 = 3 \text{ units}$$

Units used at peak rate
$$= 180 \div 60 = 3 \text{ units}$$

Total units used $= 2 + 3 + 3 = 8$

(b) A householder used 500 telephone units during one quarter and the rental charge was £13.95. If each unit was charged at 4.4 pence and VAT was levied at 15%, work out the amount of the telephone bill.

$$\text{Cost of 500 units} = 500 \times £0.044$$
$$= £22.00$$
$$\text{Rental charge} = £13.95$$
$$\text{Total charge less VAT} = £35.95$$
$$\text{VAT at 15\%} = 15\% \text{ of } £35.95$$
$$= £5.39$$
$$\text{Total cost} = £35.95 + £5.39$$
$$= £41.34$$

POSTAL CHARGES

Letter Post

The cost of postage depends upon the weight of the letter and whether it is to be sent by first or second class post. The table below gives details of the inland postal rates.

			Letter Post		
Weight not over (g)	First class (p)	Second class (p)	Weight not over (g)	First class	Second class
60	19	14	500	97 p	73 p
100	28	22	600	£1.20	90 p
150	34	26	700	£1.40	£1.05
200	42	32	750	£1.50	£1.10
250	51	39	800	£1.60	Not admissible over 750 g
300	59	46	900	£1.75	
350	67	52	1000	£1.90	
400	76	59	Each extra 250 g or part thereof 45 p		
450	86	65			

Example 16

Use the table of inland postal rates to answer the following questions.

(a) A letter weighs exactly 150 grams. Find the cost of sending it by:
   (i) first class post.
   (ii) second class post.

Directly from the table:

 (i) cost of first class post = 34 p
(ii) cost of second class post = 26 p

(b) A postal packet weighs 475 grams. Find the cost of sending it by:
   (i) first class post.
   (ii) second class post.

Since the packet weighs 475 grams we must pay the rate for a 500 gram packet. Hence

 (i) cost of first class post = 97 p
(ii) cost of second class post = 73 p

(c) A postal packet weighs 1800 grams. How much will it cost to post it?

Now

$$1800 \text{ g} = 1000 \text{ g} + 800 \text{ g}$$
$$= 1000 \text{ g} + (800 \div 250) \text{ g}$$
$$= 1000 \text{ g} + 3.2 \text{ units of } 250 \text{ g}$$

Therefore we must pay for an extra 4 units.

$$\text{Postal charge} = £1.90 + 4 \times £0.45$$
$$= £1.90 + £1.80$$
$$= £3.70$$

The postal rates for overseas mail are different to those for inland mail. A leaflet giving these rates is obtainable from any post office.

Parcel Post

The table below gives the inland postal rates for parcels.

Inland Parcel Rates

Weight not over (kg)	Postal rate	Weight not over (kg)	Postal rate
1	£1.70	7	£3.45
2	£2.10	8	£3.60
3	£2.60	9	£3.85
4	£2.80	10	£4.00
5	£3.00	25	£5.00
6	£3.30		

Example 17

Use the table of parcel post rates to answer the following questions:

(a) find the cost of posting a parcel weighing exactly 5 kg.

$$\text{Postal charge} = £3.00$$

(b) A parcel weighs 9.2 kg. How much is the postal charge?

Since the parcel weighs 9.2 kg we must pay the charge for a 10 kg parcel.

$$\text{Postal charge} = £4.00$$

1. A family estimates that their holiday will cost them £750. If they save for 40 weeks, find the amount they need to save each week.

2. A camping holiday in France is advertised for £245 all in. Other expenses are estimated to be £200. A man wants to save over 11 months to pay for this holiday. How much per month does he need to save?

3. A woman decides to take a coach holiday. The cost of her travel, food and hotels is £230. In addition she needs £70 for spending money. To pay for the holiday she saves for 30 weeks. How much per week does she save?

4. The table below has been taken from the brochure of the Wonderful Travel Company. It applies to winter holidays on the Costa Blanca in Spain. The prices per person given are in pounds for 7 nights, return flight, accommodation and full board.

Departure date	26th Oct.	3rd Nov.	10th Nov.	17th Nov.	24th Nov.	1st Dec
	189	179	155	142	124	117

Children under 15 years are charged 80% of the above rates and extra weeks are charged at £57 per week with children free.

(a) Mr Jones and his family of wife and two children want to start their holiday on 3rd November and to stay for 3 weeks. Work out the total cost of their holiday.
(b) If they depart on the 17th November, how much money will they save?

5. A hotel offers bed, breakfast and evening meal for £65 per week per person. Children under 14 years old are allowed a discount of 30%. VAT is charged at 15% on the total bill.

(a) A family consisting of a man and his wife and two children (under 14 years old) stay for 2 weeks. Work out the amount of the hotel bill excluding VAT.
(b) How much VAT is payable?
(c) What is the total bill including VAT?

6. Work out the cost of the following telephone bills:

(a) Standing charge £15 plus 100 units at 4.6 p per unit.
(b) Standing charge of £9.20 plus 243 units at 4.9 p per unit.

7. A telephone bill is made up of the following charges: rental £16.40 per quarter, 705 dialled units at 4.6 p per unit and VAT at 15% on the total bill.

(a) Work out the cost of the dialled units.
(b) Calculate the total bill excluding VAT.
(c) Calculate the amount of VAT payable.
(d) How much is the total bill including VAT?

8. During one day a telephone subscriber makes the following local calls: three calls at the cheap rate lasting 7 min, 9 min and 4 min respectively; two calls at the standard rate lasting 5 min and 6 min respectively; one call at the peak rate lasting 8 min.

(a) Using the table on page 103, work out the total number of units used on that day.
(b) If each unit used cost 4.4 pence find the total cost of the telephone calls made on that day.

9. Use the table on page 103 to answer the following questions:
   (a) A letter weighs exactly 350 grams. What is the postal charge for sending it (i) first class, (ii) second class.
   (b) A postal packet weighs 525 grams. What is the cost of sending it (i) first class, (ii) second class.
   (c) A postal packet weighs 2827 grams. How much is the postal charge?

10. Use the table of inland parcel post rates on page 104 to answer the following questions:
    (a) Find the postal charge to send a parcel weighing 6 kg.
    (b) What is the postal charge for sending a parcel weighing 7.6 kg?

11. Using the table of inland postal rates on page 103, find the second class postal charges for sending letters weighing
    (a) 500 g   (b) 550 g   (c) 475 g.

MISCELLANEOUS EXERCISE 11

1. Calculate the monthly cost of owning a house given that the outgoings are as follows: mortgage repayments £115 per month, insurance £132 per annum and rates £190 per half-year.

2. The meter readings for an electricity consumer at the beginning and end of a quarter were as follows:

   Beginning of quarter 57 469 units
   End of quarter   58 196 units

   Electricity is charged at 5.91 p per unit plus a standing charge of £7.20 per quarter. Work out the amount of the electricity bill for the quarter.

3. The rateable value of a house is £184 and the local rates are levied at 162 p in the £1.

   (a) Find the annual amount paid in local rates.
   (b) The water rate amounts to £57.30 per half-year. Calculate the total amount paid in rates per annum.
   (c) The householder pays by budget account. How much per month must she place in the account?

4. The cash price of an electric fire is £74.20. It is bought on hire purchase by paying a deposit of 20% plus 12 monthly payments of £6.50.

   (a) How much is the hire purchase price?
   (b) The fire is rated at 3 kilowatts. If it is on for 7 hours during one day, how many units of electricity has it used?

5. A television set can be bought for £270, maintained at £34.60 per year for 7 years then sold for £42. Renting the set, maintenance included, costs £8 per calendar month for 3 years, £7.60 per month for the next 2 years and £7 per month thereafter. How much is saved in the 7 years by buying the set?

6. For the next year the expenditure for a village is estimated at £313 780, some of which is to be used for making a car park. The total rateable value of the village is £432 800. Calculate:

   (a) the estimated rate in the £1.
   (b) the rates to be paid on a house with a rateable value of £312.
   (c) the estimated cost of the car park if the rate levied to meet the cost is 7.8 p in the £1. Give your answer to the nearest £100.

106

7. A man buys a house in which he has been living and for which he paid a weekly rent of £37.60. He also paid rates at £1.10 in the £1, the rateable value of the house being £320. The cost of lighting and heating is included in the rent. The house is valued at £32 000 and to purchase it the man borrows £21 600 from a building society. His expenses now are:

Heating and lighting £65 per quarter
Insurance at the rate of 0.15% per annum on the value of the house
Rates now at 124 p in the £1
Mortgage repayments of £0.90 per month per £100 borrowed
Miscellaneous expenses £216 per annum

Giving your answer to the nearest pound, work out how much extra the man pays per annum than formerly.

8. A flat is supplied with Economy 7 electricity. Details of the quarterly bill are as follows:

| Reading | | Units | Pence | Cost |
This time	Last time	used	per unit	
72864	68992(E)		2.34	
53572	52932(S)		5.61	

E against a reading means economy charge. S against a reading means standard charge. Standing charge is £10.14.

(a) Copy and complete the bill filling in the columns headed 'units used' and 'cost'.

(b) By adding in the standing charge work out the total charge for electricity for the quarter.

CHAPTER 12

Time, Distance and Speed

MEASUREMENT OF TIME

In the winter, time in the United Kingdom is measured using Greenwich Mean Time (GMT). In summer clocks are brought forward by 1 hour and this is called British Summer Time (BST). The units of time are:

$$60 \text{ seconds (s)} = 1 \text{ minute (min)}$$
$$60 \text{ minutes (min)} = 1 \text{ hour (h)}$$
$$24 \text{ hours (h)} = 1 \text{ day (d)}$$
$$7 \text{ days (d)} = 1 \text{ week (wk)}$$
$$28, 30, 31 \text{ days} = 1 \text{ calendar month}$$
$$28 \text{ days} = 1 \text{ lunar month}$$
$$365 \text{ days} = 1 \text{ year}$$
$$366 \text{ days} = 1 \text{ leap year}$$
$$52 \text{ weeks} = 1 \text{ year}$$
$$12 \text{ months} = 1 \text{ year}$$
$$13 \text{ weeks} = 1 \text{ quarter}$$

The months of January, March, May, July, August, October and December each have 31 days whilst April, June, September and November have 30 days. February normally has 28 days. When the number denoting a year is exactly divisible by 4, the year is called a leap year (unless it is a century year, e.g., 1900: then it is a leap year only if the first two figures are divisible by 4). So 1908, 1936 and 1984, for instance, were all leap years, as will be 2000, 2004, etc. A leap year has 366 days the extra day being 29th February.

Example 1

(a) Change 480 s into minutes.

$$480 \text{ s} = 480 \div 60 \text{ min}$$
$$= 8 \text{ min}$$

(b) Change 7 h into minutes.

$$7 \text{ h} = 7 \times 60 \text{ min}$$
$$= 420 \text{ min}$$

(c) How many seconds are there in 2 h?

$$2 \text{ h} = 2 \times 60 \text{ min}$$
$$= 120 \text{ min}$$
$$= 120 \times 60 \text{ s}$$
$$= 7200 \text{ s}$$

(d) How many weeks are there in 3 quarters?

$$3 \text{ quarters} = 3 \times 13 \text{ weeks}$$
$$= 39 \text{ weeks}$$

EXERCISE 12.1

1. How many minutes are there in:
   (a) 5 hours   (b) $4\frac{1}{2}$ hours
   (c) 720 seconds?

2. How many seconds are there in:
   (a) 3 min   (b) $5\frac{1}{2}$ min
   (c) 1 h   (d) $3\frac{1}{4}$ h?

3. Change to hours:
   (a) 300 min   (b) 150 min
   (c) 195 min

4. A woman earns £5460 per annum.
   (a) How much is this per month?
   (b) How much is it per week?

5. A gas bill was £104 for a quarter. How much was it per week?

6. If milk costs 20 p per pint and a householder uses 2 pints per day, calculate the weekly bill for the milk.

7. A television programme lasts for $3\frac{1}{2}$ hours. 20% of the time is devoted to cartoons, 50% to plays and the remainder to music and dancing. Work out the time in minutes devoted to cartoons, plays and music and dancing.

8. State which of the following were leap years:
   (a) 1684   (b) 1700   (c) 1876
   (d) 1936   (e) 1600   (f) 1937

9. How many days are there between 4th April and 9th July?

10. A man buys a daily paper on each weekday and one paper on Sundays. If the daily paper costs 22 p and the Sunday paper costs 40 p, calculate his annual paper bill. (Assume 52 Sundays and 313 weekdays.)

THE CLOCK

There are two ways of showing the time:

(1) With a 12-hour clock (Figure 12.1), in which there are two periods each of 12 hours duration during each day. The period between midnight and noon is called a.m. whilst the period between noon and midnight is called p.m. Thus 9.45 a.m. is a time in the morning whilst 2.30 p.m. is a time in the afternoon.

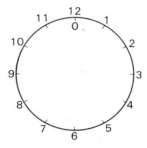

Figure 12.1

(2) With a 24-hour clock (Figure 12.2), in which there is one period of 24 hours. This clock is used for railway and airline timetables. Times between midnight and noon lie between 0000 hours and 1200 hours, whilst times between noon and midnight lie between 1200 hours and 2400 hours.

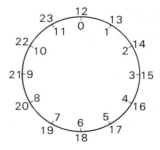

Figure 12.2

Example 2

(a) Find the length of time between 7.30 a.m. and 9.15 p.m.

7.30 a.m. to 12 noon is	4 h 30 min
12 noon to 9.15 p.m. is	9 h 15 min +
	13 h 45 min

(b) Find the length of time between 0626 hours and 1912 hours.

1912 hours is	19 h 12 min
0626 hours is	6 h 26 min −
Length of time is	12 h 46 min

EXERCISE 12.2

Find the length of time in hours and minutes between:

1. 2.52 a.m. and 6.58 a.m.

2. 3.25 p.m. and 8.41 p.m.

3. 2.43 a.m. and 8.34 p.m.

4. 0050 hours and 1038 hours

5. 0242 hours and 1748 hours

6. An aeroplane leaves Gatwick airport at 0930 hours and reaches Malaga airport 2 h 40 min after take off. At what time did it arrive at Malaga?

7. A train leaves London for Newcastle at 8.25 a.m. and travels for 2 hours and 45 minutes to York where it stops for 12 minutes. It then travels on to Newcastle which it reaches in a further 1 hour and 2 minutes. At what time does it arrive at Newcastle?

8. A car leaves Cheltenham at 8.05 a.m. and arrives at Worcester $\frac{3}{4}$ hour later. At what time does it arrive in Worcester?

TIMETABLES

Timetables are usually written using the 24-hour clock. Here is a simplified portion of a railway timetable.

Hester	0730	0830	0930	1030	1100	1230	1430	1600
Manton	0735	....	0935	1047	....	1236	1447	1606
Turley	0755	....	0955	1058	....	1255	1503	1627
Denton	0810	0900	1010	1115	1128	1310	1518	1640

Example 3

(a) I can catch either the 0930 or the 1100 train from Hester to Denton. Find the difference in the times taken for the journey.

The 0930 train arrives in Denton at 1010. Hence the time taken for the journey is 40 min.
The 1100 train arrives in Denton at 1128. Hence the time taken for the journey is 28 min.
The difference in the times taken is
40 min − 28 min = 12 min.

(b) Which is the slowest train from Hester to Denton and how long does this journey take?

The slowest train is the 1430 which arrives in Denton at 1518. The time taken for the journey is 48 min.

Using the timetable for Hester-Manton-Turley-Denton answer the following questions:

1. I want to arrive in Turley at 10.58. Which train must I catch from Hester? How long does the journey take?

2. How long must I wait for the first train from Turley after 10.00 a.m.?

3. I arrive at Manton station at 2.15 p.m. How long must I wait for a train to Denton.

4. Which train from Hester to Denton is the fastest?

5. How long does it take the fastest train to travel between Hester and Turley?

Shown below is part of a railway timetable. Use it to answer the following questions:

6. Which is the first train to Paddington from Worcester after 10.00 a.m.?

7. How long does it take the 1358 train from Gloucester to reach Swindon?

8. What time must I arrive at Stroud station in order to catch the 0943 train from Cheltenham?

9. What time train must I catch from Kemble to make sure of arriving at Reading by 2.00 p.m.?

10. How long does the 1256 train from Stonehouse take to reach Paddington?

WORCESTER · CHELTENHAM · GLOUCESTER · SWINDON · LONDON

Mondays to Fridays

WORCESTER,

Shrubb Hill	....	0653	0805	0915	....	1107	....	1317	....	1508	1554	....	1557	2022	....	....	....
CHELTENHAM	0620	0722	0828	0943	1041	1135	1230	1344	1437	1536	1624	1718	1826	2051	2138	....	....
Gloucester	0633	0741	0847	0956	1055	1148	1244	1358	1451	1550	1638	1732	1843	2105	2152	....	....
Stonehouse	0645	0755	0902	1008	1107	1200	1256	1410	1503	1602	1650	1744	1855	2117	2204	....	....
Stroud	0650	0802	0909	1013	1112	1206	1302	1415	1508	1607	1656	1749	1900	2123	2209	....	....
Kemble	0706	0819	0926	1029	1128	1222	1318	1431	1524	1623	1713	1805	1916	2140	2225	....	....
SWINDON	0723	0836	0943	1046	1145	1239	1335	1448	1541	1640	1730	1824	1933	2157	2242	....	....
Reading	0803	0915	1017	1143	1245	1353	1443	1545	1643	1718	1853	1908	2010	2245	....	....	....
LONDON,																
Paddington	0834	0938	1053	1216	1308	1426	1517	1618	1717	1747	1920	1937	2039	2314	....	....	....

Extract from British Rail timetable – not now in operation

AVERAGE SPEED

The road from Campton to Burley is 50 miles long. It takes me 2 hours to drive from Campton to Burley. Obviously I do not drive at the same speed all the time. Sometimes I drive slowly and sometimes I have to stop at crossroads and traffic lights.

However the time it takes me is exactly the same as if I were driving along a straight road at 25 miles per hour, i.e., 50 miles ÷ 2 hours. So we say that my *average speed* is 25 miles per hour.

$$\text{Average speed} = \frac{\text{Total distance travelled}}{\text{Total time taken}}$$

The unit of speed depends upon the unit of distance and the unit of time as shown in the table on p. 112.

Unit of distance	Unit of time	Unit of speed
kilometre	hour	kilometres per hour (km/h) or km h^{-1}
mile	hour	miles per hour (mile/h) or m.p.h.
metre	second	metres per second (m/s) or m s^{-1}
foot	second	feet per second (ft/s) or ft s^{-1}

Note carefully that:

$$\text{Distance travelled} = \text{Average speed} \times \text{Time taken}$$

$$\text{Time taken} = \frac{\text{Distance travelled}}{\text{Average speed}}$$

Example 4

(a) A car travels a total distance of 400 km in 5 hours. What is the average speed?

$$\text{Average speed} = \frac{\text{Distance travelled}}{\text{Time taken}}$$

$$= \frac{400}{5} \text{ km/h}$$

$$= 80 \text{ km/h}$$

(b) A lorry travels at an average speed of 40 mile/h for 3 hours. How far does it travel?

$$\text{Distance travelled} = \text{Average speed} \times \text{Time taken}$$

$$= 40 \times 3 \text{ miles}$$

$$= 120 \text{ miles}$$

(c) A train travels a distance of 240 km at an average speed of 80 km/h. How long does the journey take?

$$\text{Time taken} = \frac{\text{Distance travelled}}{\text{Average speed}}$$

$$= \frac{240}{80} \text{ hours}$$

$$= 3 \text{ hours}$$

Example 5

A car travels 136 miles at an average speed of 32 mile/h. On the return journey the speed is increased to 34 mile/h. Calculate the average speed for the complete journey.

Time taken to travel 136 miles at 32 mile/h

$$= \frac{136}{32} \text{ h}$$

$$= 4.25 \text{ h}$$

Time taken to travel 136 miles at 34 mile/h

$$= \frac{136}{34} \text{ h}$$

$$= 4.00 \text{ h}$$

Total time taken $= (4.25 + 4.00) \text{ h} = 8.25 \text{ h}$

Total distance travelled $= 2 \times 136$ miles
$$= 272 \text{ miles}$$

$$\text{Average speed} = \frac{\text{Total distance travelled}}{\text{Total time taken}}$$

$$= \frac{272}{8.25} \text{ mile/h}$$

$$= 32.97 \text{ mile/h}$$

EXERCISE 12.4

Copy the table below and work out the average speeds.

	Distance	Time	Average speed
1.	10 miles	2 h	
2.	40 km	5 h	
3.	90 m	6 s	
4.	200 ft	4 s	
5.	150 miles	$2\frac{1}{2}$ h	

Copy the table below and work out the distance travelled.

	Average speed	Time	Distance travelled
6.	30 km/h	4 h	
7.	50 mile/h	8 h	
8.	35 m/s	3 s	
9.	25 m/s	4 s	
10.	60 km/h	$3\frac{1}{2}$ h	

Copy the table below and work out the time taken.

	Distance travelled	Average speed	Time taken
11.	40 km	20 km/h	
12.	80 miles	40 mile/h	
13.	60 ft	30 ft/s	
14.	120 m	40 m/s	
15.	10 miles	4 mile/h	

16. The distance between Cheltenham and Paddington is 110 miles. A train takes $2\frac{1}{4}$ hours to make the journey. What is the average speed?

17. A motorist leaves Bristol at 10.55 a.m. and arrives in Gloucester 50 minutes later. The distance between Bristol and Gloucester is 34 miles.
    (a) At what time did he arrive in Gloucester?
    (b) What was his average speed in miles per hour?

18. The distance between Baxton and Flighton is 125 km. A car leaves Baxton at 1325 hours and arrives in Flighton at 1555 hours. Calculate the average speed of the car.

19. A boy takes 15 min to walk to school at a speed of 5 km/h. How many minutes would he take if he cycled to school at 15 km/h?

20. A car travels for 3 hours at a speed of 45 mile/h and for 4 hours at a speed of 50 mile/h. Calculate the total distance travelled by the car.

21. (a) A motorist drives for 3 hours at an average speed of 50 mile/h. How far has he travelled?
    (b) He then travels at 60 mile/h for 2 hours. Calculate the total distance he has now travelled.
    (c) Work out the total time taken for the entire journey.
    (d) Calculate the overall average speed.

22. The distance between two towns is 160 km.

  (a) How long will it take a motorist to make the journey if his average speed is 40 km/h?

  (b) The return journey takes $2\frac{1}{2}$ hours. What is the average speed for the return journey?

23. A train travels 200 miles at an average speed of 50 miles/h. It then travels 60 miles in a further 1 hour.

  (a) Calculate the total distance travelled.

  (b) What is the total time taken?

  (c) Find the overall average speed.

MISCELLANEOUS EXERCISE 12

1. (a) A clock at a bus station shows the departure of a bus to be 8.15 p.m. How would this time be written in a timetable which uses the 24-hour system?

  (b) The bus arrived at its destination, 20 miles away, at 2045 hours. What was the average speed of the bus?

2. (a) An aeroplane left town A at 1335 hours taking 2 h 30 min for its flight to town B. At what time did the aeroplane reach town B?

  (b) The distance between towns A and B is 1250 miles. What was the average speed of the aeroplane?

3. The distance between Cardiff and London is 153 miles. A car leaves Cardiff at 9.35 a.m. and arrives in London at 1.50 p.m.

  (a) How long did the journey take?

  (b) What was the average speed of the car?

4. On a train journey of 120 km, the average speed for the first 20 km was 60 km/h.

  (a) Find the time taken to travel the first 20 km.

  (b) For the remainder of the journey the average speed was 50 km/h. Calculate the time taken for this part of the journey.

  (c) Find the average speed of the train over the entire journey.

5. A greyhound runs 800 m in 100 s.

  (a) Calculate the average speed of the dog in metres per second.

  (b) Work out the average speed of the dog in kilometres per hour.

6. A car travels 50 km at 50 km/h and 70 km at 70 km/h. What is its average speed for the complete journey of 120 km?

7. A motorway journey takes 3 hours at an average speed of 60 mile/h.

  (a) How long, in miles, was the journey?

  (b) On the return journey, because of heavy traffic, the average speed was reduced to 50 mile/h. How much longer did the return journey take?

114

MENTAL TEST 12

Try to answer the following questions without writing anything down except the answer.

1. Change 180 seconds into minutes.

2. Change 5 minutes into seconds.

3. Change 240 minutes into hours.

4. Change 5 hours into minutes.

5. How many days in 240 hours?

6. Find the length of time between 8.30 a.m. and 10.45 a.m.

7. What is the length of time between 1320 hours and 1650 hours?

8. A train leaves Cheltenham at 1330 hours and arrives in Paddington at 1638 hours. How long does the journey take?

9. A car travels 140 km in 2 hours. What is its average speed?

10. A train travels 200 miles in 4 hours. Calculate its average speed.

11. A car travels for 4 hours at an average speed of 30 miles/h. How far has it travelled?

12. A car travels 90 km at an average speed of 45 km/h. How long does the journey take?

13. An aeroplane flies at an average speed of 400 mile/h. If it flies at this speed for 2 hours, how far has it flown?

14. A car takes 4 hours to travel 240 miles. What is its average speed?

15. A train travels 300 km at an average speed of 60 km/h. How long does the journey take?

CHAPTER 13

Basic Algebra

INTRODUCTION

The methods of algebra are an extension of those used in arithmetic. In algebra we use letters and symbols as well as numbers to represent quantities. We shall need to do a little algebra in some of the chapters which follow.

USE OF SYMBOLS

$m + n$ means a number m added to a second number n.

$m - n$ means a number n subtracted from a number m.

$m \times n$ means a number m multiplied by a number n.

$m \div n$ means a number m divided by a number n.

Example 1

(a) Put into symbols six times a number p.

Six times a number p is $6 \times p$

In algebra multiplication signs are often left out so that $6 \times p$ would be written as $6p$.

(b) Put into symbols eight multiplied by r multiplied by s.

Eight multiplied by r multiplied by s
$= 8 \times r \times s = 8rs$

(c) Put into symbols three times a number y minus five.

Three times a number y minus five
$= 3 \times y - 5 = 3y - 5$

(d) Put into symbols five times a number p divided by the number q.

The division sign is rarely used in algebra and we write five times a number p divided by the number q as $\dfrac{5p}{q}$.

EXERCISE 13.1

Put each of the following into symbols:

1. Five times a number a

2. Six times a number m plus seven

3. Three times a number x minus four

4. Four times a number m plus three times a number n

5. The numbers a, b and c multiplied together

6. Twice the number m divided by the number n

7. Seven times the number p minus eight times the number q

8. The numbers m and n multiplied together and then divided by three times the number p

SUBSTITUTION

Substitution means putting numbers in the place of letters and symbols.

Example 2

Find the value of $3y + 5z$ when $y = 2$ and $z = 4$.

Remembering that $3y$ means $3 \times y$ and $5z$ means $5 \times z$ we have

$$3y + 5z = 3 \times 2 + 5 \times 4 = 6 + 20 = 26$$

(Remember that we always multiply and/or divide before we add and subtract.)

EXERCISE 13.2

If $a = 2$, $b = 3$ and $c = 5$, find the values of the following:

1. $a + 7$
2. $c - 2$
3. $6 - b$
4. $6b$
5. $9c$
6. ab
7. $3bc$
8. abc
9. $5c - 2$
10. $4a + 6b$
11. $8c - 7$
12. $a + 2b + 5c$
13. $8c - 4b$
14. $\frac{1}{2}a$
15. $\frac{ab}{8}$
16. $\frac{abc}{6}$
17. $\frac{2c}{a}$
18. $\frac{5a + 10b + 8c}{a + b + c}$

POWERS

The quantity $a \times a \times a$ is usually written as a^3. a^3 is called the third power of a. The number 3 which indicates the number of threes to be multiplied together is called the index (plural: indices).

$$2^4 = 2 \times 2 \times 2 \times 2$$

$$y^6 = y \times y \times y \times y \times y \times y$$

Note carefully that, for instance a^2 is not the same as $2a$.

$$a^2 = a \times a \quad \text{but} \quad 2a = a + a$$

Similarly, y^4 is not the same as $4y$.

$$y^4 = y \times y \times y \times y \quad \text{but} \quad 4y = y + y + y + y$$

$$a^4 = a \times a \times a \times a$$

Example 3

Find the value of b^3 when $b = 2$.

$$b^3 = 2^3 = 2 \times 2 \times 2 = 8$$

When dealing with expressions like $8mn^4$ note that it is only the letter n which is raised to the fourth power.

$$8mn^4 = 8 \times m \times n \times n \times n \times n$$

Example 4

Find the value of $7p^2q^3$ when $p = 5$ and $q = 4$.

$$7p^2q^3 = 7 \times 5^2 \times 4^3 = 7 \times 25 \times 64 = 11\,200$$

EXERCISE 13.3

Write the following in index form:

1. $b \times b$

2. $c \times c \times c$

3. $n \times n \times n \times n$

4. $p \times p \times p \times p \times p \times p$

5. $q \times q \times q \times q \times q$

If $a = 2$, $b = 3$ and $c = 4$, find the values of the following:

6. a^2

7. b^4

8. ab^3

9. $2a^2c$

10. ab^2c^3

11. $5a^2 + 6b^2$

12. $a^2 + c^2$

13. $7b^3c^2$

14. $\dfrac{3a^4}{c^2}$

15. $\dfrac{c^5}{a^6}$

FORMULAE

A formula is a statement which shows the relationship between two or more quantities. The statement $E = IR$ is a formula for E in terms of I and R. The value of E may be found by simple arithmetic after substituting the given values of I and R.

Example 5

(a) If $E = IR$, find the value of E when $I = 6$ and $R = 4$.

Substituting the given values of I and R and remembering that multiplication signs are omitted in formulae, we have

$$E = IR = 6 \times 4 = 24$$

(b) The formula for the surface area of a sphere is $A = 4\pi r^2$ where $\pi = 3.142$ and r is the radius of the sphere. Work out the surface area of a sphere whose radius is 8.

We are given $\pi = 3.142$ and $r = 8$, so

$$A = 4\pi r^2 = 4 \times 3.142 \times 8^2 = 804$$

EXERCISE 13.4

1. If $V = Ah$, find the value of V when $A = 8$ and $h = 4$.

2. $S = 90(n - 4)$ is a formula used in geometry. Find S when $n = 8$.

3. The formula $K = Wa + b$ is used in engineering technology. Find K when $W = 25$, $a = 3$ and $b = 5$.

4. If $A = \frac{1}{2}BH$, find the value of A when $B = 6$ and $H = 7$.

5. If $v = u + at$, find the value of v when $u = 5$, $a = 3$ and $t = 4$.

6. If $C = \pi D$, find C when $\pi = 3.142$ and $D = 6$.

7. A formula used in business calculations is $I = \dfrac{PRT}{100}$. Find the value of I when $P = 700$, $R = 12$ and $T = 3$.

8. If $K = \dfrac{Wv^2}{2g}$, find the value of K when $W = 60$, $v = 20$ and $g = 10$.

9. If $P = 3r^4$, find P when $r = 5$.

10. If $y = \dfrac{3t}{c}$, find the value of y when $c = 6$ and $t = 12$.

118

NUMBERS IN STANDARD FORM

Any number can be expressed as a value between 1 and 10 multiplied by a power of 10. For instance,

$$8372 = 8.372 \times 1000 = 8.372 \times 10^3$$

It should be remembered that:

$$100 = 10^2$$
$$1000 = 10^3$$
$$10\,000 = 10^4$$
$$100\,000 = 10^5$$
$$1\,000\,000 = 10^6$$

Example 6

(a) $563 = 5.63 \times 100 = 5.63 \times 10^2$

(b) $75\,532 = 7.5532 \times 10\,000 = 7.5532 \times 10^4$

(c) $25\,000\,000 = 2.5 \times 10\,000\,000 = 2.5 \times 10^7$

We sometimes need to convert a number stated in standard form to a number in ordinary decimal form.

When the power of 10 is positive as in Example 6 the index, which gives the power of 10, shows the number of places that the decimal point has to be moved to the right. So

$6.187 \times 10^2 = 618.7$ (decimal point moved two places to the right)

$8.463 \times 10^5 = 846\,300$ (decimal point moved five places to the right)

Write the following numbers in standard form:

1. 827   **3.** 47 734   **5.** 7 089 000

2. 2937   **4.** 983 267

Write the following as ordinary decimal numbers (i.e., not in standard form):

6. 3.4×10^3 **8.** 3.78×10^6 **10.** 2.678×10^5

7. 8×10^2 **9.** 2.35×10^4

ADDING AND SUBTRACTING NUMBERS IN STANDARD FORM

(1) If the numbers to be added or subtracted have the same power of 10, then the numbers can be added or subtracted directly.

Example 7

(a) $3.52 \times 10^2 + 7.16 \times 10^2 + 8.53 \times 10^2$

     $= (3.52 + 7.16 + 8.53) \times 10^2$

     $= 19.21 \times 10^2$

     $= 1.921 \times 10^3$

(b) $7.543 \times 10^3 - 5.261 \times 10^3$

     $= (7.543 - 5.261) \times 10^3$

     $= 2.282 \times 10^3$

(2) If the numbers have different powers of 10, first convert them to decimal form and then add or subtract them.

Example 8

$$4.326 \times 10^3 + 5.81 \times 10^2 = 4326 + 581$$

$$= 4907$$

$$= 4.907 \times 10^3$$

119

EXERCISE 13.6

State which of the following numbers is the larger and by how much:

1. 6.8×10^2 and 3.2×10^3

2. 8.7×10^4 and 9.3×10^3

3. 8.79×10^4 and 9.98×10^2

4. 3.1×10^4 and 6.4×10^3

5. 9.73×10^3 and 2.26×10^3

State the answers to the following in standard form:

6. $4.683 \times 10^3 + 2.786 \times 10^3$

7. $6.81 \times 10^2 + 5.36 \times 10^2 + 7.14 \times 10^2$

8. $2.809 \times 10^2 - 1.783 \times 10^2$

9. $8.89 \times 10^3 - 8.85 \times 10^3$

10. $2.78 \times 10^2 + 3.68 \times 10^3$

11. $6.987 \times 10^3 + 5.26 \times 10^2 + 7.834 \times 10^4$

12. $7.902 \times 10^3 - 6.65 \times 10^2$

MISCELLANEOUS EXERCISE 13

1. For cooking a stuffed chicken the following formula is used:

$$T = 40W + 20$$

where T is the cooking time in minutes and W is the weight of the chicken in kilograms. Find the time required in minutes to cook a chicken weighing 2 kg.

2. An approximate formula for converting degrees Fahrenheit into degrees Celsius is

$$C = \tfrac{1}{2}(F - 30)$$

The recommended cooking temperature for doughnuts is 360 °F. What is this temperature in degrees Celsius?

3. What is the value of $x^2 + x + 3$ when $x = 5$?

4. If $a = 0.5$ and $b = 27$, what is the value of $\dfrac{b}{a}$?

5. If $p = 3bc$ what is the value of p when $b = 2$ and $c = 5$?

6. If $a = 3$ and $b = 6$, what is the value of $2a^2b$?

7. To calculate the amount of a telephone bill the formula

$$C = \frac{Np}{100} + R$$

is used where N is the number of units used, p is the cost per unit in pence and R is the rental charge. 200 units costing 4 p per unit are used during one quarter. If the rental charge is £5, work out the amount of the telephone bill.

8. Write the number 1 250 000 in standard form.

9. Find the value of $53 \times 4.28 \times 38$ giving the answer in standard form, correct to 3 significant figures.

10. Write 7×10^2 as a decimal number.

CHAPTER 14

Interest

INTRODUCTION

If you invest money with a bank or a building society then interest is paid to you for lending them the money. On the other hand if you borrow money you will be charged interest. Interest is usually stated as so much per cent per annum, for instance 12% per annum.

Example 1

If I invest £3000 at 8% per annum for 1 year, how much interest will I be paid at the end of the year?

$$\text{Amount of interest} = 8\% \text{ of } £3000$$
$$= £240$$

SIMPLE INTEREST

With simple interest the amount of interest earned is the same every year. If the money is invested for 2 years the amount of interest is doubled; for 3 years the amount of interest will be three times as much. For 6 months (i.e., half a year) the amount of interest will be only half as much.

In actual practice for periods of over 1 year, simple interest is virtually unknown but it is quite common for short periods.

To calculate the amount of simple interest the following formula can be used:

$$I = \frac{PRT}{100}$$

where

$I =$ the amount of interest after a period of T years

$R =$ is the rate of interest expressed as a decimal

$P =$ the principal, i.e., the amount borrowed or lent

Example 2

(a) A woman invests £5000 with a bank which pays 7% per annum simple interest on investments. At the end of each year the woman draws the interest and spends it. If she leaves the money for 4 years how much will she have received in interest payments?

We are given that $P = 5000$, $R = 7$ and $T = 4$. So

$$I = \frac{5000 \times 7 \times 4}{100} = £1400$$

(b) A man borrows £4000 for 6 months. if the rate of interest is 20% per annum, how much interest will he pay?

We are given that $P = 4000$, $R = 20$ and $T = \frac{1}{2} = 0.5$. So

$$I = \frac{4000 \times 20 \times 0.5}{100} = £400$$

Find the interest for 1 year on:

   1. £500 at 5% per annum

   2. £2000 at 8% per annum

   3. £4000 at 10% per annum

   4. £8000 at 12% per annum

   5. £15 000 at 20% per annum

Find the amount of simple interest on:

   6. £3000 at 10% per annum for 6 months

   7. £500 at 12% per annum for 3 months

   8. £5000 at 20% per annum for 3 years

   9. £7000 at 14% per annum for 4 years

   10. £150 at $7\frac{1}{2}$% per annum for 2 years

COMPOUND INTEREST

Compound interest is different from simple interest in that the interest is added to the amount invested (or borrowed) and hence also attracts interest. So after 2 years there will be more interest than after 1 year because there is more capital to attract interest.

Example 3

£500 is invested for 2 years at 10% compound interest. Calculate the value of the investment at the end of this period.

	£	
Amount invested	500	
First year's interest	50	(i.e., 10% of £500)
Value of investment after 1 year	550	(i.e., £500 + £50)
Second year's interest	55	(i.e., 10% of £550)
Value of investment after 2 years	605	(i.e., £550 + £55)

The value of an investment after a period of time is usually called the amount. Thus in Example 3, the amount after 2 years is £605. Although all problems on compound interest can be worked out in the way shown in Example 3, the work takes a long time, particularly if the period is lengthy.

The following formula will allow you to calculate the amount but you will need a calculator.

$$A = P\left(1 + \frac{R}{100}\right)^T$$

where
A = the amount after T years
P = the principal
R = the percentage rate per annum

122

Example 4

£950 is invested for 7 years at 9% per annum compound interest.

(a) Calculate the amount accruing at the end of the 7 years.

(b) How much interest was earned during the 7 year period.

(a) We are given that $P = 950$, $R = 9$ and $T = 7$. So

$$A = 950 \times \left(1 + \frac{9}{100}\right)^7$$

$$= 950 \times 1.09^7$$

$$= \text{£}1736.64$$

(b) Interest earned = £1736.64 − £950 = £786.64

The following program can be used for the calculation using an ordinary calculator.

Input	Display
1.09	1.09
××	1.09
=	1.1881
=	1.295029
=	1.4115816
=	1.538624
=	1.6771
=	1.828039
×	1.828039
950	950
=	1736.637
−	1736.637
950	950
=	786.637

COMPOUND INTEREST TABLES

In business, compound interest tables are used to find the amount of interest due at the end of a given period of time. Part of such a table is shown below.

Appreciation of £1 for periods from 1 year to 25 years

Year	5%	6%	7%	8%	9%	10%	11%	12%	13%	14%
1	1.050	1.060	1.070	1.080	1.090	1.100	1.110	1.120	1.130	1.140
2	1.103	1.124	1.145	1.166	1.188	1.210	1.232	1.254	1.277	1.300
3	1.158	1.191	1.225	1.260	1.295	1.331	1.368	1.405	1.443	1.482
4	1.216	1.262	1.311	1.360	1.412	1.464	1.518	1.574	1.603	1.689
5	1.276	1.338	1.403	1.469	1.539	1.611	1.685	1.762	1.842	1.925
6	1.340	1.419	1.501	1.587	1.677	1.772	1.870	1.974	2.082	2.195
7	1.407	1.504	1.606	1.714	1.828	1.949	2.076	2.211	2.353	2.502
8	1.477	1.594	1.718	1.851	1.993	2.144	2.304	2.476	2.658	2.853
9	1.551	1.689	1.838	1.999	2.172	2.358	2.558	2.773	3.004	3.252
10	1.629	1.791	1.967	2.159	2.367	2.594	2.839	3.106	3.395	3.707
11	1.710	1.898	2.105	2.332	2.580	2.853	3.152	3.479	3.836	4.226
12	1.796	2.012	2.252	2.518	2.813	3.138	3.498	3.896	4.335	4.818
13	1.886	2.133	2.410	2.720	3.066	3.452	3.883	4.363	4.898	5.492
14	1.980	2.261	2.579	2.937	3.342	3.797	4.310	4.887	5.535	6.261
15	2.079	2.397	2.759	3.172	3.642	4.177	4.785	5.474	6.254	7.138
16	2.183	2.540	2.952	3.426	3.970	4.595	5.311	6.130	7.067	8.137
17	2.292	2.693	3.159	3.700	4.328	5.054	5.895	6.866	7.986	9.276
18	2.407	2.854	3.380	3.996	4.717	5.560	6.544	7.690	9.024	10.575
19	2.527	3.026	3.617	4.316	5.142	6.116	7.263	8.613	10.197	12.056
20	2.653	3.207	3.870	4.661	5.604	6.727	8.062	9.646	11.523	13.743
21	2.786	3.400	4.141	5.034	6.109	7.400	8.949	10.804	13.021	15.668
22	2.925	3.604	4.430	5.437	6.659	8.140	9.934	12.100	14.714	17.861
23	3.072	3.820	4.741	5.871	7.258	8.954	11.026	13.552	16.627	20.362
24	3.225	4.049	5.072	6.341	7.911	9.850	12.239	15.179	18.788	23.212
25	3.386	4.292	5.427	6.848	8.623	10.835	13.585	17.000	21.231	26.462

123

Example 5

£750 is invested for 6 years at 5% compound interest per annum.

Using the compound interest table find:

(a) the amount accruing at the end of the period,
(b) the amount earned in interest during the period.

From the table, in 6 years at 5% per annum, £1 becomes £1.340

(a) Amount accruing = £750 × 1.340 = £1005

(b) Interest earned = £1005 − £750 = £255

EXERCISE 14.2

Using the compound interest formula, work out the amount accruing at the end of the given period:

1. £250 invested for 5 years at 8% per annum.

2. £4000 invested for 7 years at 9% per annum.

3. £1200 invested for 12 years at 10% per annum.

Using the compound interest formula, work out the amount of interest earned during the given period:

4. £4000 for 4 years at 12% per annum.

5. £3500 for 3 years at 6% per annum.

6. £8000 for 6 years at 11% per annum.

Using the compound interest table, calculate the amount accruing at the end of the given period:

7. £6000 for 8 years at 9% per annum.

8. £25 000 for 5 years at 12% per annum.

9. £5000 for 9 years at 5% per annum.

Using the compound interest table, work out the amount of interest earned during the given period:

10. £350 for 6 years at 8% per annum.

11. £7000 for 9 years at 7% per annum.

12. £20 000 for 10 years at 14% per annum.

DEPRECIATION

A business will own a number of assets such as computers, machinery, motor transport, etc. These assets will reduce in value as time goes on, that is, they will depreciate in value.

The depreciation formula is very similar to the compound interest formula and it is

$$A = P\left(1 - \frac{R}{100}\right)^T$$

where:
  A = the value after T years
  P = the original value
  R = percentage rate of depreciation per annum

Example 6

A company buys office machinery which costs £8000. The depreciation is calculated at an annual rate of 15%. Work out the value of the machinery at the end of 7 years.

We are given $P = 8000$, $R = 15$ and $T = 7$.

$$A = 8000 \times \left(1 - \frac{15}{100}\right)^7$$

$$= 8000 \times (1 - 0.15)^7$$

$$= 8000 \times 0.85^7$$

$$= 2565$$

So the machinery will be worth £2565 at the end of 7 years.

EXERCISE 14.3

1. A business buys new machinery at a cost of £18 000. It decides to calculate the depreciation at an annual rate of 25%. Work out the value of the machinery at the end of 3 years.

2. The value of a lathe depreciates at 18% per annum. If it cost £8000 when new, calculate its value after 4 years.

3. A car depreciates in value at an annual rate of 20%. If it cost £9000 when new, calculate its value after 3 years.

4. A lorry cost £25 000 when new. It depreciates in value at an annual rate of 15%. Estimate its value at the end of 5 years.

5. A machine costs £36 000 when new but its value depreicates at an annual rate of 15%. Work out its value at the end of 10 years.

MISCELLANEOUS EXERCISE 14

1. Work out the simple interest on £5000 invested for 6 months at 11% per annum.

2. A man invests £9000 for 5 years at 10% per annum compound interest. How much will the investment be worth at the end of the 5 years?

3. My grandfather left me £20 000 to be kept in trust for 5 years at 11% per annum simple interest. What will the money be worth at the end of the 5 years?

4. It is estimated that a machine costing £30 000 has a life of 8 years. If it depreciates in value at an annual rate of 14%, work out its likely value at the end of the 8 years.

5. A woman invested £5000 for one year in each of the following:
   (a) A building society paying 8.25% free of income tax.
   (b) A municipal bond paying interest at an annual rate of 11% on which income tax at 27% is payable.
   Work out the net income from both investments and find which investment realises the greatest net income.

125

CHAPTER 15

Investment

INTRODUCTION

There are very many different ways of investing and saving money.

There is a difference between saving and investing. If you put £100 in a building society or a bank and keep drawing the interest each year all that remains is the £100. The interest which is a compensation for your loan can go up or down in line with the money market rates. This is saving and it is generally safe but your capital of £100 does not appreciate and we say there has been no growth.

Investment means backing an enterprise in the hope that it will be successful thereby allowing the investors to share in the success. Hopefully not only will your income rise but the value of your holding (the price you paid for it) will also rise. You should get rising interest on your £100 and possibly in ten years time you can sell your stake in the enterprise for perhaps £200.

BUILDING SOCIETIES
Share Account

This is a very flexible way to invest, and there are few restrictions on how much and how often withdrawals can be made. Hence a share account is a good place to keep ready cash. Interest is paid on a daily basis and credited to you half-yearly.

Extra Interest Account

This pays top rates of interest. The money invested need not be committed for a period of years but a notice period of between seven days and three months is required before a withdrawal can be made. An immediate withdrawal can be made but this usually results in the interest on the amount withdrawn being lost. The minimum investment is often as much as £5000 or even £20 000.

Fixed-Term Account

This is for investors who want to keep a lump sum with the society for a fixed period of time, usually between one and five years. Most societies offer higher rates of interest on fixed-term accounts, the longer the term the higher the interest rate will be.

BANKS

Current Account

This allows money placed in the account to be withdrawn at any time usually by writing a cheque. As a rule, current accounts do not pay interest.

Deposit Account

This is an account in which funds are left on deposit. Interest is calculated daily and credited to the account half-yearly. Income tax is deducted before you get the interest.

Example 1

(a) A woman puts £800 in a building society share account paying interest at 6% per annum. How much interest will she get after 1 year?

Interest payable = 6% of £800 = £48

(b) A building society pays 7.25% to people who invest in their extra-interest account. However, withdrawals made without 90 days notice attract a penalty of the loss of 90 days interest on the amount withdrawn. Find:

(i) the amount of interest payable per annum if £5000 is invested in the account.

(ii) the amount of interest lost if £2000 is withdrawn without notice.

(i) Amount of interest payable per annum

$$= 7.25\% \text{ of } £5000$$

$$= £362.50$$

(ii) Amount of interest payable on £2000 per annum

$$= 7.25\% \text{ of } £2000$$

$$= £145$$

Since there are 365 days in a year

$$\text{Amount of interest lost} = £145 \times \frac{90}{365}$$

$$= £35.75$$

(c) A woman invests in a five-year fixed term building society account which pays 9% per annum compound. If she invests £4000, how much will her investment be worth at the end of the term?

Using the compound interest formula,

$$A = P\left(1 + \frac{R}{100}\right)^n$$

We have $P = £4000$, $R = 9\%$ and $n = 5$ years.

$$A = 4000 \times \left(1 + \frac{9}{100}\right)^5$$

$$= 4000 \times 1.09^5$$

$$= £6155$$

Hence at the end of the term the investment will be worth £6155.

(d) A man puts £2000 in a bank deposit account paying interest at 5% per annum. How much will his gross interest be at the end of 1 year? Tax is payable at 25%. How much will his net interest be?

Gross interest per annum = 5% of £2000 = £100

Tax payable = 25% of £100 = £25

Net interest per annum = £100 − £25 = £75

NATIONAL SAVINGS
Ordinary Account

This works like a bank deposit account except that you are banking with the Post Office. The minimum investment is £1 and the maximum is £10 000. Interest is paid gross (i.e., before tax has been deducted) and the first £70 of interest is tax free.

Investment Account

This also works like an ordinary account but you get higher rates of interest because it takes one month to make a withdrawal. The minimum investment is £5 and the maximum is £50 000. Again the interest is paid gross and it is added to the account once a year.

Savings Certificates

These are available in units of £25. They are designed to be held for at least five years. They can be cashed after a shorter period but the rate of return is then lower. No interest is paid out but each year the certificates increase in value.

Example 2

(a) The thirty-third issue of savings certificates offers the following terms:

> At the end of the first year the value of a £25 unit increases by 5.5%.
> At the end of 2 years by 5.75% per annum compound.
> At the end of 3 years by 6% per annum compound.
> At the end of 4 years by 6.5% per annum compound.
> At the end of 5 years the £25 unit is worth £35.06.

Work out the value of the £25 unit after 1, 2, 3 and 4 years.

Value after 1 year $= 105.5\%$ of £25 $=$ £26.37.

For the remaining years the compound interest formula should be used:

Value after 2 years $= 25 \times 1.0575^2 =$ £27.96

Value after 3 years $= 25 \times 1.06^3 =$ £29.78

Value after 4 years $= 25 \times 1.065^4 =$ £32.16

Note that the rate of increase is 7% at the end of the 5-year term.

(b) The rate of interest for a national savings investment account is 11% per annum but income tax at 27% has to be paid. Work out the gross and net amounts of interest at the end of 1 year if £3000 is invested.

Gross amount of interest $= 11\%$ of £3000 $=$ £330

Amount of tax payable $= 27\%$ of £330 $=$ £89.10

Net amount of interest $=$ £330 $-$ £89.10 $=$ £240.90

PUBLIC LOANS
Government Stocks

These are often called gilt-edged stocks, and are loans made by the public to the British Government. In return for your money you get a certificate which states the name of the stock, the date of repayment and the gross rate of interest, for instance, 8% Treasury 2002–6. This means that the stock will be redeemed between the years 2002 and 2006 and interest at 8% per annum (p.a.) will be paid.

For every £100 invested the Government promises to pay back £100 and prices of stocks are always quoted for £100. The value of a stock can fall below £100 and in some cases it might even rise above £100. Gilt-edged prices are influenced by such things as inflation, the balance of payments and the strength of the pound.

Example 3

The price of 8% Treasury stock is quoted as 94. A man desires to spend £800 in buying this stock.

(a) How much stock will he get?
(b) How much interest per annum will he get?

The price of 94 means that for each £100 of stock the purchaser pays only £94.

(a) Amount of stock bought $= \dfrac{800}{94} \times 100$

$$= £851$$

(b) The interest will be calculated on £851.

Interest payable $= 8\%$ of £851 $= \dfrac{8}{100} \times 851$

$$= £68.08 \text{ p.a.}$$

The true rate of interest is $\dfrac{68.08}{800} \times 100 = 8.51\%$

Corporation Stock

This is also quoted on the Stock Exchange. It is issued by large towns and cities when they cannot raise enough money through the rates. They work in exactly the same way as Government stock.

Shares

These are issued by companies as a means of raising capital. These shares have a nominal value, for instance 50 p, but they may fluctuate as they are bought and sold on the Stock Exchange. If the company does well the shares will go up in value.

Part of any profit the company makes is given to the shareholders in the form of a dividend which is usually so much per share. The normal way for a company to raise cash is by issuing ordinary shares but debentures, preference shares and loan stock are also used.

Example 4

The Concorde Company 50 p shares are quoted on the Stock Exchange at 65 p.

(a) How many shares will an investor get for £1300?
(b) The company pays a dividend of 4 p per share. How much will the investor get?
(c) What percentage return does the investor get on his investment?

(a) The nominal price of the shares is 50 p but the investor has to pay 65 p for each share that he buys. Therefore

Number of shares bought $= \dfrac{1300}{0.65} = 2000$

(b) Amount of the dividend $= 2000 \times 4$ pence

$$= 8000 \text{ pence}$$

$$= £80$$

(c) Percentage return on the investment

$$= \dfrac{80}{1300} \times 100 = 6.15\%$$

Note that on the nominal value of the shares the dividend is $\dfrac{4}{50} \times 100 = 8\%$.

Unit Trusts

These are another way of investing on the stock exchange. Because the values of ordinary shares can fall as well as rise there is an element of risk in investing in these shares. A unit trust puts together all the money received from investors in the trust and buys shares in a number of companies. This spreads the risk. The cost to the trust of investing in the shares of companies is built into the price of the units. If you look at the stock exchange prices of unit trusts you will notice that two prices are always quoted. The bid price is the price at which you buy the units and the offer price is the price at which you sell the units. The bid price is always higher than the offer price. The price of units may rise or fall over a period of time depending on the performance of shares in the companies in which the trust has invested. Dividends are payable but these can be re-invested to buy further units in the trust.

Example 5

A unit trust specialising in equities has a bid price of 102 p and an offer price of 93 p.

(a) What is the difference in the two prices?
(b) What is the percentage difference based upon the bid price?

(c) An investor wishes to buy 500 units in the trust. How much will these units cost?
(d) At a later date the offer price of the units has risen to 112 p. If the investor sells the 500 units how much will he get for them?

(a) Difference in the prices $= 102 - 93 = 9$ p

(b) Percentage difference $= \dfrac{9}{102} \times 100 = 8.82\%$

(c) Cost of 500 units $= 500 \times 102$ p $= £510$

(d) Amount obtained $= 500 \times 112$ p $= £560$

EXERCISE 15.1

1. A woman invests £500 in a share account of a building society. If the interest rate is $6\frac{1}{2}\%$ how much will she get, in interest, per annum?

2. A building society has an extra interest account which pays 7.75% p.a. net (i.e., income tax paid). Withdrawals may be made without notice but there is then a penalty of 3 months loss of interest. A man invests £2000 with this society. Find:

   (a) the amount of interest payable if the money is left in the account for one year,
   (b) the loss of interest if the money is withdrawn without notice at the end of the first year.

3. A woman invests in a three-year fixed-term building society account. The interest rate is 8% per annum compound. How much will her investment be worth at the end of the 3 years if she invests £7000?

4. A man puts £2000 in a bank deposit account paying 6% interest per annum. How much will this investment be worth at the end of 1 year?

5. An investor puts £8000 in a national savings investment account which pays interest at 12% gross. If income tax is levied at 25% find:

   (a) the gross interest (i.e., before tax),
   (b) the net interest (i.e., after tax).

6. One issue of savings certificates offers the following terms:
   At the end of the first year the value of a £20 unit is increased by 6.5%.
   At the end of 2 years the unit is increased by 7% p.a. compound.
   At the end of 3 years the unit is increased by 7.75% p.a. compound.
   At the end of 4 years the unit is increased by 8.5% p.a. compound.
   At the end of 5 years the unit is increased by 9% p.a. compound.
   Work out the value of the £20 unit after 1, 2, 3, 4 and 5 years.

7. 9% Transport stock is quoted on the Stock Exchange at 98. A man invests £2500 in this stock.

   (a) How much of this stock will he get?
   (b) How much interest is payable per annum?

8. Thetford Corporation stock was quoted on the Stock Exchange at 75. A woman invested £5000 in this stock which paid interest at 8% p.a.

   (a) How much stock did she buy?

   (b) How much interest is payable per annum?

9. Empress shares have a nominal value of £1 and they were quoted on the Stock Exchange at 135 p. An investor buys 2000 of these shares.

   (a) How much will the 2000 shares cost him?

   (b) If a dividend of 7 p per share is declared how much will the investor get in dividends?

   (c) Express this dividend as a percentage based on the amount paid for the shares.

10. Lion shares with a nominal value of 50 p were quoted on the Stock Exchange at 35 p.

    (a) How much did 1500 of these shares cost?

    (b) A dividend of 1.8 p per share is declared. How much will be paid on the 1500 shares?

    (c) Express the nominal dividend rate as a percentage.

    (d) Express the true dividend rate as a percentage.

11. A unit trust is quoted as having a bid price of 97 p and an offer price of 91 p per unit.

    (a) How much will 300 of these units cost an investor?

    (b) If the investor sells these units at the offer price, how much will he get for them?

12. A unit trust has an offer price of 238 p and a bid price of 255 p. A dividend of 12.8 p per unit is declared.

    (a) A man buys 2500 of these units. How much did they cost?

    (b) How much did the man get in dividends if he requested cash.

    (c) If the man decided to take accumulated units instead of cash, how many extra units would he get?

13. A high income unit trust specialising in gilt-edged stock declares a dividend of 12.1% gross (i.e., tax not deducted). A man invests £500 in this trust.

    (a) How much will he get as his gross dividend?

    (b) If the man pays tax at 40%, how much net dividend will he get?

14. One issue of national savings certificates offers a return of 8% per annum compound on a £25 unit provided it is kept for 5 years. Using the compound interest formula, work out the value of this unit at the end of the 5 years.

15. A person invests £5000 in national savings ordinary account. Interest at 6% per annum is paid gross (i.e., before tax has been deducted). The first £70 of interest is tax free. If the person pays income tax at 27%, how much is actually payable in income tax?

CHAPTER 16

Tables, Charts and Diagrams

TABLES

Conversion tables of various kinds are used in business, science and engineering.

Ready reckoners provide a quick way of determining bank loans, and hire purchase repayments. Table 1 shows an extract from hire-purchase replayment tables put out by a finance house.

TABLE 1

Outstanding Balance	Monthly instalments		
	36 months	24 months	12 months
£5	£0.23	£0.30	£0.51
£10	£0.45	£0.59	£1.01
£20	£0.90	£1.18	£2.02
£30	£1.35	£1.77	£3.02
£40	£1.80	£2.36	£4.03
£50	£2.25	£2.95	£5.04
£60	£2.70	£3.55	£6.05
£70	£3.17	£4.14	£7.05
£80	£3.62	£4.73	£8.06
£90	£4.07	£5.32	£9.07
£100	£4.52	£5.91	£10.08
£200	£9.04	£11.82	£20.16
£300	£13.56	£17.73	£30.24
£400	£18.08	£23.64	£40.32
£500	£22.60	£29.55	£50.40
£600	£27.12	£35.46	£60.48
£700	£31.64	£41.37	£70.56
£800	£36.16	£47.28	£80.64
£900	£40.68	£53.19	£90.72

Example 1

Use Table 1 to find the monthly instalments for outstanding balances of:

(a) £70 over 36 months,
(b) £95 over 24 months,
(c) £785 over 12 months.

(a) Directly from the table

$$\text{Monthly instalment} = £3.17$$

(b) £95 = £90 + £5

$$\text{Monthly instalment} = £5.32 + £0.30$$
$$= £5.62$$

(c) £785 = £700 + £80 + £5

$$\text{Monthly instalment} = £70.56 + £8.06 + £0.51$$
$$= £79.13$$

Table 2 shows part of a table which is used to convert °F into °C and vice versa.

TABLE 2

°F	0	1	2	3	4	5	6	7	8	9
TEMPERATURE	Degrees Fahrenheit to degrees Celsius									
0	−17.8	−17.2	−16.7	−16.1	−15.6	−15.0	−14.4	−13.9	−13.3	−12.8
10	−12.2	−11.7	−11.1	−10.6	−10.0	−9.4	−8.9	−8.3	−7.8	−7.2
20	−6.7	−6.1	−5.6	−5.0	−4.4	−3.9	−3.3	−2.8	−2.2	−1.7
20	−1.1	−0.6	0	0.6	1.1	1.7	2.2	2.8	3.3	3.9
40	4.4	5.0	5.6	6.1	6.7	7.2	7.8	8.3	8.9	9.4
50	10.0	10.6	11.1	11.7	12.2	12.8	13.3	13.9	14.4	15.0
60	15.6	16.1	16.7	17.2	17.8	18.3	18.9	19.4	20.0	20.6
70	21.1	21.7	22.2	22.8	23.3	23.9	24.4	25.0	25.6	26.1
80	26.7	27.2	27.8	28.3	28.9	29.4	30.0	30.6	31.1	31.7
90	32.2	32.8	33.3	33.9	34.4	35.0	35.6	36.1	36.7	37.2
100	37.8	38.3	38.9	39.4	40.0	40.6	41.1	41.7	42.2	42.8
110	43.3	43.9	44.4	45.0	45.6	46.1	46.7	47.2	47.8	48.3
120	48.9	49.4	50.0	50.6	51.1	51.7	52.2	52.8	53.8	53.9
130	54.4	55.0	55.6	56.1	56.7	57.2	57.8	58.3	58.9	59.4
140	60.0	60.6	61.1	61.7	62.2	62.8	63.3	63.9	64.4	65.0
150	65.6	66.1	66.7	67.2	67.8	68.3	68.9	69.4	70.0	70.6
160	71.1	71.7	72.2	72.8	73.3	73.9	74.4	75.0	75.6	76.1
170	76.7	77.2	77.8	78.3	78.9	79.4	80.0	80.6	81.1	81.7
180	82.2	82.8	83.3	83.9	84.4	85.0	85.6	86.1	86.7	87.2
190	87.8	88.3	88.9	89.4	90.0	90.6	91.1	91.7	92.2	92.8
Interpolation deg F:	0.1	0.2	0.3	0.4	0.5	0.6	0.7	0.8	0.9	
deg C:	0.1	0.1	0.2	0.2	0.3	0.3	0.4	0.4	0.5	

Example 2

Using Table 2, convert:

(a) 54 °F into degrees Celsius,
(b) 122.7 °F into degrees Celsius,
(c) 35 °C into degress Fahrenheit,
(d) 62.7 °C into degrees Fahrenheit,

(a) We first find 50 in the first column and move along this row until we arrive at the column headed 4. We find the number 12.2 and hence 54 °F = 12.2 °C.

(b) To convert 122.7 °F into degrees Celsius we make use of the figures given under the heading 'interpolation'. From the table we find 122 °F = 50 °C. Looking at the figures in the interpolation section we see that 0.7 °F = 0.4 °C. So

$$122.7 \text{ °F} = (50 + 0.4) \text{ °C} = 50.4 \text{ °C}$$

(c) To convert degrees Celsius into degrees Fahrenheit we use the table in reverse. To convert 35 °C into degrees Fahrenheit we search in the body of the table until we find the figure 35. This occurs in the column headed 5 in the row starting with 90. Hence 35 °C is equivalent to 95 °F.

(d) To convert 62.7 °C into degrees Fahrenheit we look in the body of the table for a number as close to 62.7 as possible, but less than 62.7. This number is 62.2 corresponding to 144 °F. Now 62.2 °C is 0.5 °C less than 62.7 °C. Using the interpolation figures we see that 0.5 °C corresponds to 0.9 °F. Therefore

$$62.7 \text{ °C} = 62.2 \text{ °C} + 0.5 \text{ °C}$$
$$= 144 \text{ °F} + 0.9 \text{ °F}$$
$$= 144.9 \text{ °F}$$

Mileage charts are often set out as in Table 3.

TABLE 3

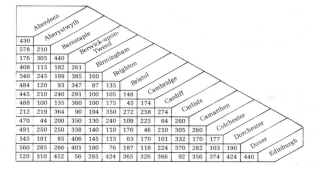

Example 3

Use Table 3 to find the distance between:

(a) Aberdeen and Carlisle,
(b) Barnstaple and Cambridge.

(a) To find the distance between Aberdeen and Carlisle, find Aberdeen and Carlisle in the sloping list. Move vertically down the column for Aberdeen and horizontally along the row for Carlisle until the two movements coincide. The figure given in the table at this point is 212. Hence the distance between Aberdeen and Carlisle is 212 miles.

(b) Find Barnstaple in the sloping list (it is third from the top of the list). The row for Cambridge is the seventh row from the top of the list. In the third column of the seventh row we find the figure 240. Hence the distance between Barnstaple and Cambridge is 240 miles.

PARALLEL SCALE CONVERSION CHARTS

A system of parallel scales may be used when we wish to convert from one set of units to another related set. Figure 16.1 is a chart relating degrees Fahrenheit and degrees Celsius.

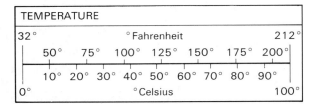

TEMPERATURE

Figure 16.1

Example 4

Using Figure 16.1 convert:

(a) 50 °F to degrees Celsius,
(b) 75 °F to degrees Celsius,
(c) 20 °C to degrees Fahrenheit.

(a) From the chart we see that 50 °F corresponds with 10 °C and therefore 50 °F is equivalent to 10 °C.

(b) From the chart we see that 75 °F roughly corresponds with 24 °C. Note carefully that when using the chart we cannot expect accuracy greater than 1°.

(c) From the chart we see that 20 °C is about 68 °F.

EXERCISE 16.1

1. Use Table 1 to find monthly instalments for outstanding balances of:
    (a) £90 over 36 months,
    (b) £700 over 12 months,
    (c) £65 over 24 months,
    (d) £805 over 12 months,
    (e) £540 over 36 months,
    (f) £735 over 24 months.

2. Use Table 2 to convert:
    (a) 83 °F to degrees Celsius,
    (b) 114.6 °F to degrees Celsius,
    (c) 55 °C to degrees Fahrenheit,
    (d) 68.7 °C to degrees Fahrenheit.

3. Use the mileage chart (Table 3) to find the distance between:
    (a) Aberdeen and Cardiff,
    (b) Birmingham and Camarthen,
    (c) Bristol and Dorchester.

4. Table 4 gives a comparison between gradients expressed as a ratio and gradients expressed as a percentage.

    Use the table to convert:
    (a) a gradient of 1:7 to a percentage,
    (b) a gradient of 7.2% to a ratio.

TABLE 4

Gradients	
Ratio	%
1:3	33.3
1:4	25
1:5	20
1:6	16.4
1:7	14.2
1:8	12.4
1:9	11.1
1:10	10
1:11	9.1
1:12	8.4
1:13	7.9
1:14	7.2
1:15	6.6
1:16	6.4
1:17	5.8
1:18	5.5
1:19	5.2
1:20	5

5. Figure 16.2 is a chart relating the pound weight to the kilogram. Use the chart to convert:

(a) 4 lb to kilograms,
(b) 568 lb to kilograms,
(c) 3.8 kg to pounds,
(d) 0.23 kg to pounds.

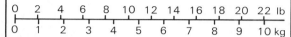

Figure 16.2

6. Table 5 shows conversions from miles to kilometres (and also from miles per hour to kilometres per hour). Use the table to convert:

(a) 15 miles to kilometres,
(b) 48.27 km/h to miles per hour,
(c) 58 miles to kilometres,
(d) 568 mile/h to kilometres per hour.

TABLE 5

Distance and speed					
Miles to kilometres					
Miles per hour to kilometres per hour					
1	1.60	20	32.18	75	120.7
2	3.21	25	40.23	80	128.7
3	4.82	30	48.27	85	136.8
4	6.43	35	56.32	90	144.8
5	8.04	40	64.37	95	152.9
6	9.65	45	72.41	100	160.9
7	11.26	50	80.46	200	321.9
8	12.87	55	88.51	300	482.8
9	14.48	60	96.55	400	643.7
10	16.09	65	104.60	500	804.7
11	24.13	70	112.70	1000	1609.3
1 mile = 1.609 344 km					
1 kilometre = 0.621 371 miles					

7. Use Figure 16.1 to convert:

(a) 100 °F to degrees Celsius,
(b) 80 °C to degrees Fahrenheit,
(c) 64 °F to degrees Celsius,
(d) 48 °C to degree Fahrenheit.

8. Table 6 shows a comparison of tyre pressures. Convert:

(a) 22 pounds per square inch to kilograms per square centimetre,
(b) 2.10 kilograms per square centimetre to pounds per square inch.

TABLE 6

Tyre pressures					
Pounds per sq in to kg per sq cm					
16	1.12	26	1.83	40	2.80
18	1.26	28	1.96	50	3.50
20	1.40	30	2.10	55	3.85
22	1.54	32	2.24	60	4.20
24	1.68	36	2.52	65	4.55

SIMPLE BAR CHARTS

A simple bar chart consists of a series of bars all of the same width. The bars may be drawn vertically or horizontally. The height (or length) of the bars represents the magnitude of the given figures.

A simple bar chart shows clearly the size of each item of information but it is not easy to obtain the total of all the items from the diagram.

Example 5

A family spends its weekly income of £300 as follows:

Food	£100
Clothes	£50
Fuel	£40
Mortgage	£90
Other expenses	£20
Total	£300

Draw (a) a horizontal bar chart, (b) a vertical bar chart to represent this information.

(a) Figure 16.3 shows the information in the form of a horizontal bar chart.

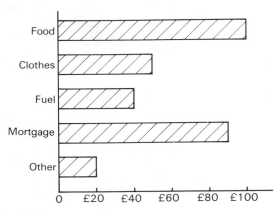

Figure 16.3

(b) Figure 16.4 shows the information in the form of a vertical bar chart.

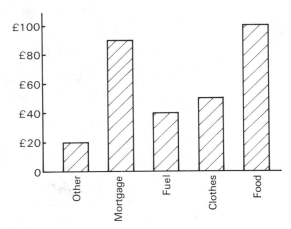

Figure 16.4

CHRONOLOGICAL BAR CHARTS

A chronological bar chart compares quantities over a period of time. It is similar to a vertical bar chart, except that the bars are often replaced by vertical lines.

Example 6

The information below gives the number of colour television sets sold in Southern England during the period 1970–5.

Year	Number of sets sold (thousands)
1970	77.2
1971	84.0
1972	91.3
1973	114.6
1974	130.9
1975	142.5

Draw a chronological bar chart to represent this information.

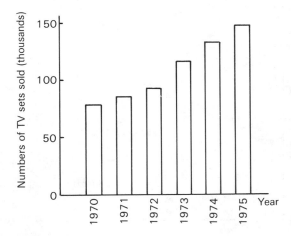

Figure 16.5

When drawing a chronological bar chart time is always marked off along the horizontal axis. The chart is drawn in Figure 16.5 and it clearly shows how the sales of television sets have increased over the period illustrated.

136

THE PROPORTIONATE BAR CHART

The proportionate bar chart (Figure 16.6) relies on heights (or areas) to convey proportions of a whole. The bar should be of the same width throughout its length or height. This diagram is accurate, quick and easy to construct and it can show quite a large number of component parts without confusion. Although Figure 16.6 shows the bar drawn vertically it can also be drawn horizontally if desired.

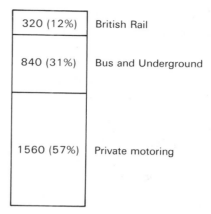

Figure 16.6

The chart is shown in Fig. 16.6.

Example 7

Draw a proportionate bar chart for the figures below which show the way some commuters in the south-east region travelled to the London area.

Type of transport	Numbers using
Private motoring	1560
Bus and Underground	840
British Rail	320

The easiest way is to draw the chart on graph or squared paper. Alternatively the proportions can be expressed as percentages which are calculated as shown below.

$$\text{Total number in the sample} = 1560 + 840 + 320 = 2720$$

Type of transport	Percentage of sample using
Private motoring	$\frac{1560}{2720} \times 100 = 57\%$
Bus and Underground	$\frac{840}{2720} \times 100 = 31\%$
British Rail	$\frac{320}{2720} \times 100 = 12\%$

PIE CHARTS

A pie chart displays the proportions of a whole as a sector angle or a sector area. The circle as a whole represents the total of the component parts.

Pie charts are very useful when component parts of a whole are to be represented, but it is not easy to discover the total quantity represented. Up to eight component parts can be represented, but above this number the chart loses its clarity and effectiveness.

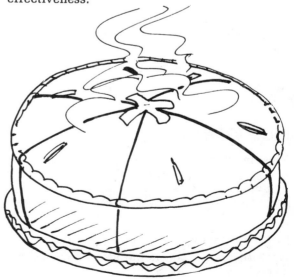

Example 8

Represent the information given in Example 7 in the form of a pie chart.

The first step is to calculate the sector angles. Remembering that a circle contains 360° the sector angles are calculated as shown below.

Type of transport	Sector angle (degrees)
Private motoring	$\frac{1560}{2720} \times 360 = 207°$
Bus and Underground	$\frac{840}{2720} \times 360 = 111°$
British Rail	$\frac{320}{2720} \times 360 = 42°$

Using a protractor the pie chart (Figure 16.7) can now be drawn. If desired, percentages can be displayed on the diagram.

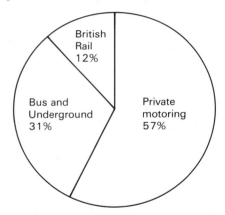

Figure 16.7

PICTOGRAMS

These are diagrams in the form of pictures which are used to present information to those who are unskilled in dealing with figures or to those who have only a limited interest in the topic depicted.

Example 9

The table below shows output of bicycles at a factory for the years 1980–84.

Year	1980	1981	1982	1983	1984
Output	2000	4000	7000	8500	9000

Represent this information in the form of a pictogram.

The pictogram is shown in Figure 16.8. It will be seen that each bicycle in the diagram represents an output of 2000 bicycles. Part of a symbol is shown in 1982, 1983 and 1984 to represent a fraction of 2000 but clearly this is not a very precise way of representing the output.

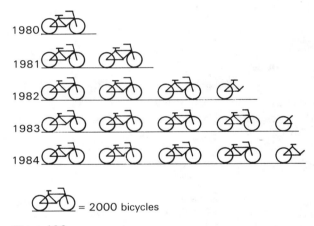

Figure 16.8

A method not recommended is shown in Figure 16.9. Comparison is difficult because the reader is not sure whether to compare heights, areas or volumes.

Sales of milk in 1960 and 1980 (millions of litres)

Figure 16.9

1. A building contractor surveying his labour force finds that 35% are engaged in constructing factories, 40% are engaged on house building and 25% are engaged on public works (schools, hospitals, etc.).

   (a) Draw a single bar chart to represent this information.
   (b) Present the information in the form of a pie chart.

2. Figure 16.10 is a pictogram showing the method used by first-year boys to travel to school.

   (a) How many come by bus?
   (b) How many come by car?

WALKING 옷 옷 옷 옷 옷 옷 옷

BUS 옷 옷 옷 옷 옷 옷 옷 옷

CYCLE 옷 옷 웃

CAR 옷 옷 ∘

옷 Represents 5 boys
(head 1, arms and legs 1 each)

Figure 16.10

3. The sales of motor cars by Mortimer & Co. Ltd. were as follows:

Year	1982	1983	1984	1985	1986
Sales	2300	2600	3400	2800	3300

   (a) Represent this information in the form of a chronological bar chart.
   (b) Draw a pictogram to represent this information.

4. The information given below gives details of the temperature range used when forging various metals. Draw a horizontal bar chart to represent this data.

Metal	Temperature (°C)
Carbon steel	770–1300
Wrought iron	860–1240
Brass	600–800
Copper	500–1000

5. Figure 16.11 is a pie chart which shows the total sales of a department store for one day. Work out the correct size of each sector angle. (The diagram is NOT drawn to scale.)

Figure 16.11

6. A firm finds that each pound received from sales is spent in the following way:

Raw materials	38 p
Wages and salaries	29 p
Machinery, etc.	8 p
Advertising	15 p
Profit	10 p

   (a) Construct a pie chart of this information.
   (b) Represent this data in the form of a vertical bar chart.

7. The information on p. 140 gives the production of tyres (in thousands) produced by the Treadwell Tyre Company for the first six months of 1987.

Month	Production
January	40
February	43
March	39
April	38
May	37
June	45

(a) Draw a pictogram to represent this information.

(b) Construct a chronological bar chart for this data.

8. In a certain factory the number of personnel employed on various jobs were as follows: Machinists 140, Fitters 120, Clerical staff 80, Unskilled workers 10, Draughtsmen 20. Represent this information:

(a) in a pie chart,

(b) in a single bar chart,

(c) in a horizontal bar chart.

MENTAL TEST 16

1. Use the mileage chart shown in Table 3 to find the distance from:

(a) Aberystwyth to Birmingham,

(b) Bristol to Carlisle,

(c) Cambridge to Edinburgh.

2. Figure 16.12 shows a diagram which can be used to change degrees Celsius into degrees Fahrenheit. Use the diagram to change:

(a) 50 °C to degrees Fahrenheit,

(b) 20 °C to degrees Fahrenheit,

(c) 50 °F to degrees Celsius.

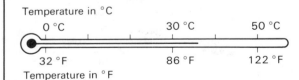

Temperature in °C

Figure 16.12

3. The bar chart (Figure 16.13) shows the ages of children in a school.

(a) How many 13-year-olds took part in the survey?

(b) How many children in total took part?

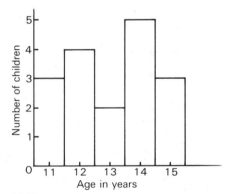

Figure 16.13

4. The pie chart (Figure 16.14) illustrates the sports preferred by a group of male students.

(a) What percentage of the group preferred tennis?

(b) What fraction preferred cricket?

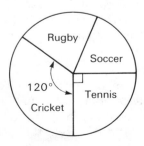

Figure 16.14

140

5. The main leisure activities of 100 fifth formers are shown below:

Soccer	40
Reading	10
Television	25
Scouts	5
Other	20

If a pie chart is drawn to represent this data, find the size of the sector angles to represent:

(**a**) reading, (**b**) television.

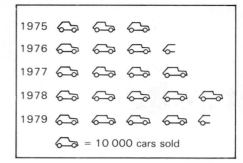

Figure 16.15

6. The pictogram (Figure 16.15) shows the sales of cars during the years 1975–79.

(**a**) In which year were most cars sold?
(**b**) How many cars were sold in 1978?
(**c**) How many cars were sold in 1976?

7. Mrs Smith has £200 per week for housekeeping. A pie chart is drawn which shows how she spent the money. If she spends £40 on food, find the size of the sector angle representing this amount.

141

CHAPTER 17

Graphs

INTRODUCTION

In newspapers, business reports and government publications great use is made of pictorial illustrations to help the reader understand the report. Some of the charts and diagrams were discussed in Chapter 16. Graphs, which are pictures of numerical information, are also commonly used as illustrations.

AXES

The first step in drawing a graph is to draw two lines, one vertical and the other horizontal. These lines are called the axes and the point where they cross is called the origin. The vertical axis is often called the y-axis and the horizontal axis is then called the x-axis (Figure 17.1). Both axes should be clearly labelled as shown, for instance, in Figure 17.2.

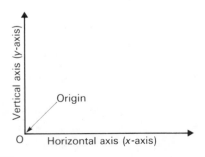

Figure 17.1

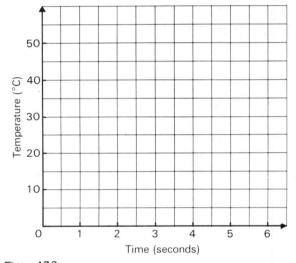

Figure 17.2

SCALES

The number of units represented by a unit length along an axis is called the scale. For instance, in Figure 17.2 the vertical scale is 1 cm = 10 degrees. The scales need not be the same on both axes. The most useful scales are 1 cm to 1, 2, 5 and 10 units. Some multiples of these are also satisfactory, for instance 1 cm to 20, 50 and 100 units.

No matter which scale is chosen it is important that it is easy to read. When graph or squared paper is used the scale will depend upon the type and size of paper used.

CARTESIAN COORDINATES

Cartesian coordinates are used to position the points on a graph. In Figure 17.3 the point P has the coordinates (4, 6). The first number, it is 4, gives the horizontal distance from the origin. The second number, it is 6, gives the vertical distance from the origin.

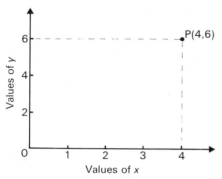

Figure 17.3

EXERCISE 17.1

1. Write down the coordinates of the points A, B, C, D, E and F (Figure 17.4).

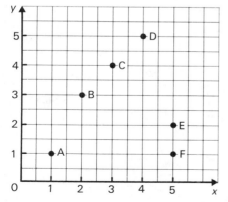

Figure 17.4

2. Write down the coordinates of the points R, S, T, U and V shown in Figure 17.5.

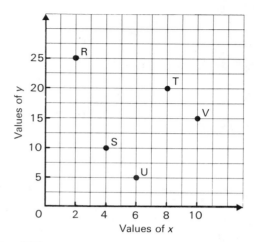

Figure 17.5

3. On graph or squared paper draw a pair of axes. Along the horizontal axis use a scale of 1 cm to represent 2 units and along the vertical axis use a scale of 1 cm to represent 10 units. Now plot the following points:

   (a) (4, 20)   (b) (6, 25)   (c) (5, 35)
   (d) (7, 60)   (e) (3, 45)

DRAWING A GRAPH

Every graph shows the relationship between two sets of numbers.

Example 1

The table below shows the speed of a racing car at various times during its first lap.

Time (seconds)	0	10	20	30	40
Speed (mile/hour)	0	10	40	90	160

Plot these points on graph paper using a scale of 1 cm to represent 5 seconds on the horizontal axis and 1 cm to represent 20 mile/hour on the vertical axis.

143

(a) Use the graph to find the speed of the car after 25 seconds.

(b) How many seconds did it take the car to attain a speed of 100 mile/hour?

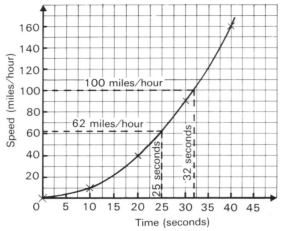

Figure 17.6

The graph is shown in Figure 17.6 and the points can be joined to give a smooth curve. When a graph is a smooth curve or a straight line it can be used to find corresponding values of the variables which are not given in the original table of values.

(a) To find the speed of the car after 25 seconds we draw horizontal and vertical lines as shown in the diagram. We find that the speed of the car after 25 seconds is 62 mile/hour.

(b) Working in a similar way we find that it takes 32 seconds for the car to reach a speed of 100 mile/hour.

The numbers given in a table of corresponding values do not have to be whole numbers. As shown in Example 2, they can include decimal numbers.

Example 2

The table below gives the average diameter of ash trees of varying ages.

Age (years)	10	20	30	40	50
Diameter (cm)	9.3	16.2	27.7	43.8	64.5

Plot these values on graph paper and join them to form a smooth curve. Use the graph to find:

(a) the diameter of a tree which is 35 years old,
(b) the age of a tree with a diameter of 20 cm.

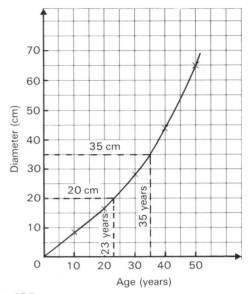

Figure 17.7

The graph is shown in Figure 17.7

(a) The diameter of a tree which is 35 years old is 35 cm.

(b) The age of a tree having a diameter of 20 cm is 23 years.

144

1. Figure 17.8 shows a graph of values of y plotted against values of x. Find:
   (a) the values of y when x = 4, x = 7 and x = 11.
   (b) the values of x when y = 7, y = 11 and y = 23.

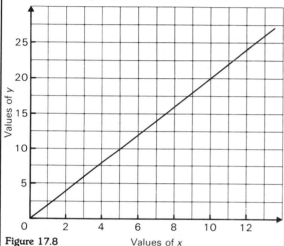

Figure 17.8   Values of x

2. Figure 17.9 shows the distance a car travels (in metres) after various times (in seconds). Find:
   (a) the distances travelled after times of 2, 3 and 5 seconds,
   (b) the times taken to travel 28, 53 and 70 metres.

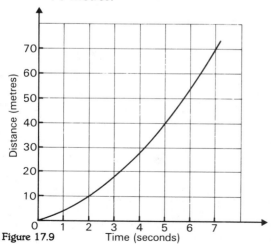

Figure 17.9   Time (seconds)

3. Figure 17.10 shows how the height of a girl alters with her age. Use the graph to find:
   (a) her age when she attained a height of 108 cm,
   (b) her height when she was 7 years old.

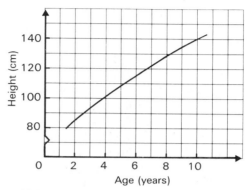

Figure 17.10

4. The figures below show corresponding values for units of electricity used and the cost of the electricity bill in £. Draw a graph of this information with units used on the horizontal axis and the cost on the vertical axis. Use a scale on the horizontal axis of one large square to represent 200 units and one large square to represent £5 on the vertical axis.

Units used	0	300	600	900	1200
Cost (£)	2	8	14	20	26

Use your graph to find:
   (a) the cost of the electricity bill when 800 units are used,
   (b) the number of units used when the bill is £12.

5. A car was tested for fuel consumption (in miles per gallon) at various speeds (in miles per hour). The results of the test were as follows:

Speed	10	30	50	70	80
Fuel consumption	20	35	40	30	23

   (a) Plot the points and draw a smooth curve through them. Suitable scales

145

are one large square to represent 5 miles per gallon along the horizontal axis and one large square to represent 20 miles per hour on the vertical axis.

(b) Use your graph to answer the following questions.

   (i) What is the fuel consumption when the speed is 40 miles per hour?

   (ii) At what speeds is the fuel consumption 25 miles per gallon?

   (iii) What is the most economical speed?

6. A quantity of gas is contained in a cylinder and subjected to various pressures. The volume occupied by the gas under different pressures is as follows:

Pressure	1	2	3	4	5	6
Volume	2.4	1.2	0.8	0.6	0.48	0.4

Plot a graph of volume against pressure with pressure on the horizontal axis. Suitable scales are one large square to 0.5 units on the horizontal axis and one large square to 0.5 units on the vertical axis. Use your graph to find:

(a) the volume when the pressure is 3.5,
(b) the pressure when the volume is 0.5.

7. An electric train starts from A and travels to its next stop 5 km from A. The following results were obtained at various times (in minutes) since leaving A and the distance (in kilometres) from A.

Time	1.0	1.5	2.0	2.5	3.0
Distance	0.20	0.45	0.80	1.25	1.80

Time	3.5	4.0	4.5	5.0
Distance	2.45	3.20	4.05	5.00

Draw a graph of these values with time as the horizontal axis. Suitable scales are 2 cm to one unit on both axes. Use your graph to estimate the time taken to travel 2 km from A.

CONVERSION GRAPHS

These are used to convert one set of units into another set of units. For example, inches into centimetres, German marks into pounds sterling and degrees Celsius into degrees Fahrenheit.

Example 3

The rate of exchange between the pound sterling and the French franc is £1 = 11 francs. Draw a graph to show the value of the franc in pounds. Your graph should cover the range from £0 to £12. From your graph find the value of:

(a) 60 francs in pounds,
(b) £9 in francs.

The first step is to make a table of corresponding values as follows.

Pounds	0	2	4	6	8	10	12
Francs	0	22	44	66	88	110	132

The graph is shown in Figure 17.11 where it will be seen to be a straight line passing through the origin. If one quantity is directly proportional to another (as they are in this case) a straight line passing through the origin always results.

From the graph:

(a) 60 francs = £5.50
(b) £9 = 99 francs

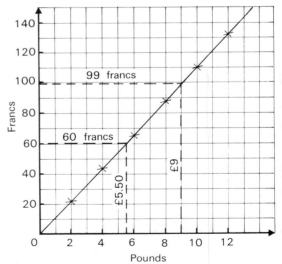

Figure 17.11

Not all conversion graphs pass through the origin. For instance the cost of electricity consists of a fixed charge plus so much per unit used. This means that even if no units are used the fixed charge must be paid. If we draw a graph of cost of electricity against the number of units used, the straight line will start at some point above the origin on the vertical axis as shown in Example 4.

Example 4

In a certain area electricity costs 6 p per unit plus a fixed charge of £7. Draw a graph of units used against the cost of electricity with cost on the vertical axis. The graph should cater for up to 250 units. Use your graph to find the cost of 180 units.

When 0 units are used:

$$\text{Cost} = (700 + 6 \times 0) \text{ pence}$$
$$= (700 + 0) \text{ pence}$$
$$= 700 \text{ pence}$$
$$= £7$$

When 50 units are used:

$$\text{Cost} = (700 + 6 \times 50) \text{ pence}$$
$$= (700 + 300) \text{ pence}$$
$$= 1000 \text{ pence}$$
$$= £10$$
$$\text{and so on}$$

The graph is shown in Figure 17.12 and from it the cost of 180 units is £17.80.

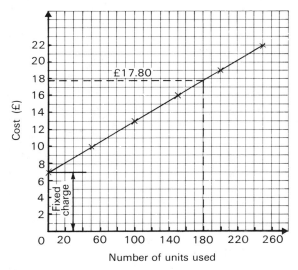

Figure 17.12

The first step is to make a table of corresponding values as follows:

Units used	0	50	100	150	200	250
Cost (£)	7	10	13	16	19	22

The values in the table have been worked out as follows.

147

1. The conversion graph (Figure 17.13) shows the rate of exchange from pounds sterling to German marks. Use the diagram to find:

   (a) the number of marks equivalent to £20,

   (b) the cost in pounds for a gift bought in Germany for 140 marks,

   (c) if a new exchange rate gives £1 = 2.5 marks, draw another graph to represent this.

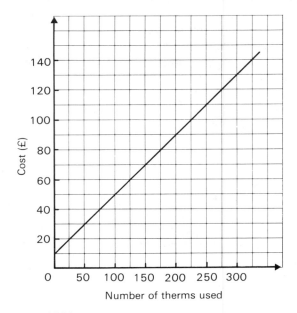

Figure 17.14

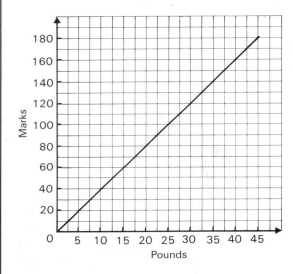

Figure 17.13

3. The graph shown in Figure 17.15 shows the relation between the number of units used and the cost of a telephone bill. Use the graph to find:

   (a) the telephone bill when 50 units are used,

   (b) the number of units used when the bill is £15.

   (c) If the bill is made up of a rental charge plus so much per unit, what is the rental charge?

2. The graph shown in Figure 17.14 shows the increase in the cost of a gas bill as the number of therms used increases. Use the diagram to find:

   (a) the standing charge,

   (b) the cost of gas per therm,

   (c) the cost of the gas bill when 250 therms are used,

   (d) the number of therms used when the gas bill is £90.

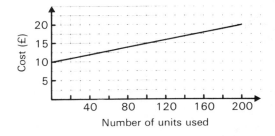

Figure 17.15

4. To convert inches into millimetres we multiply the number of inches by 25.

(a) Copy and complete the following table:

Inches	0	5	10	15	20	25
Millimetres						

(b) From these corresponding values draw a graph. Suitable scales are 1 cm to represent 1 in on the horizontal axis and 1 cm to represent 20 mm on the vertical axis.

(c) Use your graph to convert (i) 8 in into millimetres, (ii) 400 mm into inches.

5. The table below shows corresponding values of degrees Celsius and degrees Fahrenheit.

°C	0	5	10	15	20	25	30
°F	32	41	50	59	68	77	86

(a) Draw a graph of this information taking values of degrees Celsius along the horizontal axis. Suitable scales are one large square to 5° along the horizontal axis and one large square to 10° on the vertical axis.

(b) Use your graph to convert (i) 18 °C to °F, (ii) 80 °F to °C.

6. In calculating the amount of a telephone bill dialled calls are charged at 4 p per unit.

In addition a rental charge of £7 is charged.

(a) Copy and complete the following table:

Units used	0	200	400	600	800	1000	1200
Cost (£)							

(b) Construct a graph from the completed table taking the number of units used on the horizontal axis. Use one large square to represent 10 units and one large square to represent £5 on the vertical axis.

(c) Use your graph to find (i) the cost when 800 units are used, (ii) the number of units used when the cost is £23.

7. The rate of exchange between pounds sterling and the United States dollar is £1 = $1.8.

(a) Copy and complete the following table:

£	0	2	4	6	8	10	12
$							

(b) Draw a graph showing the relationship between dollars and pounds. Suitable scales are one large square on the horizontal axis to represent £2 and one large square on the vertical axis to represent $5.

(c) Use your graph to convert (i) £7 into dollars and (ii) $20 into pounds.

MISCELLANEOUS EXERCISE 17

1. The speed of a body (v metres per second) at various times (t seconds) was as follows:

t	2	4	6	8	10	12
v	6.4	7.7	9.0	10.2	11.7	13.0

Plot a graph of this information with t on the horizontal axis. Hence estimate the speed when t = 7 seconds and the time when the speed is 9.5 metres per second. Use scales of one large square to represent 2 seconds on the horizontal axis and one large square to represent 2 metres per second on the vertical axis.

2. Figure 17.16 shows the seating plan for a cinema. Tom's seating position is written as B5. Write down the seating positions of:

    (a) Sue   **(b)** Dick   **(c)** Madge

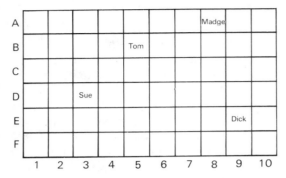

Figure 17.16

3. Use the conversion graph of Figure 17.17 to convert £40 into Swiss francs.

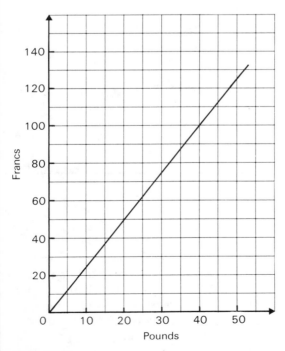

Figure 17.17

4. Figure 17.18 shows the screen of a computer game.

    (a) W shows the position of a space ship. Write down the rectangular co-ordinates of W.

    (b) A second spaceship S is at a point with the coordinates (4, 3). Copy the diagram and mark on it the position of S.

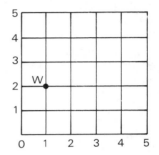

Figure 17.18

5. The figures below show the fusing current (in amperes) for wires of various diameters (in millimetres).

Current	7.5	10.0	17.5	20.0	22.5	25.0
Diameter	7.5	10.0	12.5	20.0	30.0	35.0

    (a) Draw a graph of this information taking diameter along the horizontal axis. Suitable scales are one large square to represent 5 mm on the horizontal axis and one large square to represent 5 amp on the vertical axis.

    (b) Use your graph to find the fusing current for a wire with a diameter of 18 mm.

6. Using a 1 cm grid plot the following points: A(2, 2), B(4, 2) and C(2, 4). Join the points to form the triangle ABC and find the lengths of the sides AB and AC.

150

7. The following figures show how the resistance of a conductor (R ohms) varies as the temperature (t °C) increases.

t	25	50	75	100	150
R	20.7	21.5	22.3	23.1	23.9

Plot a graph of this information with t on the horizontal axis. Use a scale of one large square to represent 25 °C on the horizontal axis and one large square to represent 1 ohm on the vertical axis. You may start the graph at 20 ohms on the vertical axis. Use your graph to find the resistance at a temperature of 80 °C.

CHAPTER 18

Geometry

ANGLES

When two lines meet at a point they form an angle. The size of the angle depends upon the amount of opening between the two lines. It does not depend upon the lengths of the lines forming the angle. Thus in Figure 18.1 the angle A is larger than the angle B even although its arms are shorter.

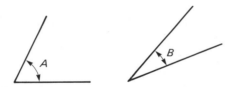

Figure 18.1

MEASUREMENT OF ANGLES

An angle may be looked upon as the amount of rotation or turning. In Figure 18.2 the line OA has been turned about O until it takes up the position OB. The angle through which the line OA has turned is the amount of opening between the lines OA and OB.

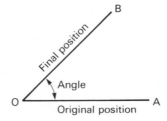

Figure 18.2

If the line OA is rotated past B until it returns to its starting place it will have completed one revolution. Therefore we can measure an angle as a fraction of a revolution.

Figure 18.3 shows a circle divided into 36 equal parts. The first division is split up into ten equal parts so that one small division is equal to $\dfrac{1}{360}$ of a complete revolution. This small division is called a *degree.* So

$$360 \text{ degrees} = 1 \text{ revolution}$$

which is written, for brevity, as

$$360° = 1 \text{ rev}$$

The small symbol ° stands for degrees.

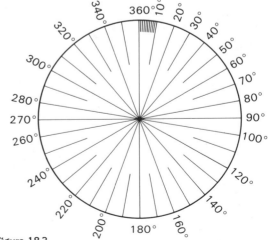

Figure 18.3

The degree can be split up into smaller units as follows:

$$60 \text{ seconds} = 1 \text{ minute}$$

$$60 \text{ minutes} = 1 \text{ degree}$$

An angle of 30 degrees 17 minutes and 5 seconds would be written 30°17′5″.

However, with the introduction of the electronic calculator most angles nowadays are stated in degrees and decimals of a degree. A typical angle might be 43.9° or 217.8°.

Example 1

(a) Find the angle in degrees corresponding to $\frac{1}{3}$ rev.

$$1 \text{ rev} = 360°$$

$$\tfrac{1}{3} \text{ rev} = \tfrac{1}{3} \times 360°$$

$$= 120°$$

(b) Find the angle in degrees corresponding to 0.8 rev.

$$0.8 \text{ rev} = 0.8 \times 360°$$

$$= 288°$$

Angles expressed in degrees and decimals of a degree can be added and subtracted in exactly the same way as decimal numbers.

Example 2

(a) Add together 15.4° and 48.7°.

$$\begin{array}{r} 15.4° \\ 48.7° + \\ \hline 64.1° \\ \hline \end{array}$$

(b) Subtract 35.9° from 93.2°.

$$\begin{array}{r} 93.2° \\ 35.9° - \\ \hline 57.3° \\ \hline \end{array}$$

EXERCISE 18.1

Find the angle in degrees corresponding to each of the following:

1. $\frac{2}{3}$ of a revolution

2. $\frac{5}{8}$ of a revolution

3. 0.3 of a revolution

4. 0.7 of a revolution

5. 0.35 of a revolution

Add the following angles:

6. 28.7° and 43.2°

7. 78.9° and 43.6°

8. 56.8° and 78.9°

Work out the following:

9. 64.6° − 19.3°

10. 56.1° − 45.7°

TYPES OF ANGLE

An *acute* angle is less than 90° (Figure 18.4).

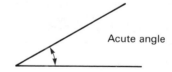

Acute angle

Figure 18.4

A *right-angle* equals 90° or $\frac{1}{4}$ of a revolution (Figure 18.5). Note carefully how a right-angle is marked.

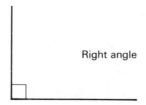

Right angle

Figure 18.5

153

An *obtuse* angle is an angle between 90° ($\frac{1}{4}$ rev) and 180° ($\frac{1}{2}$ rev) see Figure 18.6.

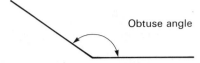

Obtuse angle

Figure 18.6

A *reflex* angle is greater than 180° ($\frac{1}{2}$ rev) see Figure 18.7.

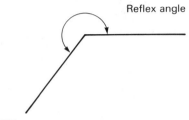

Reflex angle

Figure 18.7

PARALLEL LINES

A plane is a flat surface such as a sheet of paper or metal. Two lines in a plane that have no points in common no matter how far they are extended are called parallel lines. Arrowheads like those in Figure 18.8 are used to show that two lines are parallel.

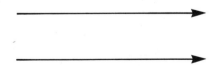

Figure 18.8

TRIANGLES

A triangle is a plane figure with three sides. There are a number of different kinds of triangles as follows:

An *acute-angled* triangle (Figure 18.9) has each of its angles less than 90°.

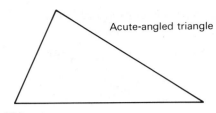

Acute-angled triangle

Figure 18.9

A *right-angled* triangle has one of its angles equal to 90° (Figure 18.10). The side opposite to the right angle is the longest side and it is called the *hypotenuse.*

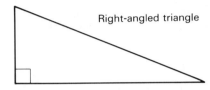

Right-angled triangle

Figure 18.10

An *isosceles* triangle has two sides and two angles equal (Figure 18.11). The equal sides lie opposite to the equal angles.

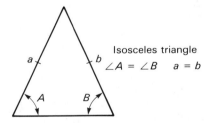

Isosceles triangle
$\angle A = \angle B \quad a = b$

Figure 18.11

An *equilateral* triangle has all its sides and all its angles equal (Figure 18.12). Each angle of an equilateral triangle is 60°.

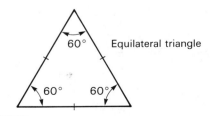

Equilateral triangle

Figure 18.12

154

An *obtuse-angled* triangle (Figure 18.13) has its largest angle greater than 90°.

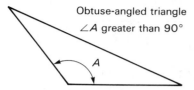

Obtuse-angled triangle
∠A greater than 90°

Figure 18.13

A *scalene* triangle has all three angles of different size and all three sides of different length.

EXERCISE 18.2 _____

1. Figure 18.14 shows a number of different angles. Name each one.

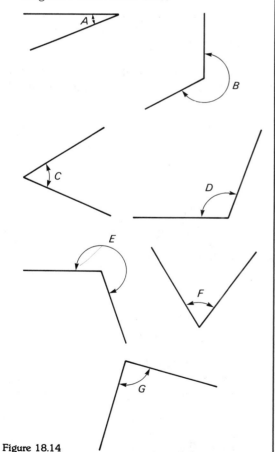

Figure 18.14

2. In each of the diagrams (Figure 18.15), the angles at the centre are of equal size. Find the number of degrees in each of the angles.

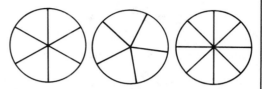

Figure 18.15

3. Look at each of the triangles shown in Figure 18.16 and decide which are:

(a) equilateral (b) acute-angled
(c) right-angled (d) isosceles
(e) obtuse-angled

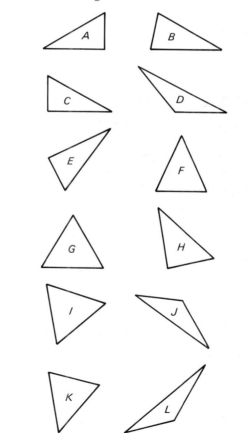

Figure 18.16

155

4. Using a protractor, measure each of the angles shown in Figure 18.17.

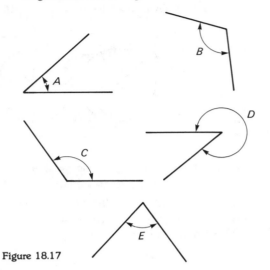

Figure 18.17

5. Make a table with the headings shown below:

Acute	Obtuse	Reflex

Now write the following angles in the appropriate columns:

31°, 186°, 217°, 156°, 63°, 235°, 163°, 62°, 116°, 279°, 143°, 81°, 168°, 315°, 20°, 340°, 16°, 120°, 96°, 225°.

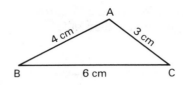

Figure 18.18

Draw BC = 6 cm (Figure 18.19). Using compasses set at 4 cm and centred at B draw an arc. Now set the compasses at 3 cm and with centre at C draw a second arc to cut the first arc at A. Finally draw straight lines between A and B and also A and C. ABC is then the required triangle.

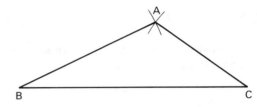

Figure 18.19

To construct a triangle like the one shown in Figure 18.20, a rule and protractor are needed.

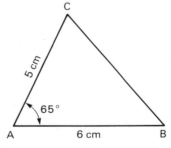

Figure 18.20

CONSTRUCTING TRIANGLES

To construct a triangle, given the lengths of the three sides, only a rule and compasses are needed.

Example 3

Construct accurately the triangle ABC which is shown in Figure 18.18.

Example 4

Construct the triangle ABC shown in Figure 18.20.

First draw AB = 6 cm. Then, using a protractor, draw AX (Figure 18.21) so that BAX = 65°. Along AX mark off AC = 5 cm. Finally join B and C, then ABC is the required triangle.

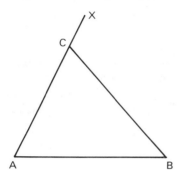

Figure 18.21

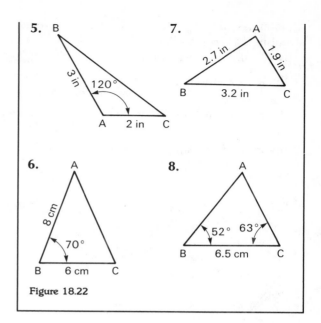

5.

6.

7.

8.

Figure 18.22

EXERCISE 18.3

Construct each of the triangles shown in Figure 18.22. Measure the lengths of the sides not given and using a protractor measure the sizes of the angles not given.

1.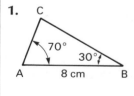

2.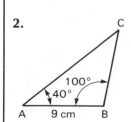

3.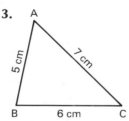

4.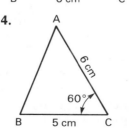

THE RIGHT-ANGLED TRIANGLE

In any right-angled triangle the hypotenuse is the longest side and it always lies opposite to the right angle. Thus in Figure 18.23 the side AC is the hypotenuse because it lies opposite to the right angle at B.

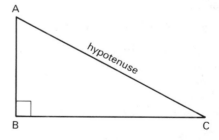

Figure 18.23

Figure 18.24 on p. 158 shows a triangle ABC which is right-angled at B. The side AB is 3 cm long and the side BC is 4 cm long. By accurately constructing the triangle the side AC (the

157

hypotenuse) is found to be 5 cm long. By constructing squares on each of the three sides as shown in the diagram we find that:

the area of the square on AC $= 5 \times 5 = 5^2$
$$= 25 \text{ cm}^2$$

the area of the square on BC $= 4 \times 4 = 4^2$
$$= 16 \text{ cm}^2$$

the area of the square on AB $= 3 \times 3 = 3^2$
$$= 9 \text{ cm}^2$$

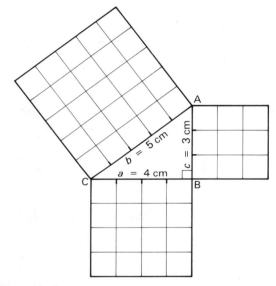

Figure 18.24

Therefore

the area of the square on AC

= the area of the square on BC

+ the area of the square on AB

That is

the area of the square on the hypotenuse

= the sum of the area of the squares on the other two sides

No matter how many right-angled triangles we draw we will always find this statement to be true. This statement is known as Pythagoras' theorem after the Greek mathematician who discovered it.

The theorem is usually written in an abbreviated form. For the triangle of Figure 18.24 we write

$$AC^2 = BC^2 + AB^2$$

It is worth remembering that triangles with sides of 3:4:5, 5:12:13 and 7:24:25 are all right-angled triangles. Triangles with sides which are multiples of these lengths are also right-angled. So triangles with sides 10, 24, 26 and 14, 48, 50 are right-angled.

Example 5

Find the length of the hypotenuse for the triangle ABC shown in Figure 18.25.

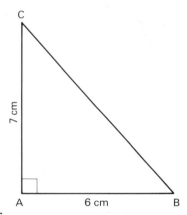

Figure 18.25

BC is the hypotenuse since it lies opposite to the right angle. So, by Pythagoras' theorem,

$$BC^2 = AB^2 + AC^2 = 6^2 + 7^2$$
$$= 36 + 49$$
$$= 85$$
$$BC = \sqrt{85}$$
$$= 9.22 \text{ cm}$$

Therefore the hypotenuse is 9.22 cm long.

Sometimes we are given the lengths of the hypotenuse and one other side and we have to find the third side. In such cases we rearrange Pythagoras' theorem in the way shown in Example 6.

158

Example 6

Find the side AB for the triangle shown in Figure 18.26.

Figure 18.26

Pythagoras' theorem gives

$$BC^2 = AB^2 + AC^2$$

Since we want to find AB we rearrange the equation to give

$$AB^2 = BC^2 - AC^2 = 6.4^2 - 5.2^2$$

$$= 40.96 - 27.04$$

$$= 13.92$$

$$AB = \sqrt{13.92}$$

$$= 3.73$$

Hence the length of AB is 3.73 cm

ISOSCELES AND EQUILATERAL TRIANGLES

It will be remembered that an isosceles triangle (Figure 18.27) has two sides and two angles equal. The equal sides lie opposite to the equal angles.

If we draw a perpendicular from A to the base BC it divides BC into two equal parts (i.e., it bisects BC). That is, in the diagram BD = CD.

Since an equilateral triangle is only a special type of isosceles triangle similar considerations apply.

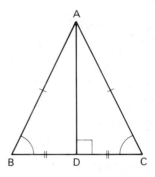

Figure 18.27

Example 7

(a) Triangle ABC (Figure 18.28) is isosceles with the perpendicular AD 10.2 in long and the base BC 8.4 in long. Work out the lengths of the equal sides.

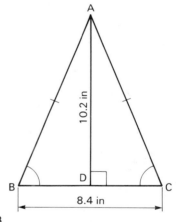

Figure 18.28

Since AD is the perpendicular drawn from the apex A, $\angle ADB = 90°$ and $BD = 8.4 \div 2 = 4.2$ in.

In $\triangle ABD$, AB is the hypotenuse and using Pythagoras' theorem,

$$AB^2 = AD^2 + BD^2 = 10.2^2 + 4.2^2$$

$$= 104.04 + 17.64$$

$$= 121.68$$

$$AD = \sqrt{121.68}$$

$$= 11.0$$

Hence the equal sides are 11.0 in long.

(b) An equilateral triangle has sides 8.5 cm long. Find the altitude of the triangle.

Looking at Figure 18.29 we see that the altitude AD bisects the base AC so that $AD = 8.5 \div 2 = 4.25$ cm.

In $\triangle BAD$, by Pythagoras,

$$BD^2 = AB^2 - AD^2 = 8.5^2 - 4.25^2$$

$$= 72.25 - 18.06$$

$$= 54.19$$

$$BD = \sqrt{54.19}$$

$$= 7.36$$

Hence the altitude of the equilateral triangle is 7.36 cm

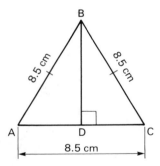

Figure 18.29

1. Figure 18.30 shows several right-angled triangles. For each triangle name the hypotenuse.

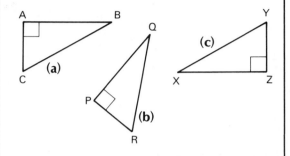

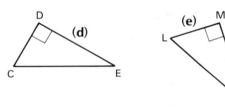

Figure 18.30

2. Figure 18.31 shows a number of right-angled triangles. For each triangle calculate the length of the side marked x.

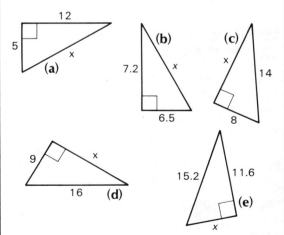

Figure 18.31

160

3. Figure 18.32 shows some isosceles triangles. For each triangle find the altitude AD.

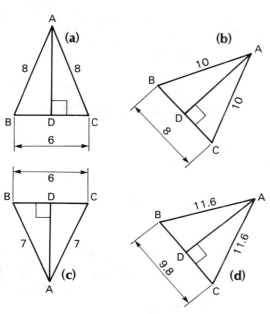

Figure 18.32

4. Figure 18.33 shows some more isosceles triangles. For each triangle work out the lengths of the equal sides.

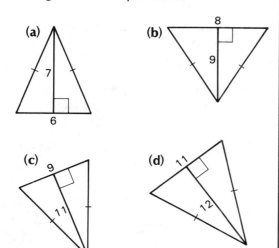

Figure 18.33

5. Figure 18.34 shows some equilateral triangles. For each triangle find the altitude.

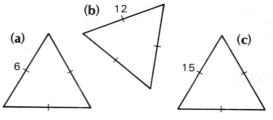

Figure 18.34

6. Figure 18.35 shows an equilateral triangle with sides 8 ft long. Work out the length of the altitude AD of the triangle.

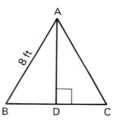

Figure 18.35

QUADRILATERALS

A *quadrilateral* is any plane figure bounded by four straight lines (Figure 18.36).

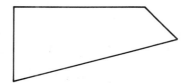

Figure 18.36

A *parallelogram* is a quadrilateral with both pairs of opposite sides parallel. The opposite sides are also equal in length so in Figure 18.37 on p. 162, AB = CD and AD = BC.

161

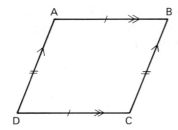

Figure 18.37

A *trapezium* is a quadrilateral with one pair of sides parallel (Figure 18.40).

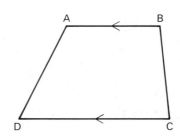

Figure 18.40

A *rectangle* is a quadrilateral with each of its angles equal to 90°. Its opposite sides are equal in length so that in Figure 18.38, AB = CD and BC = AD.

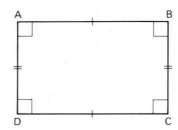

Figure 18.38

Example 8

(a) Figure 18.41 shows a rectangle ABCD with AB = 11 cm and BC = 7 cm. Calculate the length of the diagonal AC.

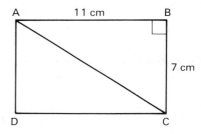

Figure 18.41

In the triangle ABC, $\angle ABC = 90°$ and hence AC is the hypotenuse. Using Pythagoras,

$$AC^2 = AB^2 + BC^2 = 11^2 + 7^2$$

$$= 121 + 49$$

$$= 170$$

$$AC = \sqrt{170}$$

$$= 13.0$$

Therefore the diagonal is 13.0 cm long.

A *square* is a rectangle with all its sides equal in length as shown in Figure 18.39.

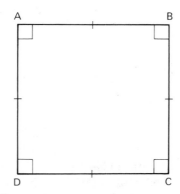

Figure 18.39

(b) Figure 18.42 shows a trapezium ABCD with the parallel sides AB and CD 8 in and 12 in long respectively. The distance between the parallel sides is 9 in and DE = CF. Work out the length of the side AD.

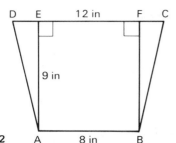

Figure 18.42

$DE = \frac{1}{2} \times (12 - 8) = \frac{1}{2} \times 4 = 2$ in

In $\triangle ADE$, $\angle AED = 90°$ and so AD is the hypotenuse. By Pythagoras' theorem,

$$AD^2 = AE^2 + DE^2 = 9^2 + 2^2$$
$$= 81 \div 4$$
$$= 85$$
$$= \sqrt{85}$$
$$= 9.22$$

Hence the side AD is 9.22 in long.

EXERCISE 18.5

1. Figure 18.43 shows the rectangle ABCD with AB = 12 cm and BC = 6 cm. Find the length of the diagonal AC.

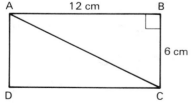

Figure 18.43

2. ABCD is a rectangle with its diagonal BD = 8 ft long. If the side AB = 5 ft long, work out the length of the side AD (Figure 18.44).

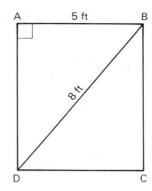

Figure 18.44

3. WXYZ is a square with sides 6 in long. Find the length of its diagonal WY.

4. For the parallelogram ABCD (Figure 18.45), the side AB is 15 cm long, the altitude BE = 8 cm and CE = 3 cm. Find the lengths of the sides CD and AD.

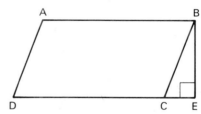

Figure 18.45

4. A square has a diagonal 9 in long. Find the lengths of its sides.

6. The trapezium WXYZ (Figure 18.46) has its parallel sides WX and YZ, 5 ft and 8 ft long respectively. The side WZ is 6 ft long and it is perpendicular to YZ. Work out the length of the side XY.

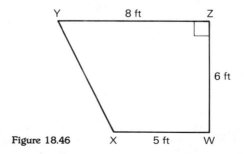

Figure 18.46

163

1. Find the angle in degrees which corresponds to:

  (a) $\frac{3}{4}$ of a revolution,
  (b) 0.45 of a revolution,
  (c) two right angles.

2. (a) Find the value of $28.36° + 19.78°$.
  (b) Subtract $27.9°$ from $86.2°$.

3. Using a protractor measure each of the angles shown in Figure 18.47.

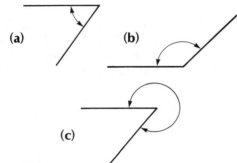

(a)   **(b)**

(c)

Figure 18.47

4. Accurately construct the triangle ABC shown in Figure 18.48 and measure and write down the sizes of each of the three angles.

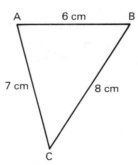

Figure 18.48

5. Figure 18.49 shows a square surmounted by an equilateral triangle. What is the size of the angle EAD?

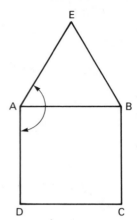

Figure 18.49

6. Figure 18.50 shows a triangular plot of land. The owner wishes to fence the plot. What length of fencing does he need?

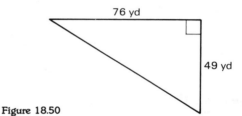

Figure 18.50

7. The rectangle ABCD (Figure 18.51) has a diagonal BD = 16 cm and the side AB = 10 cm. Work out the length of the side BC.

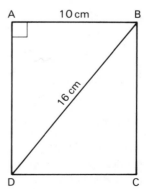

Figure 18.51

164

8. The isosceles triangle LMP (Figure 18.52) has its equal sides 12 cm long and its base MP 8 cm long. Find the length of its altitude LX.

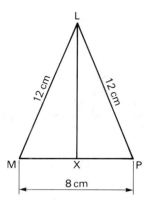

Figure 18.52

MENTAL TEST 18

1. Find the angle in degrees corresponding to one-sixth of a revolution.

2. Find the angle in degrees equivalent to 0.3 rev.

3. What is the angle shown in Figure 18.53 called?

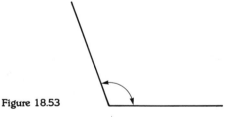

Figure 18.53

4. Write down the value of the angle marked x in Figure 18.54.

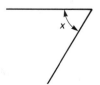

Figure 18.54

5. Add 33° to 47°.

6. Subtract 25° from 62°.

7. Figure 18.55 shows a right-angled triangle. Find the length of its hypotenuse.

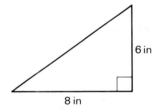

6 in

8 in

Figure 18.55

8. A quadrilateral has four sides of equal length and all its angles are right angles. What is its name?

9. What kind of a triangle has been drawn in Figure 18.56?

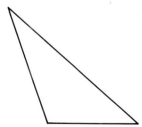

Figure 18.56

10. Add 25.3° and 34.7°.

CHAPTER 19

Map Scales and Bearings

MAP SCALES

Maps are always drawn to a scale, for example, 1 cm = 5 km. This means that a distance of 5 km on the ground would be represented by 1 cm on the map.

On maps scales are often expressed as a ratio, for example, 1:1 000 000. This means that 1 cm on the map represents 1 000 000 cm (i.e., 10 000 m or 10 km) on the ground.

Example 1

(a) A map is drawn to a scale of 1 cm = 5 km. Express this scale as a ratio.

$$1 \text{ cm} = 5 \text{ km}$$
$$= 5 \times 100 \text{ m}$$
$$= 5 \times 1000 \times 100 \text{ cm}$$
$$= 500\,000 \text{ cm}$$

When the units are the same on both sides of an equation they can be omitted and the scale, as a ratio, is then 1:500 000.

(b) A road map is drawn to a scale of 1:1 000 000. Measured on the map the distance between Luxembourg and Paris is 35 cm. What is the actual distance between these two cities?

The map scale is:

$$1 \text{ cm represents } 1\,000\,000 \text{ cm}$$
$$= (1\,000\,000 \div 100) \text{ m}$$
$$= 10\,000 \text{ m}$$
$$= (10\,000 \div 1000) \text{ km}$$
$$= 10 \text{ km}$$

So 35 cm represents: $35 \times 10 \text{ km} = 350 \text{ km}$

Hence the distance between Luxembourg and Paris is 350 km.

(c) A road map is drawn to a scale of 16 miles to the inch. Express this scale as a ratio.

$$1 \text{ inch represents } 16 \text{ miles}$$
$$= 16 \times 5280 \text{ ft}$$
$$= 16 \times 5280 \times 12 \text{ in}$$
$$= 1\,013\,760 \text{ in}$$

So the map scale is 1:1 013 760, i.e., 1:1 000 000 approximately.

1. A road map is drawn to a scale of 20 miles to 1 inch. On the map the distance between Birmingham and Bristol is $4\frac{1}{2}$ inches. Work out the actual distance between the two cities.

2. A map of Scandinavia is drawn to a scale of 1:1 500 000. On the map the distance between Oslo and Stockholm measures 22 cm. What is the actual distance between the two places?

3. A road map is drawn to a scale of 24 miles to 1 inch. Express this scale as a ratio.

4. Figure 19.1 shows a map of part of Spain. By scaling the map, find the actual distance, in miles, between Alicante and Villena.

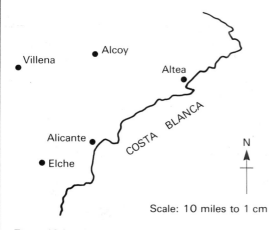

Figure 19.1

Scale: 10 miles to 1 cm

5. A map is drawn to a scale of 12 km to 1 cm. Express this scale as a ratio.

6. A map of Turkey is drawn to a scale of 1:1 250 000. What distance is represented by 1 cm?

7. A map of Europe is drawn to a scale of 120 km to 1 cm. Express this scale as a ratio.

8. Figure 19.2 shows a map of part of south-east England. By scaling the map find the distances between:

   (a) Dungeness and Dymchurch by rail,
   (b) Camber and Old Romney,
   (c) Lydd and St Mary.

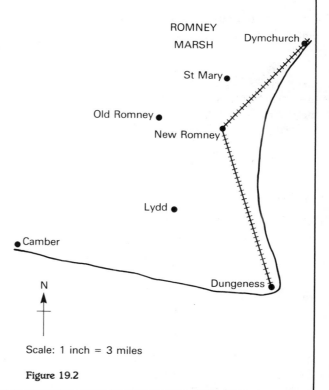

Scale: 1 inch = 3 miles

Figure 19.2

COMPASS BEARINGS

The four cardinal directions are north, south, east and west but the intermediate points north-east (NE), south-east (SE), south-west (SW) and north-west (NW) (Figure 19.3) are also often used.

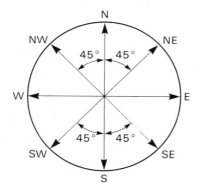

Figure 19.3

Directions between the cardinal points are called bearings.

One way of stating a bearing is to give the angle measured from the north—south line towards either east or west. A compass bearing of N 25° E means an angle of 25° measured from north towards east as shown in Figure 19.4.

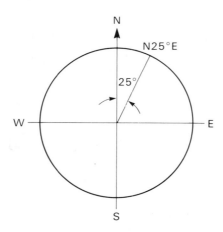

Figure 19.4

A bearing of S 60° W means an angle of 60° from south towards west as shown in Figure 19.5.

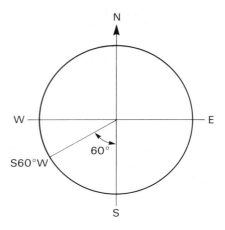

Figure 19.5

Note that bearings are always measured from north and south and never from east and west.

EXERCISE 19.2

Draw accurate diagrams to represent each of the following compass bearings:

1. N 50° W   **3.** S 35° E   **5.** S 45° E

2. N 70° E   **4.** S 55° W

Using a protractor measure each of the angles shown in Figure 19.6 and then write down the compass bearing for each angle.

6.  **7.**

(cont.)

8.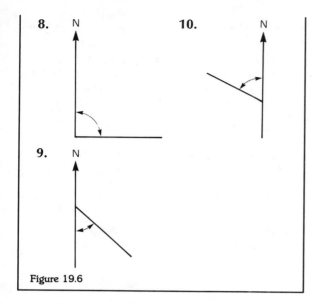

10.

9.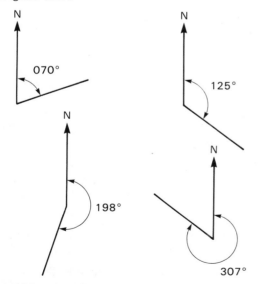

Figure 19.6

THREE-DIGIT BEARINGS

A second way of stating a bearing is to measure the angle in a clockwise direction from north.

Three figures are always used, north being 000°, 005° is written instead of 5° and 029° is written instead of 29°.

Some typical three-digit bearings are shown in Figure 19.7.

070°

125°

198°

307°

Figure 19.7

EXERCISE 19.3 ___

Draw accurately five separate diagrams to show the following three-digit bearings:

1. 050°   **3.** 240°   **5.** 350°

2. 150°   **4.** 310°

Use a protractor to measure each of the angles shown in Figure 19.8. Then using three-digit bearings, write down each of the directions.

6. N 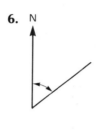   **9.** N

7. N 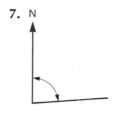   **10.** N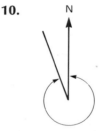

8. N

Figure 19.8

Example 2

B is a point due west of a harbour A. C is a point on the coast which is 6 miles south of A. If the distance BC is 7 miles, find, by making a scaled drawing, the bearing of C from B.

First choose a suitable scale to represent the distances AC and BC. In Figure 19.9, a scale of 1 cm = 1 mile has been chosen and a scale drawing made.

The bearing is found by using a protractor placed at B. It is S 31° E or, as a three-digit bearing 149°.

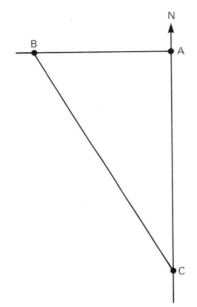

Figure 19.9

EXERCISE 19.4

1. Figure 19.10 shows part of a map of Devon and Cornwall drawn to a scale of 1 inch = 40 miles.

   Find:

   (a) the bearing of Exeter from Plymouth,

   (b) the bearing of Plymouth from Exeter,

   (c) the distance from Plymouth to Newquay,

   (d) the bearing of Newquay from St Austell.

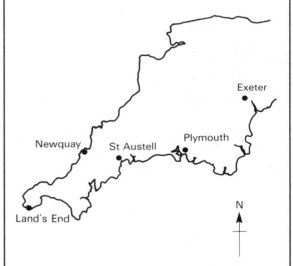

Scale: 1 inch = 40 miles

Figure 19.10

2. The bearing of a town A from a town B is 189°. What is the bearing of B from A?

3. A ship is on a bearing of 076° from a lighthouse.

   Work out the bearing of the lighthouse from the ship.

170

4. B and C (Figure 19.11) are both 200 km from A. B is on a bearing of 110° from A and C is on a bearing of 240° from B. Make a scale drawing of this information using a scale of 1 cm = 40 km. From your drawing find:

(**a**) the bearing of A from B,
(**b**) the size of the angle ABC,
(**c**) the distance BC.

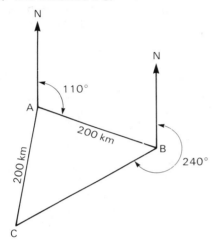

Figure 19.11

5. Figure 19.12 shows part of a map of the Costa del Sol which is in Spain. Use the map to find the following as three-digit bearings:

(**a**) the bearing of Marbella from Malaga,
(**b**) the bearing of Malaga from Marbella,
(**c**) the bearing of Antequera from Malaga,
(**d**) the bearing of Ronda from Marbella.

Scale: 1 cm = 19 km

Figure 19.12

MISCELLANEOUS EXERCISE 19

1. Write down three-digit bearings for the directions:

(**a**) south-east
(**b**) north-east

2. The map (Figure 19.13) shows the positions of a crossroads, an electric pylon, a church, an oak tree and a barn.

(**a**) Which object is north-west of the crossroads?
(**b**) What is the bearing of the barn from the crossroads?
(**c**) What is the bearing of the oak tree from the church?

Give your answers as three-digit bearings.

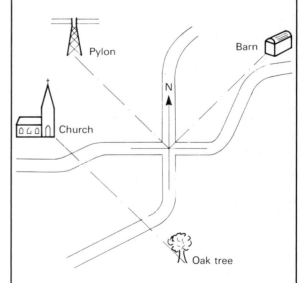

Fig. 19.13

3. The scale of a map is 1:1 500 000. What distance on the ground does 6 cm represent? Give your answer correct to the nearest kilometre.

171

4. Figure 19.14 shows a map of the Shrewsbury area, drawn to a scale of 10 miles to 1 inch.

    (a) Express this scale as a ratio.

    (b) Find the bearing of Much Wenlock from Shrewsbury.

    (c) A helicopter flies direct from Much Wenlock to Diddlebury. How many miles does it fly?

    (d) What bearing does the helicopter follow?

(b) An aeroplane flies from Barry to Aberystwyth. Find the distance, in miles between the two places.

(c) A fishing boat sails from Aberystwyth to a point P at sea. The bearing of P from Aberystwyth is 320°. Find the size of the angle marked x on the map.

(d) The boat sails from P to a point Q which is due west of Aberystwyth. By scaling the map find the distance PQ.

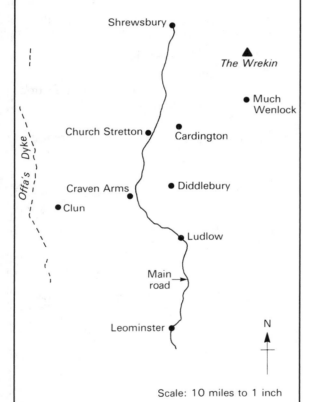

Scale: 10 miles to 1 inch

Figure 19.14

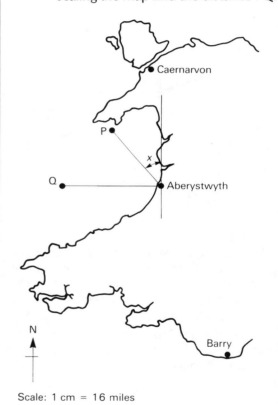

Scale: 1 cm = 16 miles

Figure 19.15

5. A map of Wales is shown in Figure 19.15. It is drawn to a scale of 1 cm = 16 miles.

    (a) If 1 km = $\frac{5}{8}$ mile, express this scale as a ratio.

6. A ship sails from a harbour H on a bearing of 075° for a distance of 12 miles to a point P. It then sails due south for 12 miles to a point Q.

    (a) Using a scale of 1 cm = 2 miles make a scale drawing to represent the journey of the ship.

172

(b) Use your drawing to find:
  (i) the bearing of Q from H,
  (ii) the distance of Q from H.

7. The distances from a town A to towns B and C are 180 km and 360 km respectively. The bearing of B from A is 327° and the bearing of C from A is 032°. Using a scale of 1 cm = 20 km make a scale drawing of this information and from it find:
  (a) the distance from B to C,
  (b) the three-digit bearing of C from B.

8. An aeroplane flies direct from Moscow to Leningrad. Using Figure 19.16 find out how long the flight will last if an average speed of 500 miles per hour is maintained.

9. Using the map of Figure 19.16, measure the distances, in inches (or fractions of an inch), between:
  (a) Uzhgorod and Rovno,
  (b) Rovno and Kiev,
  (c) Kiev and Orel,
  (d) Orel and Moscow.
  (e) Using the scale given on the map find the actual distances between the towns and cities.
  (f) An aeroplane flies direct from Rovno to Moscow. How far is the flight?
  (g) What is the three-digit bearing of Rovno from Moscow?

10. The map of Figure 19.16 shows a road from Berlin to Moscow via Warsaw, Brest, Minsk and Smolensk. By scaling the map find the distances by road between:
  (a) Berlin and Warsaw,
  (b) Warsaw and Brest,
  (c) Brest and Minsk,
  (d) Minsk and Smolensk,
  (e) Smolensk and Moscow,
  (f) Berlin and Moscow.

Scale: 1 inch = 400 miles

Figure 19.16

MENTAL TEST 19

1. The scale of a map is 1:100. Find, in metres, the distances on the ground represented by:
  (a) 1 cm on the map,
  (b) 3 cm on the map,
  (c) 0.5 cm on the map.

2. The scale of a map is 1 cm = 5 km.

Find, in kilometres, the distances on the ground represented by
  (a) 3 cm on the map,
  (b) 0.4 cm on the map.

3. The scale of a map is 1 cm = 10 km. What lengths on the map represent:
  (a) 20 km on the ground,
  (b) 5 km on the ground?

4. Figure 19.17 shows a map of Dublin drawn to a scale of 1 inch = 1 mile. By measuring the map find the actual distances between:

(a) Guiness Brewery and Four Courts,
(b) Bank of Ireland and Custom House,
(c) Four Courts and General Post Office.

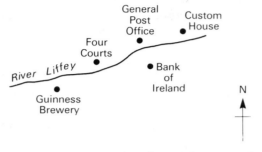

Scale: 1 inch = 1 mile

Figure 19.17

5. Write down three-digit bearings for:

(a) south-west   (b) north-west

6. Using a protractor and measuring the angle clockwise, express as three-digit bearings the directions shown in Figure 19.18.

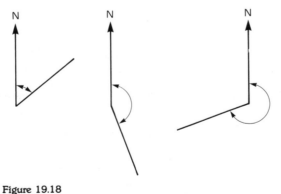

Figure 19.18

7. In Figure 19.19, what is the three-digit bearing of:

(a) B from A   (b) A from B?

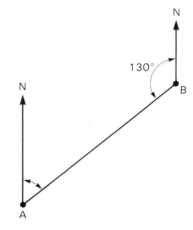

Figure 19.19

8. Using Figure 19.20 write down the three-digit bearing of:

(a) B from A
(b) C from A

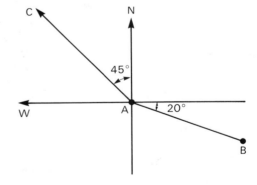

Figure 19.20

CHAPTER 20

Areas and Perimeters

PLANE FIGURES

A plane figure is flat like a sheet of paper or metal. It is made up of lines called the sides of the figure. A triangle (Figure 20.1) has three sides and a rectangle (Fig. 20.2) has four sides.

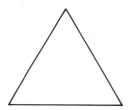

Figure 20.1

Figure 20.2

PERIMETERS

The distance all the way round a plane shape is called its *perimeter*.

Example 1

(a) Find the perimeter of the triangle shown in Figure 20.3.

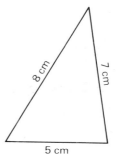

Figure 20.3

Perimeter = (5 + 8 + 7) cm = 20 cm

(b) Work out the perimeter of the rectangle shown in Figure 20.4.

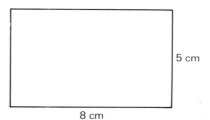

Figure 20.4

Perimeter = (8 + 5 + 8 + 5) = 26 cm

(c) Find the perimeter of the plane shape shown in Figure 20.5.

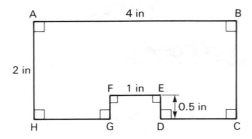

Figure 20.5

$$\text{Perimeter} = AB + BC + CD + DE + EF + FG + GH + AH$$

$$= (4 + 2 + 1.5 + 0.5 + 1 + 0.5 + 1.5 + 2) \text{ in}$$

$$= 13 \text{ in}$$

CIRCUMFERENCE OF A CIRCLE

The main parts of a circle are shown in Figure 20.6. The perimeter of a circle is called its *circumference*.

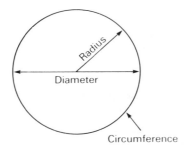

Figure 20.6

Note also that

$$\text{Diameter} = 2 \times \text{Radius}$$

For any size of circle that you care to draw it will be found that its circumference is just over three times its diameter. That is

$$\text{Circumference} \div \text{Diameter} = 3 \text{ (approximately)}$$

The exact value of circumference ÷ diameter has never been worked out, but for most problems a value of 3.14 is accurate enough when working in decimals. When working in fractions a value of $\frac{22}{7}$ may be used. When working mentally a value of $\frac{25}{8}$ is often used. The value circumference ÷ diameter is so important in mathematics that it has been given the special symbol π (the Greek letter pi). We take the value of π as being 3.14 or $\frac{22}{7}$. We then say

$$\text{Circumference} = \pi \times \text{Diameter}$$

or as an algebraic formula

$$C = \pi \times d$$

where C is the circumference, d is the diameter and $\pi = 3.14$ or $\frac{22}{7}$.

Since the diameter of a circle is twice its radius we can write

$$C = 2 \times \pi \times r$$

where C is the circumference, r is the radius and $\pi = 3.14$ or $\frac{22}{7}$.

When working in decimals a calculator should be used when working out circumferences.

Example 2

(a) A circle has a diameter of 4 inches. Work out its circumference.

$$C = \pi \times d = 3.14 \times 4 \text{ in} = 12.56 \text{ in}$$

(b) The radius of a circle is 14 cm. Calculate its circumference.

$$C = 2 \times \pi \times r = \frac{2}{1} \times \frac{22}{\cancel{7}} \times \frac{\cancel{14}^{2}}{1} \text{ cm}$$

$$= 2 \times 22 \times 2 \text{ cm}$$

$$= 88 \text{ cm}$$

(When the radius or the diameter has a value which is divisible by 7 it is best to use $\pi = \frac{22}{7}$ because the numbers will then cancel.)

1. Work out the perimeters of each of the triangles shown in Figure 20.7.

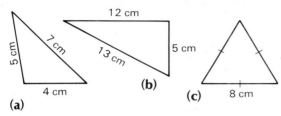

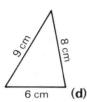

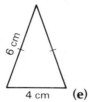

Figure 20.7

2. Figure 20.8 shows a number of rectangles. Find the perimeters of each of them.

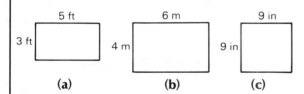

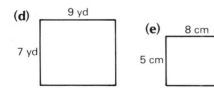

Figure 20.8

3. Find the perimeters of the following rectangles:

(a) length 7 cm, width 4 cm
(b) length 7 cm, width 5 cm
(c) length 6.8 cm, width 5.9 cm
(d) length 4.6 in, width 3.8 in

4. Calculate the perimeters of the following squares having sides:

(a) 6 ft long,   (b) 43 mm long,
(c) 9.2 in long.

5. The dots in Figure 20.9 are spaced 1 cm apart. Find the perimeters of each rectangle shown.

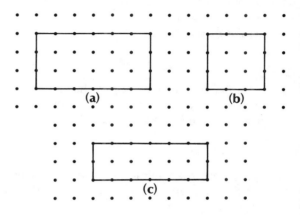

Figure 20.9

6. Taking $\pi = 3.14$, calculate the circumferences of each of the following circles:

(a) 8 cm diameter,
(b) 3 ft diameter,
(c) 4.6 in diameter,
(d) 9.8 cm diameter,
(e) 2 in radius,
(f) 5 cm radius,
(g) 6.7 in radius,
(h) 5.9 m radius.

7. Taking $\pi = \frac{22}{7}$, work out the circumferences of each of the following circles:

(a) 28 cm diameter,
(b) 84 in diameter,
(c) 49 mm radius,
(d) 63 in radius.

8. A circular flower bed has a diameter of 7 ft. How far it it around its edge? (Take $\pi = \frac{22}{7}$)

9. A circular garden pool has a radius of 9 ft. What is the circumference of the pool? (Take $\pi = 3.14$)

10. A wheel has a diameter of 70 cm. Work out the circumference of the wheel. (Take $\pi = \frac{22}{7}$)

11. The flywheel of a motor car has a radius of 6 cm. What is the circumference of the flywheel? (Take $\pi = 3.14$)

12. Work out the perimeters of each of the shapes shown in Figure 20.10. The dots are spaced 1 cm apart.

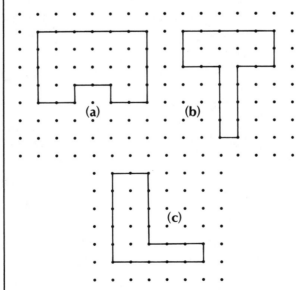

Figure 20.10

13. Figure 20.11 shows the shape of a piece of wood which is to be cut out of a plywood sheet using a bandsaw. How far does the bandsaw travel in cutting out the shape? (Take $\pi = 3.14$)

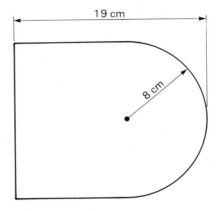

Figure 20.11

14. Find the perimeter of the shape shown in Figure 20.12. (Take $\pi = 3.14$)

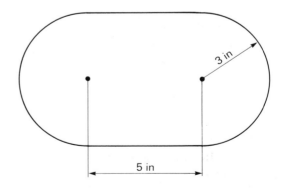

Figure 20.12

178

AREA

Area is the space taken up by a plane shape. The area of a plane shape is found by counting the number of equal squares contained in the shape.

Example 3

Figure 20.13 shows three different shapes. By counting up the number of equal squares contained in each of the shapes, find out which shape has the greatest area.

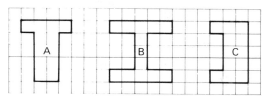

Figure 20.13

Shape A contains 12 equal squares.
Shape B contains 13 equal squares.
Shape C contains 12 equal squares.

We see that shape B has the greatest area because it contains the largest number of equal squares.

In practice, the squares used for measuring area have sides of 1 metre, 1 centimetre or 1 millimetre if we are using the metric system and 1 inch, 1 foot or 1 yard if we are using the imperial system.

A square having a side of 1 metre has an area of 1 square metre (abbreviation: m^2).

A square having a side of 1 centimetre has an area of 1 square centimetre (abbreviation: cm^2).

A square having a side of 1 millimetre has an area of 1 square millimetre (abbreviation (mm^2).

A square having a side of 1 inch has an area of 1 square inch (abbreviation: in^2).

A square having a side of 1 foot has an area of 1 square ft (abbreviation: ft^2).

A square having a side of 1 yard has an area of 1 square yard (abbreviation: yd^2).

AREAS OF RECTANGLES

The rectangle shown in Figure 20.14 contains eight equal squares each with a side of 1 cm and an area of 1 cm^2. We say that the area of the rectangle is 8 cm^2.

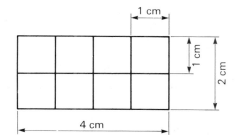

Figure 20.14

Looking at the diagram again we see that we have two rows of equal squares each having four of these squares. So

$$Area = 4 \times 2 \ cm^2 = 8 \ cm^2$$

All we have done is to multiply the length of the rectangle by its breadth. No matter how many rectangles we measure we will always find that:

Area of rectangle = Length × Breadth

or as a formula:

$$A = l \times b$$

where A is the area, l is the length and b is the breadth. It is important to realise that l and b must be in the same units, i.e., both in centimetres or both in inches, etc.

Example 4

A carpet measures 7 ft by 5 ft. What is its area?

We are given that $l = 7$ and $b = 5$. So

$$A = l \times b = 7 \times 5 = 35$$

The area of the carpet is 35 ft^2.

179

AREA OF A SQUARE

A square is a rectangle with all its sides equal in length. So

Area of a square = Side × Side = Side²

or as a formula

$$A = a^2$$

where A is the area of the square and a is the length of the sides.

Example 5

A floor tile has sides 9 in long. What is its area?

We are given that $a = 9$, so

$$A = 9^2 = 9 \times 9 = 81$$

So the area of the floor tile is 81 in².

EXERCISE 20.2

1. Find the areas of the rectangles shown in Figure 20.15.

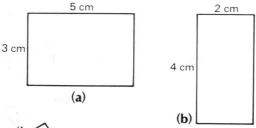

(a)

(b)

(c) **(d)**

Figure 20.15

2. Find the areas of the following rectangles:
   (a) length 30 mm breadth 15 mm,
   (b) length 36 ft breadth 9 ft,
   (c) length 19.7 in breadth 8.4 in,
   (d) length 7.9 cm breadth 5.3 cm,
   (e) length 12.1 ft breadth 9.8 ft.

3. A piece of metal is rectangular in shape. Its length is 15.8 cm and it is 11.3 cm wide. What is its area?

4. A rectangular floor is 16.2 ft long and 11.5 ft wide. What area of carpet is needed to cover it completely?

5. A square ceramic tile has sides 8 in long. What is its area?

6. A square carpet tile has sides 30 cm long. Work out its area.

7. Figure 20.16 shows four rectangles. Which two have the same area?

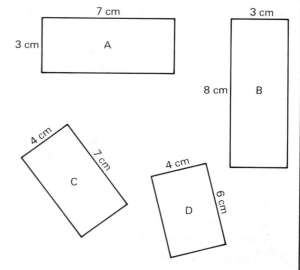

Figure 20.16

180

8. Calculate the areas of each of the rectangles shown in Figure 20.17. The spots are 1 cm apart each way.

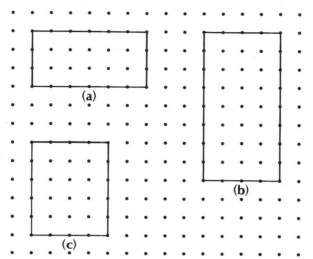

(a)

(b)

(c)

Figure 20.17

9. To tile one wall of a bathrom square tiles of 15 cm side are used. It took 150 tiles to complete the job. What is the area of the wall?

10. Sheet metal is sold at £9.25 per square foot. How much will a rectangular sheet 4.5 ft by 3.2 ft cost?

AREAS OF SHAPES MADE FROM RECTANGLES

The areas of many different shapes can often be found by splitting the shape up into various rectangles and squares.

Example 6

Figure 20.18 shows the cross-section of a steel girder. Work out its area.

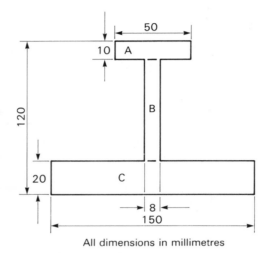

All dimensions in millimetres

Figure 20.18

The shape can be split up into three rectangles as shown in the diagram.

$$\text{Area of shape} = \text{Area of rectangle A}$$
$$+ \text{Area of Rectangle B}$$
$$+ \text{Area of Rectangle C}$$

$$= [(50 \times 10) + (90 \times 8)$$
$$+ (150 \times 20)] \text{ mm}^2$$

$$= [500 + 720 + 3000] \text{ mm}^2$$

$$= 4220 \text{ mm}^2$$

So the area of the girder is 4220 mm^2.

By splitting up the shapes shown in Figure 20.19 into appropriate rectangles, find the area of each shape.

1.

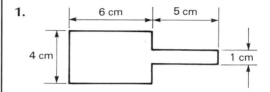

2.

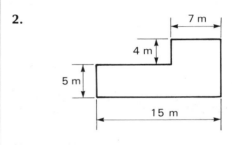

3.

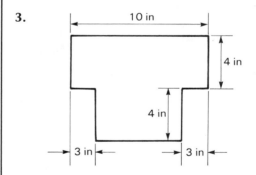

4.

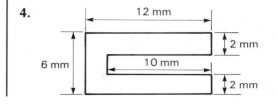

182

5.

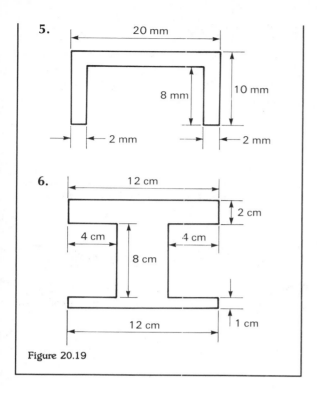

6.

Figure 20.19

AREAS OF BORDERS

To find the area of a border, work out the area of the outer rectangle and subtract from it the area of the inner rectangle as shown in Example 7.

Example 7

Figure 20.20 shows a room fitted with a carpet so as to leave a surround. Calculate the area of the surround.

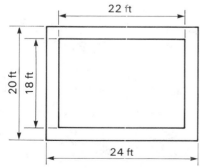

Figure 20.20

Area of room $= (24 \times 20)$ ft^2 $= 480$ ft^2

Area of carpet $= (22 \times 18)$ ft^2 $= 396$ ft^2

Area of border $= (480 - 396)$ ft^2 $= 84$ ft^2

So the area of the surround is 84 ft^2.

EXERCISE 20.4

Find the areas of the shaded borders in Figure 20.21.

1.

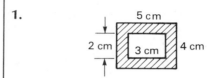

2.

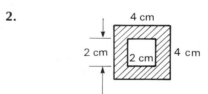

3.

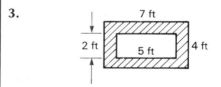

4.

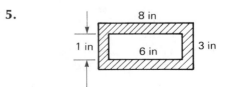

5.

6.

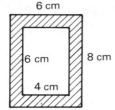

6 cm

6 cm   8 cm

4 cm

7.

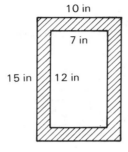

10 in

7 in

15 in   12 in

Figure 20.21

8. A rectangular lawn is 43 yards long and 27 yards wide. It has a path 2 yards wide all round it. Work out the area of the path.

9. A room 7 metres long and 6 metres wide is to be carpeted so as to leave a surround 1 metre wide. Work out the area of the surround.

10. A rectangular swimming pool 50 yards long and 20 yards wide is to have a tiled path around its perimeter. If the path is to be $1\frac{1}{2}$ yards wide, what is its area?

DOMESTIC PROBLEMS

The popularity of 'do it yourself' makes it necessary to be able to calculate, for instance, the number of tiles needed to tile a kitchen or a bathroom or the number of rolls of wallpaper needed to decorate a room.

Example 8

(a) A rectangular floor is 7 metres long by 5 metres wide. It is to be tiled with tiles of side 20 cm. How many tiles are needed to complete the job?

Number of tiles needed to give a length of 7 metres

$$= 700 \div 20 = 35$$

Number of tiles needed to give a length of 5 metres

$$= 500 \div 20 = 25$$

Total number of tiles needed

$$= 35 \times 25 = 875$$

(b) A room 20 ft long and 16 ft wide is to be decorated using wallpaper. The wallpaper is packed in rolls containing 30 ft and each strip of paper needs to be 7 ft long. Estimate the number of rolls of wallpaper needed ignoring the fact that doors and windows are not papered and given that each strip of paper is 21 inches wide.

Perimeter of room $= (20 + 16 + 20 + 16)$ ft

$$= 72 \text{ ft}$$

Number of strips of paper needed

$$= (72 \times 12) \div 21 = 41.1$$

Therefore 42 strips are needed.

Number of complete strips that can be cut from one roll is $30 \div 7 = 4$.

Number of rolls needed $= 42 \div 4 = 10.5$

Therefore 11 rolls of wallpaper are needed.

1. A floor 8 m long and 6 m wide is to be covered with square carpet tiles of 50 cm side. How many tiles are needed to completely cover the floor?

2. A bathroom wall measures 3.9 m by 2.25 m. It is to be tiled using 15 cm square tiles. How many tiles are needed for this job?

3. An area of floor measures 6 ft by $4\frac{1}{2}$ ft.

   (a) It is covered with 18 inch square tiles. How many of these tiles were needed to cover the floor?

   (b) Each of these large tiles is made up of small square tiles with a side of $\frac{3}{4}$ inch. How many of these small tiles are needed to make one of the larger tiles?

4. A room is 18 ft long, 15 ft wide and 7 ft high. It is to be decorated using wallpaper. Each roll contains 30 ft of paper 21 inches wide. How many rolls of wallpaper are needed to finish the work? (Assume that 4 complete strips can be cut from a roll and ignore doors and windows.)

5. A room is 9 metres long, 7 metres wide and 2.2 metres high. The walls are to be painted with emulsion paint.

   (a) Work out the area to be painted if the door has an area of 2.5 m^2 and the window has an area of 2.1 m^2.

   (b) The manufacturer of the paint states that a 2.5 litre tin should cover an area of 27 m^2. How many 2.5 litre tins are needed to paint the walls of the room?

AREA OF A PARALLELOGRAM

A parallelogram is really a rectangle pushed out of square as shown in Figure 20.22, where the equivalent rectangle is shown in dotted outline.

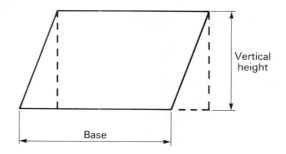

Figure 20.22

Hence,

Area of parallelogram = Length of base × Vertical height

Example 9

Find the area of a parallelogram whose base is 8 cm long and whose vertical height is 5 cm.

$$\text{Area} = (8 \times 5)\,\text{cm}^2 = 40\,\text{cm}^2$$

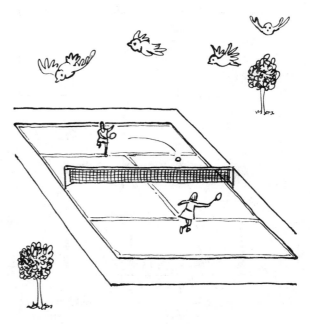

Find the areas of the following parallelograms:

1. Base 8 cm, vertical height 7 cm

2. Base 9 in, vertical height 12 in

3. Base 8.7 ft, vertical height 5.3 ft

4. Figure 20.23 shows the cross-section of a steel girder. Calculate its area in square centimetres.

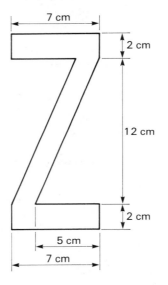

Figure 20.23

AREA OF A TRIANGLE

If you look at Figure 20.24 you will see that the area of triangle ABC is exactly half that of the parallelogram ABCD. Since the area of the parallelogram is length of base × vertical height

Area of triangle $= \frac{1}{2} \times$ Base $\times$ Vertical height

As a formula

$$A = \frac{1}{2} \times b \times h$$

where A is the area of the triangle, b is the length of the base and h is the vertical height (sometimes called the altitude of the triangle) see Figure 20.25.

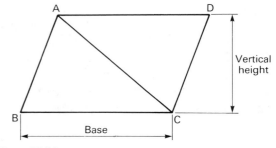

Figure 20.24

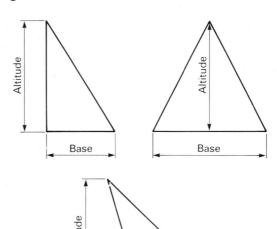

Figure 20.25

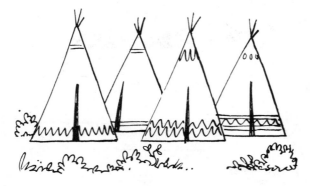

186

Example 10

Work out the area of each of the triangles shown in Figure 20.26.

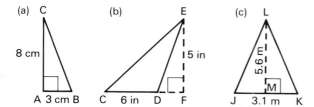

Figure 20.26

(a) Here the base is $AB = 3$ cm and the vertical height is $AC = 8$ cm. So

Area of triangle $ABC = \frac{1}{2} \times 3 \times 8$ cm$^2 = 12$ cm^2

(b) Here the base is $CD = 6$ in and the vertical height is $EF = 5$ in.

Area of triangle $CDE = \frac{1}{2} \times 6 \times 5$ in$^2 = 15$ in^2

(c) Here the base is $JK = 3.1$ m and the vertical height is $LM = 5.6$ m.

Area of triangle $JKL = \frac{1}{2} \times 3.1 \times 5.6$ m$^2 = 8.68$ m^2

EXERCISE 20.7

1. Calculate the areas of the triangles shown in Figure 20.27.

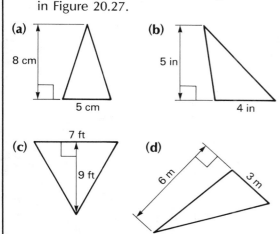

Figure 20.27

2. Figure 20.28 shows several right-angled triangles. Find the area of each.

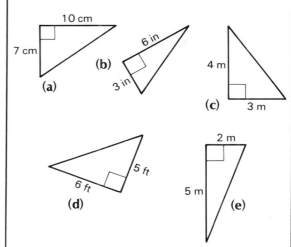

Figure 20.28

3. Calculate the areas of the following triangles:
  (a) base 7 cm, altitude 4 cm,
  (b) base 9 cm, altitude 8 cm,
  (c) base 4.2 in, altitude 5.3 in,
  (d) base 4.5 ft, vertical height 8.7 ft.

AREA OF A TRAPEZIUM

A trapezium is a four-sided figure with one pair of sides parallel (see Figure 20.29).

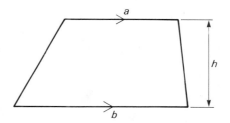

Figure 20.29

187

Area of trapezium $= \frac{1}{2} \times$ Sum of the parallel sides $\times$ Distance between the parallel sides

As a formula this becomes

$$A = \frac{1}{2}(a + b)h$$

where A is the area of the trapezium, a and b are the lengths of the parallel sides and h is the distance between the parallel sides.

Example 11

Find the area of the trapezium shown in Figure 20.30.

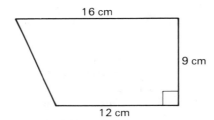

Figure 20.30

The lengths of the parallel sides are 12 and 16 cm.

The sum of the parallel sides $= (12 + 16)$ cm
$\qquad\qquad\qquad\qquad\qquad\; = 28$ cm.

Distance between parallel sides $= 9$ cm.

Area of trapezium $= \frac{1}{2} \times 28 \times 9$ cm^2 $= 126$ cm^2.

Alternatively the formula may be used with $a = 12$, $b = 16$ and $h = 9$.

$$A = \frac{1}{2}(a + b)h = \frac{1}{2} \times (12 + 16) \times 9$$

$$= \frac{1}{2} \times 28 \times 9$$

$$= 126$$

Hence the area of the trapezium is 126 cm^2.

EXERCISE 20.8

1. Find the area of the trapezium shown in Figure 20.31.

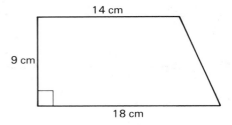

Figure 20.31

2. A trapezium has parallel sides 9 in and 11 in long. The distance between these parallel sides is 8 in. Work out the area of the trapezium.

3. Find the area of a trapezium whose parallel sides are 9 and 13 cm long, if the distance between them is 5 cm.

4. Find the area, in square yards, of the field shown in Figure 20.32.

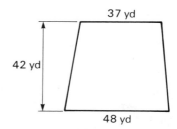

Figure 20.32

5. Find the area of a trapezium whose parallel sides are 23 ft and 27 ft long if the distance between them is 20 ft.

AREA OF A CIRCLE

It can be shown that

$$\text{Area of a circle} = \pi \times \text{Radius}^2$$

or as a formula

$$A = \pi r^2$$

Example 12

(a) Find the area of a circle whose radius is 4 cm.

$$A = \pi \times 4^2 = 3.14 \times 16 \text{ cm}^2 = 50.2 \text{ cm}^2$$

(b) Work out the area of a circle having a diameter of 28 cm.

Since the diameter is 28 cm, the radius $= 28 \div 2$
$= 14$ cm.

$$A = \pi \times 14^2 = \frac{22}{7_1} \times \frac{\overset{2}{\cancel{14}}}{1} \times \frac{14}{1}$$

$$= 22 \times 2 \times 14 \text{ cm}^2$$

$$= 616 \text{ cm}^2$$

AREA OF AN ANNULUS

An annulus consists of two concentric circles (i.e., circles having the same centre) as shown in Figure 20.33.

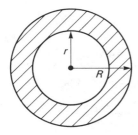

Figure 20.33

The area of the annulus is the shaded area in the diagram. It is found by subtracting the area of the inner circle from the area of the outer circle. So

$$\text{Area of annulus} = \pi \times (\text{outer radius})^2$$
$$- \pi \times (\text{inner radius})^2$$

or as a formula

$$A = \pi \times R^2 - \pi \times r^2$$

which may be written as

$$A = \pi \times (R^2 - r^2)$$

Example 13

Work out the area of an annulus which has an outer diameter of 20 cm and an inner diameter of 12 cm.

We are given that the outer radius is 10 cm and the inner radius is 6 cm. Hence:

Area of outer circle $= 3.14 \times 10^2 = 314 \text{ cm}^2$

Area of inner circle $= 3.14 \times 6^2 = 113 \text{ cm}^2$

Area of annulus $= 314 - 113 = 201 \text{ cm}^2$

Alternatively, using the formula with $R = 10$ and $r = 6$,

$$A = \pi \times (10^2 - 6^2)$$

$$= 3.14 \times (100 - 36)$$

$$= 3.14 \times 64$$

$$= 201$$

Hence, as before, the area of the annulus is 201 cm^2.

EXERCISE 20.9

1. Taking $\pi = \frac{22}{7}$, work out the areas of the following circles:

   (a) radius 7 cm   (b) radius 28 in
   (c) radius 140 mm   (d) diameter 42 ft
   (e) radius 35 m

2. Taking $\pi = 3.14$, find the areas of the following circles:

   (a) radius 3 cm   (b) radius 5.6 in
   (c) diameter 15 ft   (d) diameter 9.4 m

189

3. An annulus has an outer radius of 6 in and an inner radius of 4 in. Work out its area. (Take $\pi = 3.14$)

4. A copper pipe has a bore (inside diameter) of 30 mm and an outside diameter of 40 mm. Work out the cross-sectional area of the pipe. (Take $\pi = \frac{22}{7}$)

5. A garden pond with a diameter of 12 metres has a path 1 metre wide around its circumference. Calculate the area of the path. (Take $\pi = 3.14$)

LARGE AREAS

The area of a country is usually stated in square miles (mile^2) or square kilometres (km^2). The area of farmland etc. is often measured in hectares (ha) or in acres such that:

$$1 \text{ hectare} = 10\,000 \text{ square metres}$$

$$1 \text{ acre} = 4840 \text{ square yards}$$

Example 14

(a) A rectangular plot of land is 600 m long and 200 m wide. What is its area in hectares?

$$\text{Area} = 600 \times 200 \text{ m}^2 = 120\,000 \text{ m}^2$$

$$= (120\,000 \div 10\,000) \text{ ha}$$

$$= 12 \text{ ha}$$

(b) An island has a shape roughly corresponding to a triangle with a base 9 miles long and a vertical height of 7.2 miles. Find the area of the island in square miles.

$$\text{Area} = \tfrac{1}{2} \times 9 \times 7.2 \text{ mile}^2 = 32.4 \text{ mile}^2$$

1. A triangular plot of land has a base 250 yards long and a vertical height of 300 yards. Work out the area of the plot in acres.

2. A rectangular field has a length of 400 m and a width of 350 m. What is the area of the field in hectares?

3. The land making up a farm is shown in Figure 20.34. Work out the area of the farm in hectares.

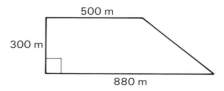

Figure 20.34

4. A town may be considered as being contained in a circle having a diameter of 6 miles. What is the area of the town in square miles?

5. A small island is approximately a trapezium with parallel sides 80 km and 60 km, the distance between these parallel sides being 70 km. Work out the area of the island in square kilometres.

AREAS OF COMPOSITE SHAPES

Many shapes are made up of straight lines and circles. The areas of such shapes are found by splitting up the shape into figures such as rectangles, triangles and parts of circles.

Example 15

(a) Find the area of the shape shown in Figure 20.35. The shape consists of a rectangle and a semicircle.

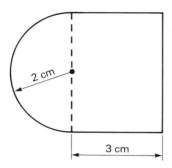

Figure 20.35

Area of semicircle $= \frac{1}{2} \times \text{Radius}^2$

$\qquad = \frac{1}{2} \times 3.14 \times 2^2 \text{ cm}^2$

$\qquad = 6.28 \text{ cm}^2$

Area of rectangle $= \text{Length} \times \text{Breadth}$

$\qquad = 4 \times 3 \text{ cm}^2$

$\qquad = 12 \text{ cm}^2$

Area of shape $= (6.28 + 12) \text{ cm}^2$

$\qquad = 18.28 \text{ cm}^2$

(b) Find the area of the shaded part of Figure 20.36.

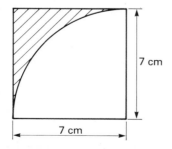

Figure 20.36

The area of the shaded part is found by subtracting the area of the quarter circle from the area of the square.

Area of square $= 7^2 \text{ cm}^2$

$\qquad = 49 \text{ cm}^2$

Area of quarter circle $= \frac{1}{4} \times \pi \times \text{Radius}^2$

$\qquad = \frac{1}{4} \times 3.14 \times 7^2 \text{ cm}^2$

$\qquad = 38.5 \text{ cm}^2$

Area of shaded part $= (49 - 38.5) \text{ cm}^2$

$\qquad = 10.5 \text{ cm}^2$

EXERCISE 20.11

Find the areas of the shapes shown in Figure 20.37. They are all made up of squares or rectangles and parts of circles.

1.

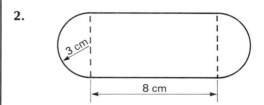

2.

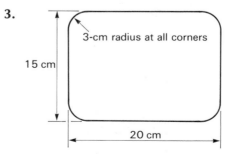

3.

Figure 20.37

191

Find the areas of the shaded parts of the shapes shown in Figure 20.38.

4.

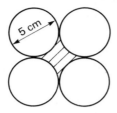

5.

6.

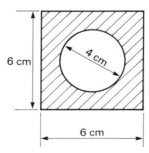

7.

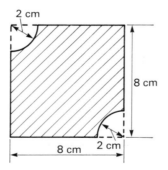

8.

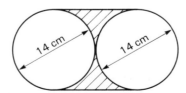

Figure 20.38

MISCELLANEOUS EXERCISE 20

1. A rectangle is 6.9 in long and 3.7 in wide. Work out:

   (a) its perimeter,
   (b) its area.

2. A circular pond has a radius of 14 metres.

   (a) What is its diameter?
   (b) Taking $\pi = \frac{22}{7}$, find its circumference.
   (c) Work out the area of the pond.

3. The pins on a pinboard are 1 centimetre apart. The pinboard and a rubber band can be used to show a variety of rectangles.

   (a) What is the perimeter of the rectangle ABCD shown in Figure 20.39?
   (b) Work out the area of ABCD.
   (c) Write down the length and width of a rectangle with the same perimeter as ABCD which can be shown on the pinboard.

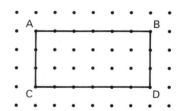

Figure 20.39

4. Which of the triangles in Figure 20.40 have the same area as triangle ABC?

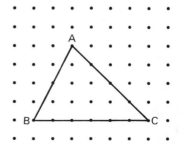

192

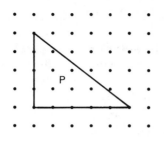

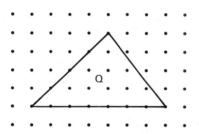

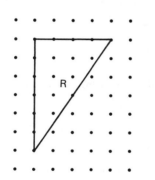

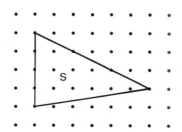

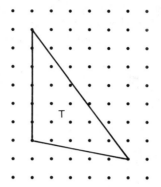

Figure 20.40

5. Work out the area of the shaded border shown in Figure 20.41.

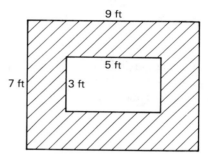

Figure 20.41

6. A square has a perimeter of 20 cm. What is its area?

7. Figure 20.42 shows a trapezium. Work out its area.

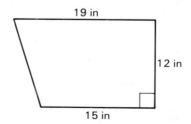

Figure 20.42

193

8. In Figure 20.43, ABCD is a rectangle 12 cm by 8 cm. The shaded portions are cut off. Calculate the area of DLMNPC.

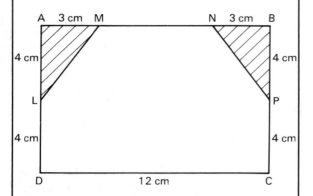

Figure 20.43

9. A rectangular field measures 350 metres by 240 metres. What is its area in hectares? (1 ha = 10 000 m²)

10. Figure 20.44 shows a plane shape composed of a rectangle and two semicircles. Work out the area of the shape. (Take $\pi = 3.14$)

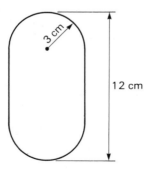

Figure 20.44

MENTAL TEST 20

1. Find the area of a rectangle whose length is 8 cm and whose width is 5 cm.

2. A square has sides 6 cm long.
  (a) What is its perimeter?
  (b) What is its area?

3. A parallelogram has a base 7 in long and a vertical height of 6 in. What is its area?

4. A triangle has a base 6 cm long and an altitude of 4 cm. Find its area.

5. The rectangle shown in Figure 20.45 is drawn on a 1 cm grid. What is its perimeter?

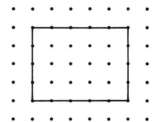

Figure 20.45

6. What is the area of the rectangle shown in Figure 20.45?

7. Find the area of the triangle in Figure 20.46.

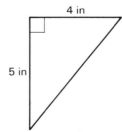

Figure 20.46

8. Taking $\pi = \frac{25}{8}$, find the circumference of a circle whose diameter is 16 cm.

CHAPTER 21

Solid Figures

INTRODUCTION

In Chapter 20 we found out that a plane shape like a rectangle had length and width but no height or thickness. Another way of describing a plane shape is to call it a two-dimensional figure.

Every solid figure has three dimensions which are length, width and height (or thickness). You can see that this is so by looking at a biscuit tin.

TYPES OF SOLID FIGURE

A *sphere* (Figure 21.1) is a circular solid. Examples are a football and a ball bearing.

Figure 21.1

A *cuboid* (Figure 21.2) is a rectangular solid. It has a cross-section which is a rectangle. Examples are a breakfast cereal packet and a plank of wood.

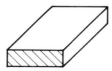

Figure 21.2

A *cube* (Figure 21.3) has all its edges equal in length and each of its faces is a square. Dice of various sizes are examples of cubes.

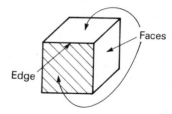

Figure 21.3

A *triangular prism* (Figure 21.4) has a constant cross-section which is a triangle. A ridge tent is an example.

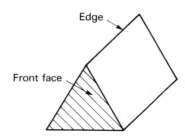

Figure 21.4

195

Some prisms have a constant cross-section which is a regular polygon. Figure 21.5 shows a *hexagonal prism.* Steel bars used in the engineering industry are sometimes made in this shape.

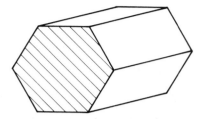

Figure 21.5

Figure 21.6 shows a joist which has a constant cross-section in the form of an I. Steel bars used by the construction industry are often made in this shape.

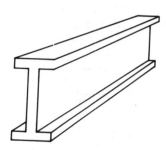

Figure 21.6

A *cylinder* (Figure 21.7) has a constant cross-section which is a circle. Many tins are cylindrical.

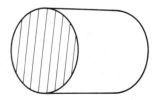

Figure 21.7

A *pyramid* is a solid figure which stands upon a flat base which may be a triangle, a square, a rectangle or a regular polygon. As shown in Figure 21.8 a pyramid tapers to a point which means that each of its faces is a triangle.

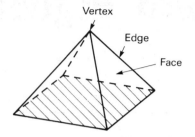

Figure 21.8

A *cone* (Figure 21.9) has a circular base and tapers to a point. An example is an ice-cream cone.

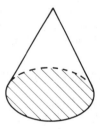

Figure 21.9

Example 1

Figure 21.10 shows a triangular prism. How many edges, faces and vertices does it have?

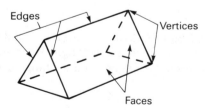

Figure 21.10

As shown in the diagram the prism has 9 edges, 5 faces and 6 vertices.

196

DRAWING SOLID FIGURES

We often need to draw solid figures on paper. Now a sheet of paper has only two dimensions, length and width. But a solid figure has three dimensions, length, width and height. So we need a special way of representing solid figures on paper. The method, called isometric projection is as follows. Start off by drawing three lines OX, OY and OZ as shown in Figure 21.11. These three lines which are called the isometric axes allow the drawing of a solid figure to be made.

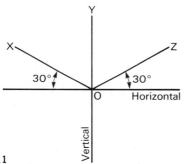

Figure 21.11

Example 2

Make a drawing of a cuboid which is 5 cm long, 3 cm wide and 2 cm high.

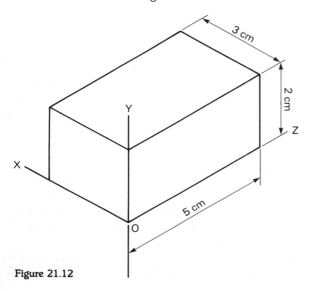

Figure 21.12

Start off by drawing the three axes OX, OY and OZ (Figure 21.12). In the three-dimensional drawing the vertical edges of the cuboid are represented by vertical lines and for a rectangular solid like a cuboid all the lines representing its edges either lie along the axes or are parallel to them.

Example 3

Draw a three-dimensional picture of a pyramid with a rectangular base 3 cm by 4 cm and a vertical height of 5 cm.

As before, start off by drawing the three axes OX, OY and OZ (Figure 21.13). Now draw the base OABC and plot the point D which is at the intersection of the diagonals BO and AC. The vertex V lies vertically, 5 cm above D. Join VA, VB, VC and VO to complete the drawing.

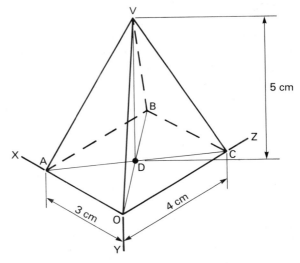

Figure 21.13

REPRESENTING CIRCLES

Drawing circles on a three-dimensional picture sometimes causes difficulty. Figure 21.14 gives the clue necessary for partly overcoming this difficulty. Diagram (a) shows a true circle drawn in a square. At the points marked X the circumference of the circle and the sides of the square touch. This must be the same in the isometric view shown at (b).

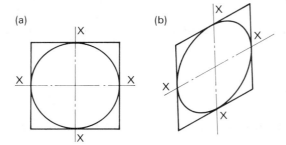

(a)　　　　　　　(b)

Figure 21.14

Example 4

Draw a three-dimensional picture of a cylinder which has a diameter of 4 cm and a height of 7 cm.

Start off by drawing the three axes OX, OY and OZ. Next draw the cuboid ABCODEFG which is needed to obtain the shape of the circular ends of the cylinder. The finished drawing is shown in Figure 21.15.

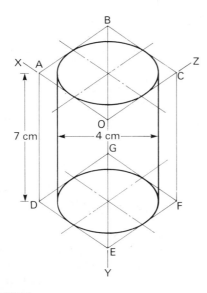

Figure 21.15

EXERCISE 21.1

Make three-dimensional drawings of each of the following solid figures. For each figure in questions 1–4, write down the number of edges, faces and vertices:

1. A cuboid with a length of 6 cm, a width of 3 cm and a height of 4 cm.

2. A cube having an edge 5 cm long.

3. A pyramid with a square base of side 4 cm and a vertical height of 6 cm.

4. A triangular prism with measurements as shown in Figure 21.16.

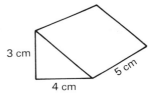

Figure 21.16

5. Draw a cylinder with a diameter of 4 cm and a height of 6 cm.

6. Make a picture of a cone with a base diameter of 5 cm and a vertical height of 6 cm.

NETS

Suppose that we want to make a cube out of cardboard. We need a pattern giving us the shape of the cardboard required to make the cube. As shown in Figure 21.17 the pattern consists of six squares. This shape, which is called a net of a cube, can be folded to make a cube.

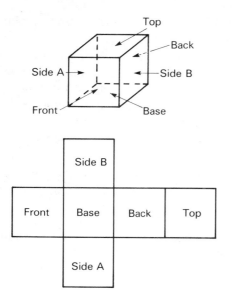

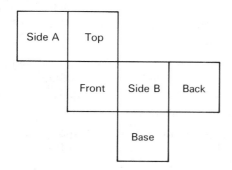

Figure 21.17

It is possible for there to be more than one net for a solid object. For instance, a cube can also be made from the net shown in Figure 21.18.

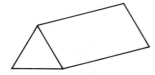

Figure 21.18

Example 5

Sketch the net of the prism shown in Figure 21.19.

Figure 21.19

The net is sketched in Figure 21.20 and it consists of three rectangles representing the base and the two sides together with two triangles representing the two ends.

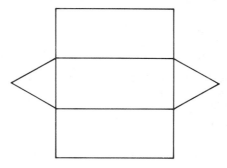

Figure 21.20

Nets of circular objects like cylinders can also be drawn. Figure 21.21 shows the net of the curved part of a cylinder. It is a rectangle whose length is equal to the circumference of the base of the cylinder and whose breadth is equal to its height.

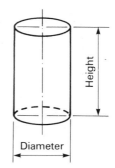

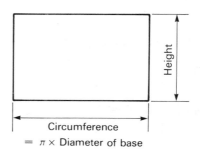

Figure 21.21

199

SURFACE AREA OF SOLIDS

We often need to find the surface areas of solids. The surface area of a solid can always be found by drawing its net and then calculating the area of the net.

Example 6

A cuboid is 8 cm long, 5 cm wide and 4 cm high. Find its total surface area.

The net is drawn in Figure 21.22. The total surface area is found by adding together the areas of the six rectangles making up the net.

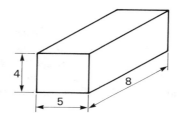

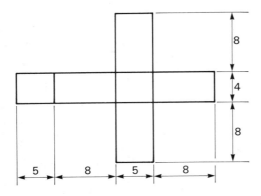

All dimensions in centimetres

Figure 21.22

$$\text{Total surface area} = (2 \times 5 \times 4) + (2 \times 4 \times 8)$$
$$+ (2 \times 5 \times 8)$$
$$= 40 + 64 + 80$$
$$= 184 \text{ cm}^2$$

We could find the total surface area by using the formula:

$$\text{Total surface area} = \text{Perimeter of end}$$
$$\times \text{Length of cuboid}$$
$$+ \text{Area of ends}$$

This formula may be used to find the area of any solid which has a constant cross-section.

Example 7

Work out the total surface area of a cylinder with a base diameter of 14 in and a height of 9 in.

Area of base $= \pi \times 7^2 = 154 \text{ in}^2$

Circumference of base $= 2 \times \pi \times 7 = 44 \text{ in}$

$$\text{Total surface area} = 44 \times 9 + 2 \times 154$$
$$= 396 + 308$$
$$= 704 \text{ in}^2$$

EXERCISE 21.2

1. Draw the net of a cuboid which is 5 cm long, 4 cm wide and 2 cm high and hence calculate the total surface area of the cuboid.

2. A pyramid has a square base of 4 in side and a vertical height of 5 in. Sketch the net of the pyramid and hence find its total surface area.

3. Sketch the net of the triangular prism shown in Figure 21.23 and hence work out its total surface area.

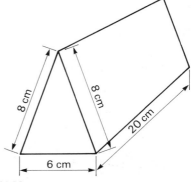

Figure 21.23

4. Figure 21.24 shows the nets of various solids. Name the solids.

(a)

(b)

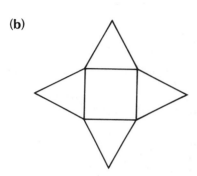

(c)

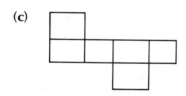

Figure 21.24

5. Work out the total surface area of the solid shown in Figure 21.25.

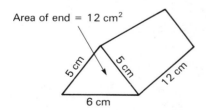

Area of end = 12 cm²

5 cm

5 cm

12 cm

6 cm

Figure 21.25

UNITS OF VOLUME

The volume of a solid object is measured by seeing how many cubic units it contains. Figure 21.26 shows a cube whose edge is 1 cm long.

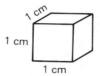

1 cm

1 cm

1 cm

Figure 21.26

Its volume is 1 cubic centimetre (cm^3)
In the metric system the following units of volume are used:

cubic millimetres mm^3
cubic centimetres cm^3
cubic metres m^3

In the imperial system the following are used:

cubic inches in^3
cubic feet ft^3
cubic yards yd^3

VOLUME OF A CUBOID

Figure 21.27 shows a cuboid. Three layers of cubes with 1 cm edges fit into the solid shape. Each layer consists of 5×4 cubes. So the total number of 1 cm cubes fitted into the solid shape is $5 \times 4 \times 3 = 60$. We say that the cuboid has a volume of 60 cubic centimetres.

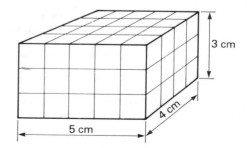

3 cm

5 cm

4 cm

Figure 21.27

To calculate the volume of the cuboid we have multiplied its length by its breadth by its height.

That is:

Volume of cuboid = Length × Breadth × Height

Since the area of the end of a cuboid is breadth × height we can also write:

Volume of cuboid = Area of end × Length

This statement is true for any solid which has the same cross-section throughout its length.

Example 8

(a) Find the volume of a rectangular tin which is 16.3 in long, 9.7 in wide and 4.6 in high.

$$\text{Volume of tin} = (16.3 \times 9.7 \times 4.6) \text{ in}^3$$
$$= 727.3 \text{ in}^3$$

(b) A block of wood has the constant cross-section shown in Figure 21.28. If the block is 80 cm long work out its volume.

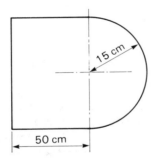

Figure 21.28

$$\text{Area of cross-section} = (\tfrac{1}{2} \times \pi \times 15^2) + (30 \times 50) \text{ cm}^2$$
$$= (353 + 1500) \text{ cm}^2$$
$$= 1853 \text{ cm}^2$$

Volume of block = Area of cross-section × Length
$$= (1853 \times 80) \text{ cm}^3$$
$$= 148\,240 \text{ cm}^3$$

Example 9

Find the volume of the solid shape shown in Figure 21.29.

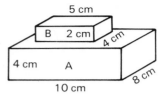

Figure 21.29

The solid shape can be split up into the two cuboids A and B.

$$\text{Volume of A} = (10 \times 8 \times 4) \text{ cm}^3$$
$$= 320 \text{ cm}^3$$
$$\text{Volume of B} = (5 \times 4 \times 2) \text{ cm}^3$$
$$= 40 \text{ cm}^3$$
$$\text{Volume of solid} = (320 + 40) \text{ cm}^3$$
$$= 360 \text{ cm}^3$$

EXERCISE 21.3

Work out the volume of each of the solid shapes shown in Figure 21.30.

1.

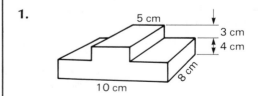

2.

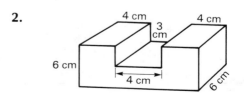

3.

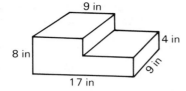

4.

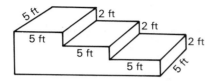

5.

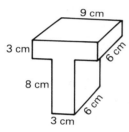

Figure 21.30

6. Figure 21.31 shows the cross-section of an angle bar. If it is 180 mm long, work out its volume.

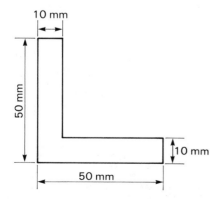

Figure 21.31

7. A block of wood 200 mm long has the cross-section shown in Figure 21.32. Work out the volume of the block.

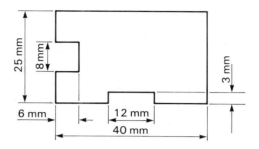

Figure 21.32

8. A tank which is 5 m in height has the cross-section shown in Figure 21.33. Find the volume of the tank. (Take $\pi = 3.14$)

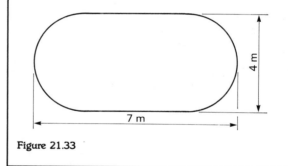

Figure 21.33

VOLUME OF A CYLINDER

A cylinder has a constant cross-section which is a circle (Figure 21.34). So

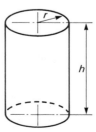

Figure 21.34

Volume of cylinder = Area of cross-section
$\qquad\qquad\qquad$ × Height

$\qquad\qquad$ = Area of circle × Height

$\qquad\qquad$ = π × Radius^2 × Height

As a formula we write

$$V = \pi r^2 h$$

where V stands for the volume, r for the radius of the cross-section and h for the height of the cylinder.

Example 10

(a) Work out the volume of a cylinder which has a radius of 9 cm and a height of 12 cm.

We are given $r = 9$ and $h = 12$. So

$$V = \pi r^2 h = (3.14 \times 9^2 \times 12) \text{ cm}^3$$

$$= 3052 \text{ cm}^3$$

(b) Figure 21.35 shows a pipe. Calculate the volume of metal contained in it.

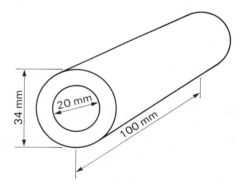

Figure 21.35

Area of cross-section = π × (outer radius)^2
$\qquad\qquad\qquad\qquad$ − π × (inner radius)^2

$\qquad\qquad$ = $3.14 \times 17^2 - 3.14 \times 10^2$

$\qquad\qquad$ = $907 - 314$

$\qquad\qquad$ = 593 mm^2

Volume of metal = Area of cross-section
$\qquad\qquad\qquad\quad$ × Length

$\qquad\qquad$ = $(593 \times 100) \text{ mm}^3$

$\qquad\qquad$ = $59\,300 \text{ mm}^3$

VOLUME OF A CONE

The volume of a cone (Figure 21.36) is one-third of the volume of an equivalent cylinder (i.e., a cylinder with the same radius as the base radius of the cone and the same height). That is:

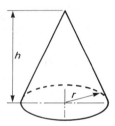

Figure 21.36

$$V = \tfrac{1}{3} \times \text{Area of the base} \times \text{Height}$$

$$= \tfrac{1}{3} \times \pi \times \text{Radius}^2 \times \text{Height}$$

As a formula we write

$$V = \tfrac{1}{3}\pi r^2 h$$

where V stands for the volume of the cone, r for its base radius and h its height.

Example 11

A cone has a base radius of 8 cm and a height of 6 cm. Work out its volume.

We are given $r = 8$ and $h = 6$. So

$$V = \tfrac{1}{3} \times 3.14 \times 8^2 \times 6 = 402 \text{ cm}^3$$

VOLUME OF A PYRAMID

The volume of a pyramid (Figure 21.37) is one-third of the volume of the equivalent prism, that is

Volume of a pyramid $= \frac{1}{3} \times$ Area of base $\times$ Height

As a formula we write

$$V = \frac{1}{3}Ah$$

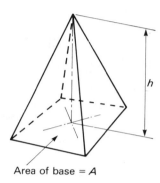

Area of base $= A$

Figure 21.37

Example 12

Find the volume of a pyramid whose base is a square of side 4 in and whose height is 6 in.

Area of base $= 4 \times 4 = 16$ in^2

We now have $A = 16$ and $h = 6$.

$$V = \frac{1}{3} \times 16 \times 6 = 32 \text{ in}^3$$

THE SPHERE

It can be shown that:

Volume of a sphere $= \frac{4}{3} \times \pi \times$ Radius^3

As a formula we write

$$V = \frac{4}{3}\pi r^3$$

where V stands for the volume of the sphere and r stands for its radius.

Surface area of a sphere $= 4 \times \pi \times$ Radius^2

As a formula we write

$$A = 4\pi r^2$$

where A stands for the surface area of the sphere and r stands for its radius.

Example 13

A ball has a diameter of 28 cm. Calculate its volume and its surface area.

We are given that $r = 28 \div 2 = 14$. So

$$V = \frac{4}{3} \times 3.14 \times 14^3 = 11\,488 \text{ cm}^3$$

$$A = 4 \times 3.14 \times 14^2 = 2462 \text{ cm}^2$$

EXERCISE 21.4

1. A cylindrical tin has a diameter of 7 inches and a height of 8 inches. Calculate the volume of the tin. (Take $\pi = 3.14$)

2. A hole 40 mm diameter is drilled in a metal plate which is 60 mm thick. Calculate the volume of metal removed in drilling the hole. (Take $\pi = 3.14$)

3. Calculate the volume of material in a tube which has an outside diameter of 14 cm and an inside diameter of 10 cm if it is 40 cm long. (Take $\pi = 3.14$)

4. A cone has a base radius of 14 cm and a height of 8 cm. Calculate its volume. (Take $\pi = \frac{22}{7}$)

5. A pyramid has a rectangular base 5 ft long and 3 ft wide. If its height is 7 ft, work out its volume.

6. A concrete dome is in the shape of a hemisphere. Its internal and external diameters are 5.2 m and 5.4 m respectively. Calculate the volume of concrete used in its construction. (Take $\pi = 3.14$)

7. A small roof is in the form of a pyramid. Its base is a regular pentagon (five-sided polygon) whose area is 45 square feet and its height is 12 feet. Work out the volume enclosed by the roof.

8. Figure 21.38 shows a laboratory flask which may be considered as a sphere with a cylindrical neck. Calculate the volume of the flask. (Take $\pi = 3.14$)

3 cm

35 cm

20 cm

Figure 21.38

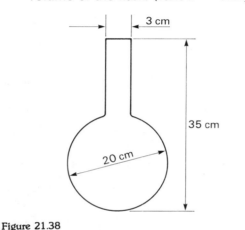

CAPACITY

The capacity of a container is the volume of liquid that it will hold. Capacity is sometimes measured in the same units as volume (i.e., cubic metres, cubic feet, etc.) but more often it is measured in litres, pints, gallons, etc.

In the metric system the standard unit of capacity is the litre (abbreviation l) such that

1 litre = 1000 cm^3

Small capacities are measured in centilitres (cl) or millilitres (ml).

100 centilitres = 1000 millilitres = 1 litre
1 millilitre = 1 cm^3

In the imperial system:

20 fluid ounces (fl oz) = 1 pint (pt)
8 pints (pt) = 1 gallon (gal)

Example 14

(a) How many 5 millilitre doses of medicine can be obtained from a full bottle which has a volume of 250 cubic centimetres?

$$250 \text{ cm}^3 = 250 \text{ millilitres}$$

Number of doses = $250 \div 5 = 50$

(b) A rectangular water tank is 5 metres long, 3 metres wide and 6 metres high. How many litres of water will it hold when full?

Volume of tank = $(500 \times 300 \times 600)$ cm^3

= 90 000 000 cm^3

Since   1 litre = 1000 cm^3

Capacity of tank = $(90\,000\,000 \div 1000)$ litres

= 90 000 litres

EXERCISE 21.5

1. A small tin is in the form of a cylinder. Its radius is 7 cm and its height is 9 cm. (Take $\pi = \frac{22}{7}$)

   (a) Work out the volume of the tin in cubic centimetres.

   (b) What is the capacity of the tin in litres?

2. A rectangular water tank is 4 m long, 3 m wide and 2 m high.

   (a) Express each of the dimensions of the tank in centimetres and hence find its volume in cubic centimetres.

   (b) Work out the capacity of the tank in litres.

3. A basin may be considered to be a hemisphere with a radius of 28 cm. How many litres of water will it hold when full? (Take $\pi = \frac{22}{7}$)

4. A circular garden pool has a diameter of 6 metres. How many litres of water will it take to fill it to a depth of 0.75 metres? (Take $\pi = 3.14$)

5. A rectangular medicine bottle is 8 cm wide, 4 cm long and 12 cm high.

   (a) How many centilitres will it hold when full?

   (b) How many 5-millilitre doses can be obtained from a full bottle?

6. A conical wine glass has a maximum diameter of 4.5 cm and it is 6 cm in height.

   (a) How many centilitres does the glass hold when full?

   (b) How many such glasses would be filled from a bottle of wine containing 70 centilitres? (Take $\pi = 3.14$)

7. An ice-cream carton is cylindrical in shape. It has a diameter of 6 cm and it is 8 cm tall. Work out the amount of ice-cream, in litres, needed to fill 50 such cartons. (Take $\pi = 3.14$)

MISCELLANEOUS EXERCISE 21

1. Beef cubes have an edge 2 cm long. They are packed in boxes which are cubic in shape with an edge 8 cm long. How many beef cubes are needed to fill a box?

2. (a) Draw, in good proportion, a pyramid with a square base of side 4 cm and a height of 7 cm.

   (b) How many edges has the pyramid?

   (c) How many faces does it have?

3. Work out the volume of a cylindrical water tank which has a diameter of 5 ft and a height of 6 ft. (Take $\pi = 3.14$)

4. A thin cardboard sleeve is shown in Figure 21.39.

   (a) Draw a net of this sleeve.

   (b) Use your net to work out the area of cardboard needed to make the sleeve.

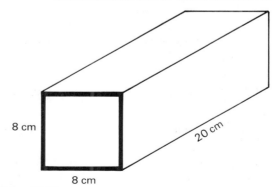

8 cm

8 cm

20 cm

Figure 21.39

5. Figure 21.40 shows the cross-section of a steel bar used in the construction industry. If it is 120 inches long, calculate the volume of steel contained in it.

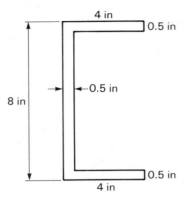

Figure 21.40

6. A cone has a base diameter of 6 m and a vertical height of 8 m.

   (a) Taking $\pi = 3.14$, work out the volume of the cone in cubic metres.
   (b) If it is filled with water, how many litres will it hold?

7. Figure 21.41 shows two solid wooden blocks taken from a child's building outfit. Work out:

   (a) the volume of block A,
   (b) the total surface area of block B,
   (c) the volume of block B.

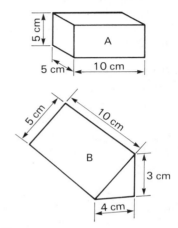

Figure 21.41

8. Soup is sold in a closed cylindrical can whose diameter is 7 cm and whose height is 10 cm. Work out, in litres, the quantity of soup contained in a can which is completely filled. (Take $\pi = \frac{22}{7}$)

MENTAL TEST 21

1. What is the volume of a cube with edges 3 cm long?

2. A match box is 7 cm wide, 3 cm high and 10 cm long. Work out the volume of the box.

3. How many faces does a rectangular pyramid possess?

4. A triangular block has a constant cross-sectional area of 3 square centimetres. If the block is 8 centimetres long, what is its volume?

5. A cylindrical tin has a cross-sectional area of 12 square centimetres. If it has a height of 8 centimetres, work out its volume.

6. A cone has a base area of 21 square inches and a vertical height of 5 inches. Work out the volume of the cone.

7. A pyramid has a base area of 12 square centimetres and a height of 10 centimetres. What is its volume?

8. A small tank has a volume of 3000 cubic centimetres. It is filled with water. How many litres of water are needed?

CHAPTER 22

Statistics

Statistics is the name given to the science of collecting and analysing facts. It is used in business, medicine, pure science, insurance, etc.

RAW DATA

Raw data is collected numerical information which is not arranged in any kind of order.

Consider the following scores obtained by 50 students in a mathematics test:

4	3	3	5	5	6	5	8	7	6
7	8	9	5	4	1	8	7	5	6
6	7	5	2	5	2	6	9	5	7
6	5	6	2	8	6	7	3	3	8
7	6	5	5	6	4	3	4	5	7

This is an example of raw data and we see that the figures are not arranged in any kind of order.

FREQUENCY DISTRIBUTIONS

The information about the scores of students given on the left does not mean very much as it stands. However if the scores are grouped and made into a table then it is easier to see if a pattern emerges.

Example 1

Form a frequency distribution for the scores of 50 students in a mathematics test given on the left. The easiest way to form a frequency distribution is to use a tally chart.

On looking at the figures we see that the lowest score is 1 whilst the highest score is 9. The scores 1 to 9 are written in the first column of the tally chart. We now take each figure in the raw data just as it comes and put a tally mark in the appropriate row.

The fifth tally mark for each score is made in an oblique direction thereby tying the tally marks into bundles of five. This makes the counting of the tally marks very much easier. When all the figures have been entered the tally marks for each score are counted and their total is written in the column headed frequency. Thus the frequency is simply the number of times each score occurs in the raw data.

From the tally chart we see that the score 2 occurs three times (a frequency of 3) whilst the score 6 occurs ten times (a frequency of 10).

Score	Tally	Frequency
1	1	1
2	111	3
3	1111	5
4	1111	4
5	1111 1111 11	12
6	1111 1111	10
7	1111 111	8
8	1111	5
9	11	2

The frequencies can be displayed on a bar chart (Figure 22.1) with all the rectangles of equal width. The frequencies are represented by the heights of the rectangles. A bar chart which displays a frequency distribution is called a histogram.

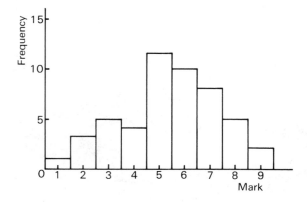

Figure 22.1

GROUPED DISTRIBUTIONS

When a large amount of information has to be organised a grouped frequency distribution is used.

Example 2

The distances, in metres, achieved by competitors in a discus throwing event were:

19	37	42	19	27	42	37	27	7	33
30	12	6	31	24	25	50	29	38	35

Use these figures to obtain a grouped frequency distribution with classes 1–10, 11–20, 21–30, 31–40 and 41–50.

Distance (m)	Tally	Frequency
1–10	11	2
11–20	111	3
21–30	1111 1	6
31–40	1111 1	6
41–50	111	3

The class interval for the third class is 21–30. The end numbers 21 and 30 are called the class limits for the third class, 21 being the lower class limit and 30 being the upper class limit. In the tally chart for the grouped distribution the distances have been recorded to the nearest metre. The class interval 21–30, theoretically includes all the distances between 20.5 m and 30.5 m. These figures are called the lower and upper class boundaries respectively.

The width of a class interval is the difference between the upper and lower class boundaries, i.e.,

Width of class interval = Upper class boundary − Lower class boundary

So for the third class of the distribution:

Width of class interval = $(30.5 - 20.5)$ m

$= 10.0$ m

A histogram (Figure 22.2 on p. 212) for the grouped distribution of Example 2 may be drawn by using the mid-points of the class intervals as the centres of the rectangles.

210

Note that the extremes of each rectangle represent the lower and upper class boundaries.

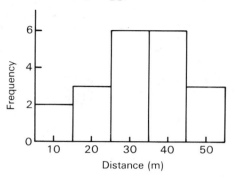

Figure 22.2

Example 3

The figures in the table below are part of a grouped frequency distribution. Write down the upper and lower class boundaries for the second class and hence find the width of the class interval.

Weight (kg)	Frequency
350–379	27
380–409	34
410–439	43

For the second class the upper and lower class boundaries are 409.5 kg and 379.5 kg respectively.

Width of class interval = (409.5 − 379.5) kg

= 30.0 kg

EXERCISE 22.1

1. In a swimming match the times taken, to the nearest second, by 20 children to swim one length were:

   31 27 24 26 31 25 26 32 27 31
   26 32 30 32 29 25 29 27 26 28

   (a) Construct a tally chart and hence form a frequency distribution.
   (b) Use your frequency distribution to draw a histogram.

2. The goals scored by a football team in 30 matches were as follows:

   4 1 3 2 0 1 1 1 1 0
   2 5 0 0 4 1 1 0 1 1
   5 1 2 1 1 0 2 1 2 0

   (a) Arrange this information in a frequency table using classes of 0 goals, 1 goal, 2 goals, 3 goals, 4 goals and 5 goals.
   (b) Draw a histogram to represent this frequency distribution.

3. The histogram shown in Figure 22.3 gives the heights of a group of 54 fourteen-year-old boys. Copy and complete the following table:

Height (cm)	150	151	152	153	154	155
Frequency						
Height (cm)	156	157	158	159	160	161
Frequency						

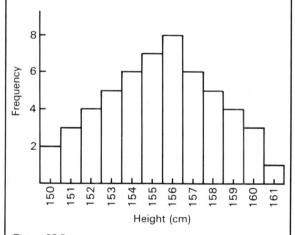

Height (cm)

Figure 22.3

4. A teacher asked his class of 32 pupils to write down how long a particular question took them to answer. The following table summarises their times:

Time (min)	10	11	12	13	14	15	16
Frequency	1	3	6	8	7	5	2

Draw a histogram to depict this information.

211

5. A survey was made one evening of the ages of 30 members of a youth club with the following results:

14　16　16　15　15　14　14　17　18　15
14　16　16　14　14　15　17　15　14　15
14　14　18　16　15　14　15　17　17　15

Form a frequency distribution of this information using classes 14, 15, 16, 17 and 18 years. Draw a bar chart to represent the results of the survey.

6. Look at the following table:

Length (cm)	Frequency
11–15	4
16–20	7
21–25	12
26–30	8
31–35	3

(a) Write down the upper and lower class boundaries for the third class.

(b) Work out the width of the third class.

(c) Draw a histogram of this information.

7. The table is a record of the heights of 100 people in a random sample. The heights are given correct to the nearest centimetre.

Height (cm)	Frequency
100–109	1
110–119	3
120–129	7
130–139	9
140–149	18
150–159	32
160–169	13
170–179	8
180–189	5
190–199	4

(a) Work out the class width for each of the classes.

(b) Display this distribution in a histogram.

STATISTICAL AVERAGES

Three kinds of statistical average are generally used. They are the arithmetic mean (usually called the *mean*), the *median* and the *mode*.

The arithmetic mean is found by adding all the values in the set and dividing this sum by the number of values in the set.

$$\text{Mean} = \frac{\text{Sum of all the values}}{\text{Number of values}}$$

Example 4

Work out the mean of the numbers 3, 5, 8, 9 and 10.

$$\text{Mean} = \frac{3 + 5 + 8 + 9 + 10}{5} = \frac{35}{5} = 7$$

When a set of values is arranged in ascending or descending order the median is the value which lies half-way along the set.

Example 5

Find the median of the numbers 5, 4, 2, 8, 7, 2, 9, 7 and 3.

Arranging the numbers in ascending order we have

$$2, \ 2, \ 3, \ 4, \ 5, \ 7, \ 7, \ 8, \ 9$$

The median is 5 because there are four numbers below this value and four numbers above it.

When there are an even number of values in a set the median is found by calculating the mean of the two middle values.

Example 6

Find the median of the numbers 8, 5, 4, 7, 9, 10, 2 and 6.

Arranging the numbers is descending order we have:

$$10, 9, 8, 7, 6, 5, 4, 2$$

The middle two values are 7 and 6 and so:

$$\text{Median} = \frac{7+6}{2} = 6.5$$

The mode of a set of values is the value which occurs most frequently.

Example 7

Find the mode of the numbers 4, 5, 7, 4, 8, 5, 6, 5, 7, 5 and 9.

The mode is 5 because there are more fives than any other number.

Example 8

The marks obtained in a test taken by a class of 30 pupils were as follows:

Mark	1	2	3	4	5
Frequency	2	8	13	5	2

Find (a) the modal mark, (b) the median mark, (c) the mean mark.

(a) The modal mark is the most frequently occurring mark. Looking at the table we see that 3 marks occurs 13 times which is more than any other mark in the distribution. Therefore the modal mark is 3.

(b) Since there are 30 children the median mark must lie between the 15th and 16th items in the distribution. We now look at the 15th and 16th items and we find that these are both 3. Therefore the median mark is 3.

$$\text{(c) Mean mark} = \frac{\begin{aligned}(1 \times 2) + (2 \times 8) + (3 \times 13) \\ + (4 \times 5) + (5 \times 2)\end{aligned}}{2 + 8 + 13 + 5 + 2}$$

$$= \frac{2 + 16 + 39 + 20 + 10}{30}$$

$$= \frac{87}{30}$$

$$= 2.9$$

Hence the mean mark is 2.9.

Uses of Statistical Averages

The mean is the most commonly used statistical average. Indeed when most people talk about an average the average they are talking about is the arithmetic mean, for example, batting averages in cricket or average marks in examinations.

Example 9

The hourly rate of pay for four office workers are £4.06, £4.32, £9.40 and £2.22. Calculate their average rate of pay.

$$\text{Mean} = \frac{4.06 + 4.32 + 9.40 + 2.22}{4}$$

$$= \frac{20.00}{4}$$

$$= 5$$

So the mean rate of pay is £5 per hour.

This mean rate of pay is greatly distorted by the very low rate of £2.22 (paid to the office junior?) and the very high rate of £9.40 (paid to the office manager?). Therefore the mean is not a reliable guide to the wages paid to the four office workers. In fact the median rate of pay will give a better guide.

Example 10

Find the median for the rates of pay given in Example 9.

Arranging the values in ascending order we have:

2.22, 4.06, 4.32, 9.40

The two middle values are 4.06 and 4.32.

$$\text{Median} = \frac{4.06 + 4.32}{2} = 4.19$$

So the median rate of pay is £4.19 which is a better average to use in this case.

Example 11

A shop sells two pairs of shoes of size 4, three pairs of size 5, four pairs of size 7 and three pairs of size 8. Work out the mean, median and modal sizes.

The mean size   = 6.25

The median size = 7

The modal size   = 7

The mean tells us something about the size of feet but it is not a stock size and is not of much use to the shopkeeper. The median is a stock size and the modal size tells us that more shoes of size 7 were sold than any other size. This is what the shopkeeper wants to know when ordering more shoes.

EXERCISE 22.2

1. Work out the mean of the numbers 6, 9, 10 and 11.

2. Find the mean of £24, £28, £31, £29 and £33.

3. The heights of some men are 173, 171, 169, 182, 176, 180 and 174 cm. Calculate the mean height of these men.

4. Find the median of the numbers 4, 2, 7, 4, 3, 2 and 7.

5. Find the median of the numbers 3, 5, 7, 6, 9, 7, 5 and 8.

6. Find the mode of the numbers 4, 6, 5, 9, 4, 7, 6, 9, 6, 5 and 8.

7. Eleven people were asked to guess the weight of a cake to the nearest half-pound. Their estimates were:

$3\frac{1}{2}$, $2\frac{1}{2}$, 2, $1\frac{1}{2}$, $3\frac{1}{2}$, 3, 3, 1, $1\frac{1}{2}$, $2\frac{1}{2}$, $3\frac{1}{2}$

What was:

(a) the estimated mean weight?
(b) the estimated modal weight?
(c) the estimated median weight?

8. During a census a check was made to find out how many people were living in each house in a certain street. The results were:

Number of people per house	1	2	3	4	5	6	7
Frequency	3	6	8	9	3	1	0

(a) How many houses were checked?
(b) Write down the modal number of people per house.
(c) Work out the mean number of people per house.
(d) What is the median number of people per house?

9. The marks of 100 students in a test were as follows:

Mark	1	2	3	4	5	6	7
Frequency	2	8	20	37	18	12	3

(a) Calculate the mean mark.
(b) What is the modal mark?
(c) What is the median mark?

10. The following table shows the number of runs scored by a sample of cricketers in a limited-over competition.

Runs scored	18	19	20	21	22	23	24	25
Frequency	5	10	12	28	36	30	10	3

(a) How many cricketers are in the sample?
(b) What is the modal score?
(c) What is the median score?
(d) Work out the mean score correct to 1 decimal place.

PROBABILITY

Probability has great importance in insurance (the risks have to be carefully calculated before the premium can be set), investment in business, medical research and so on.

If a fair coin is tossed the result is equally likely to be heads or tails. We say that the events of tossing heads or tossing tails are equiprobable events.

Similarly if we throw a die (plural dice) with six faces the events of throwing a 1, 2, 3, 4, 5 or 6 are equiprobable events.

The probability of an event occuring is defined as:

$$\frac{\text{Number of ways the event can occur}}{\text{Total number of equiprobable events}}$$

Example 12

A fair coin is tossed once. What is the probability that a head will result?

Number of ways in which a head can occur = 1

Total number of equiprobable events = 2

Probability of a head = $\frac{1}{2}$ = 0.5

Example 13

Work out the probability of throwing a four in a single roll of a fair die.

Number of ways of throwing a four = 1

Number of equiprobable events = 6

Probability of a four = $\frac{1}{6}$ = 0.167

Example 14

A card is dealt from a well shuffled pack of 52 playing cards. Work out the probability that it will be an ace.

Number of ways an ace can occur = 4
 (there are four aces in a pack of cards)

Number of equiprobable events = 52

Probability of an ace = $\dfrac{4}{52} = \dfrac{1}{13}$

$$= 0.0769$$

All probabilities have a value between 0 and 1. As shown in the example above probabilities may be written as fractions or as decimal numbers. A probability of 0 means that the event is an impossibility (for example, the probability that you can swim the Atlantic Ocean unaided). A probability of 1 means that the event is absolutely certain to occur (for example, the probability of picking the winner of a one-horse race).

Example 15

A die has six faces numbered 1, 2, 3, 4, 5 and 6. It is rolled once only. Find the probability of

(a) throwing a seven,
(b) throwing a 1, 2, 3, 4, 5 or 6.

(a) Throwing a seven with a die possessing six faces is impossible, so the probability of this occurring is 0.

215

(b) When the die is thrown one of the numbers 1, 2, 3, 4, 5, 6 must turn up. So we are certain to throw a 1, 2, 3, 4, 5 or 6. Hence the probability of this occurring is 1.

TOTAL PROBABILITY

If we toss a fair coin it will come down either heads or tails. That is:

Probability of a head $= \frac{1}{2}$

Probability of a tail $\quad = \frac{1}{2}$

Total probability covering all possible outcomes

$$= \tfrac{1}{2} + \tfrac{1}{2} = 1$$

Another way of saying this is

Probability of success + Probability of failure $= 1$

Example 16

A bag contains 5 blue balls, 3 red balls and 2 black balls. A ball is drawn from the bag. Calculate the probability tht it will not be black.

Number of ways of drawing a black ball $= 2$ because there are 2 black balls in the bag.

Number of equiprobable events $= 10$ because there are a total of 10 balls in the bag.

Probability of drawing a black ball $= \frac{2}{10}$

$$= 0.2$$

Probability of not drawing a black ball $= 1 - 0.2$

$$= 0.8$$

EXPERIMENTAL PROBABILITY

Although it is possible to calculate many probabilities in the way previously shown, in a great number of cases we have to rely upon an experiment or a survey to establish the probability of an event happening.

Example 17

100 ball bearings were examined and 4 were found not to be perfectly round. Find the probability of choosing a non-round ball bearing by choosing one bearing at random from the 100 checked.

Total number of trials $= 100$

Number of ways of choosing a non-round bearing $= 4$

Probability of choosing a non-round bearing

$$= \frac{4}{100}$$

$$= \frac{1}{25}$$

$$= 0.04$$

In industry, probabilities are worked out just like this and these experimental probabilities can usually be relied upon. In the test on the ball bearings the calculated probability of 0.04 would be used to estimate the number of defective (i.e. non-round) ball bearings that will be produced as production proceeds. The sample size (in this case 100) is very important and, generally speaking, the larger the sample the more accurate the probability will be.

When we say that the probability of an event happening is $\frac{1}{3}$ we do not mean that if we repeat the experiment three times the event will happen once. Even if we repeat the experiment 30 times it is very unlikely that the event will happen exactly 10 times.

Probability tells us what to expect in the long run. If the experiment is repeated 300 times then we would expect the event to happen about 100 times.

216

EXERCISE 22.3

1. A die has six faces numbered 1, 2, 3, 4, 5 and 6. It is rolled once. Find the probability that:
   (a) a 3 will turn up,
   (b) a number less than 4 will turn up,
   (c) an even number will turn up.

2. A letter is chosen at random from the word TERRIFIC. Work out the probability that it will be
   (a) an F   (b) an R.

3. A card is dealt from a well shuffled pack of 52 playing cards. Calculate the probability that it will be:
   (a) the jack of diamonds,
   (b) a king,
   (c) a red card,
   (d) a club,
   (e) an ace, king, queen or jack.

4. The probability of a particular couple having a child with blue eyes is 0.4. What is the probability that the child will not have blue eyes?

5. The probability that Sheila will be selected for the school hockey team is 0.7. What is the probability that she will not be selected?

6. It states on the box of a certain brand of matches that the average contents is 36 matches. 9 boxes were counted with the following results: 36, 40, 36, 32, 37, 35, 29, 32. What is the probability of selecting a box from this sample which contains less than 36 matches?

7. 20 discs numbered 1 to 20 are placed in a box and one disc is chosen at random. Determine the probability that the number on the disc will be:
   (a) odd,   (b) more than 7,
   (c) less than 7.

8. A bag contains 5 red balls, 2 blue balls and 3 green balls. A ball is drawn at random from the bag. Find the probability that it will be:
   (a) red,   (b) blue,
   (c) green,   (d) not green.

MISCELLANEOUS EXERCISE 22

1. The lengths of 50 pieces of wood were measured, to the nearest millimetre, with the following results:

Length (mm)	Frequency
295	1
296	2
297	6
298	9
299	15
300	10
301	4
302	2
303	1

   (a) Draw a histogram of this information.
   (b) What is the class width of each of the classes?
   (c) What is the modal length?
   (d) What is the median length?

2. The marks of five students in a test were 54, 63, 49, 78 and 61. Calculate the mean mark.

3. The figures which follow give the population of seven villages taken after a census: 1864, 2467, 1392, 1459, 2134, 9083, 5072. Find the median population.

4. The pointer shown in Figure 22.4 is spun once. Find the probability that the pointer stops in:

(a) section G,   (b) in R or B sections.

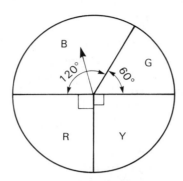

Figure 22.4

5. As part of an experiment in botany the lengths of 40 laurel leaves were measured, to the nearest millimetre, with the following results:

161 146 168 146 138 164 158 126 173 145
135 142 138 140 150 132 147 176 147 142
150 135 163 136 144 156 153 120 148 125
145 140 154 152 149 128 135 165 144 157

(a) Make a tally chart to form a grouped distribution using the classes 120–129, 130–139, 140–149, 150–159, 160–169, and 170–179.

(b) Draw a histogram for this frequency distribution.

6. The shoe sizes of nine girl pupils were: 2, 4, 4, 6, 5, 7, 4, 2, 6. What is the modal shoe size?

7. In a certain town it was calculated that the probability of a child catching measles is 0.14. What is the probability that the child will not catch measles?

8. 50 students had their height measured, to the nearest centimetre, with the following results:

Height (cm)	160	161	162	163	164	165	166
Frequency	1	5	10	16	10	6	2

(a) Calculate the mean height.
(b) What is the modal height?
(c) What is the median height?

MENTAL TEST 22

1. The tally marks show the distribution of sports preferred by a sample of school-boys.

Hockey	1111
Rugby	1̶1̶1̶1̶ 11
Soccer	1̶1̶1̶1̶ 1̶1̶1̶1̶ 11
Cricket	1̶1̶1̶1̶ 111
Tennis	1̶1̶1̶1̶

(a) How many preferred rugby?

(b) How many boys were there in the sample?

2. Find the median of 2, 4, 6, 7, 8, 9, 10.

3. Work out the mean of £14 and £16.

4. Find the mode of 3, 5, 2, 7, 8, 5, 2, 2.

5. The following numbers give the probability of an event happening: 0, 0.6, 1 and 2. One of these probabilities must be incorrect. Which one?

6. A girl's purse contains 7 five-pence coins and 3 ten-pence coins. She chooses one coin at random. What is the Probability that it will be a ten-pence coin?

7. One letter is chosen at random from the word EMERGENCY. What is the probability that it will be an E?

8. What is the modal score for the following frequency distribution?

Score	5	6	7	8	9	10
Frequency	5	3	4	6	2	1

Answers

ANSWERS TO CHAPTER 1

Exercise 1.1

1. 49	**7.** 91 000
2. 375	**8.** 35 240
3. 705	**9.** 600 000
4. 240	**10.** 735 000 000
5. 3523	**11.** 537 350 407
6. 8326	**12.** 976 000 000

13. Three hundred and seventy-four
14. Eight hundred and five
15. Four hundred and four
16. Two hundred and seventy
17. Three hundred and fifty
18. Eighty-two thousand
19. Eight hundred and sixty-two thousand
20. Eight hundred and seven thousand
21. Ninety-seven thousand six hundred and nine
22. Three hundred and four thousand and sixty-nine
23. Seven hundred and ninety thousand and sixty-eight
24. Six million eight hundred and ninety-three thousand and thirty-six
25. Eight million thirteen thousand seven hundred and nine.
26. 123, 132, 213, 231, 312, 321
27. (a) seven hundred
  (b) seven units
  (c) seven tens
  (d) seven hundred thousand
  (e) seven million

Exercise 1.2

1. 17	**6.** 20	**11.** 13
2. 25	**7.** 27	**12.** 18
3. 28	**8.** 19	**13.** 29
4. 26	**9.** 14	**14.** 13
5. 39	**10.** 23	**15.** 26

Exercise 1.3

1. 5 tens		**9.** 5 hundreds
2. 1 ten		**10.** 8 hundreds
3. 7 tens		**11.** 4 thousands
4. 9 tens		**12.** 1 thousand
5. 9 tens		**13.** 7 thousands
6. 6 hundreds		**14.** 8 thousands
7. 6 hundreds		**15.** 7 thousands
8. 1 hundred		

Exercise 1.4

1. 3515	**6.** 3 531 962
2. 5725	**7.** 6 793 597
3. 3232	**8.** 6826
4. 3982	**9.** 5388
5. 4603	**10.** 376 278

Exercise 1.5

1. 4	**6.** 4	**11.** 11 586
2. 3	**7.** 3	**12.** 330 131
3. 6	**8.** 6	**13.** 1 224 084
4. 5	**9.** 397	**14.** 17
5. 9	**10.** 4669	**15.** 11 434

Exercise 1.6

1. 21	**3.** 3	**5.** 4	**7.** 36	**9.** 15
2. 2	**4.** 6	**6.** 32	**8.** 18	**10.** 134

Exercise 1.7

1. 60	**5.** 280	**9.** 43 056
2. 42	**6.** 3922	**10.** 146 880
3. 90	**7.** 23 805	
4. 240	**8.** 19 152	

Exercise 1.8

1. 89	**5.** 326
2. 141	**6.** 31
3. 57	**7.** 2949
4. 32	

Exercise 1.9

1. 7, remainder 1	**5.** 6, remainder 4
2. 3, remainder 1	**6.** 6, remainder 5
3. 5, remainder 1	**7.** 3, remainder 2
4. 2, remainder 1	**8.** 5, remainder 3

Exercise 1.10

1. 27	**6.** 30	**11.** 2
2. 12	**7.** 14	**12.** 9
3. 15	**8.** 2	**13.** 22
4. 38	**9.** 7	**14.** 29
5. 11	**10.** 19	**15.** 1

Exercise 1.11

1. 892	**5.** 18	**9,** 0
2. 8716	**6.** 0	**10.** 0
3. 0	**7.** 19	**11.** 42
4. 7	**8.** 8	**12.** 6

Exercise 1.12

1. 897	**3.** 2	**5.** 1454	**7.** 930
2. 361	**4.** 3333	**6.** 8664	**8.** 929

Exercise 1.13

1. 375, 1875	**6.** 78, 158	**11.** 7, 11
2. 9, 11	**7.** 37, 69	**12.** 256, 1024
3. 29, 35	**8.** 162, 486	**13.** 28, 46
4. 32, 16	**9.** 12, 17 or 13, 21	**14.** 3, 4, 5
5. 15, 21	**10.** 8, 13	**15.** 10, 21, 36

Exercise 1.14

1. 13 mm
2. 867 litres
3. £1798
4. (a) 7786   (b) 879
5. 8 m
6. 16 cm
7. 7 p
8. £787 000 000
9. £24 956
10. (a) 60 °F   (b) 78 °F   (c) 90 °F

Miscellaneous Exercise 1

1. (a) 17	(b) 63	(c) 368	(d) 56
2. (a) 24	(b) 4	(c) 11	(d) 2
3. (a) 9, 12, 18	(b) 30, 22, 18	(c) 8, 4, 2	
(d) 27, 44	(e) 20, 27		
4. (a) 5 tens	(b) 9 hundreds	(c) 8 thousands	
5. 365 min			
6. 12 °C			
7. (a) 21 021 000	(b) 900 000		
8. 27 litres			
9. (a) 2	(b) 8		
10. (a) 22	(b) 16, 7, 2		

Mental Test 1

1. 21	**6.** 54	**11.** 14	**16.** 2
2. 15	**7.** 9	**12.** 2	**17.** 4
3. 7	**8.** 14	**13.** 8	**18.** 16
4. 9	**9.** 0	**14.** 6	**19.** 9
5. 80	**10.** 16	**15.** 60	**20.** 7

ANSWERS TO CHAPTER 2

Exercise 2.1

1. Odd	**22.** 1936
2. Even	**23.** 3025
3. Even	**24.** 7921
4. Odd	**25.** 15 129
5. Odd	**26.** 294 849
6. Even	**27.** 126 736
7. Even	**28.** 27
8. Odd	**29.** 343
9. 6	**30.** 4913
10. 8	**31.** 54 872
11. 13	**32.** 205 379
12. 16	**33.** 2 299 968
13. 25	**34.** 8 741 816
14. 30	**35.** 64
15. 56	**36.** 81
16. 60	**37.** 15 625
17. 1080	**38.** 4096
18. 49	**39.** 50 625
19. 64	**40.** 21 952
20. 169	**41.** 531 441
21. 729	

Exercise 2.2

1. 8 and 36	**6.** 21, 28 and 35
2. 6, 12, 30, 33 and 54	**7.** 18, 27 and 36
3. 8, 12, 24, 36 and 44	**8.** 3, 9 and 21
4. 15, 20, 30, 35 and 55	**9.** 1, 2, 3, 4, 6, 8, 9, 12
5. 20, 60, 90, 120 and 240	**10.** 1, 2, 4, 5, 10, 20

Exercise 2.3

1. 1, 2, 3, 4, 6, 9, 12, 18, 36
2. 1, 2, 4, 7, 8, 14, 28, 56
3. 1, 2, 4, 5, 10, 20, 25, 50, 100
4. 1, 2, 3, 4, 6, 7, 12, 14, 21, 28, 42, 84
5. 1, 2, 3, 4, 5, 6, 10, 12, 15, 20, 30, 60
6. 1, 3, 5, 7, 15, 21, 35, 105
7. 1, 2, 5, 7, 10, 14, 35, 70
8. 1, 2, 3, 4, 6, 8, 12, 16, 24, 32, 48, 96

Exercise 2.4

1.	6	3.	20	5.	30	7.	30	9.	30
2.	8	4.	18	6.	30	8.	48	10.	36

Miscellaneous Exercise 2

1. (a) 2, 4, 6, 8   (b) 3, 6, 9
   (c) 2, 3, 5, 7
2. (a) 55, 60   (b) 204
   (c) 9
3. (a) 61, yes   (b) 5291, no
4. (a) 13, 31   (b) 5
5. (a) 8, 16, 24, 32, 40   (b) 29, 31, 37
6. 36
7. 25
8. 28
9. 2401
10. 30
11. 1
12. 1, 2, 3, 4, 5, 6, 8, 10, 12, 15, 20, 24, 30, 40, 60, 120

Mental Test 2

1. Yes
2. No
3. 49
4. 16
5. No
6. 8
7. 42
8. Yes
9. 1, 2, 3, 4, 6, 8, 12, 24
10. 4, 8, 12, 16, 20, 24, 28, 32
11. $1 \times 2 \times 3^2$
12. 10
13. 33

ANSWERS TO CHAPTER 3

Exercise 3.1

1.	$4\frac{1}{2}$	6.	$\frac{13}{4}$	11.	$\frac{2}{5}$
2.	$3\frac{2}{3}$	7.	$\frac{13}{5}$	12.	$\frac{3}{4}$
3.	$4\frac{3}{5}$	8.	$\frac{47}{8}$	13.	$\frac{1}{3}$
4.	$2\frac{5}{7}$	9.	$\frac{67}{20}$	14.	$\frac{3}{5}$
5.	$4\frac{7}{8}$	10.	$\frac{41}{8}$	15.	$\frac{5}{6}$

Exercise 3.2

1.	$\frac{1}{3}, \frac{2}{5}, \frac{3}{7}$	9.	$1\frac{13}{120}$	17.	$\frac{7}{20}$
2.	$\frac{2}{3}, \frac{7}{10}, \frac{3}{4}$	10.	$5\frac{7}{8}$	18.	$1\frac{3}{8}$
3.	$\frac{21}{32}, \frac{11}{16}, \frac{3}{4}, \frac{7}{8}$	11.	$8\frac{4}{15}$	19.	$2\frac{5}{48}$
4.	$\frac{13}{20}, \frac{7}{10}, \frac{3}{4}, \frac{4}{5}$	12.	$8\frac{23}{56}$	20.	$1\frac{13}{16}$
5.	$\frac{13}{15}$	13.	$13\frac{1}{30}$	21.	$2\frac{7}{12}$
6.	$\frac{5}{8}$	14.	$13\frac{11}{40}$	22.	$\frac{31}{40}$
7.	$\frac{53}{72}$	15.	$\frac{5}{12}$		
8.	$1\frac{11}{12}$	16.	$\frac{7}{24}$		

Exercise 3.3

1.	$\frac{5}{14}$	8.	108	15.	$1\frac{1}{6}$
2.	$\frac{3}{20}$	9.	18	16.	$1\frac{1}{2}$
3.	$1\frac{13}{27}$	10.	72	17.	8
4.	$1\frac{3}{32}$	11.	12	18.	$\frac{1}{6}$
5.	$\frac{3}{11}$	12.	$\frac{1}{5}$	19.	$\frac{2}{3}$
6.	$\frac{10}{21}$	13.	$\frac{9}{32}$	20.	$\frac{3}{4}$
7.	$15\frac{2}{5}$	14.	$1\frac{1}{4}$		

Exercise 3.4

1.	$\frac{5}{9}$	3.	$\frac{5}{6}$	5.	$2\frac{1}{2}$	7.	$1\frac{1}{3}$
2.	$2\frac{1}{2}$	4.	$\frac{2}{3}$	6.	$\frac{2}{3}$	8.	$1\frac{1}{2}$

Exercise 3.5

1.	£150	5.	330
2.	4	6.	160 p
3.	(a) $\frac{13}{20}$ (b) $\frac{7}{20}$	7.	30 min
4.	$262\frac{1}{2}$ l	8.	£15 950

Exercise 3.6

1.	$\frac{1}{16}$	8.	$\frac{25}{36}$	15.	$\frac{1}{6}$
2.	$\frac{9}{16}$	9.	$1\frac{7}{25}$	16.	13
3.	$\frac{9}{49}$	10.	$\frac{2}{9}$	17.	12
4.	$\frac{8}{27}$	11.	$\frac{2}{3}$	18.	3
5.	$1\frac{7}{9}$	12.	$\frac{9}{10}$	19.	12
6.	$5\frac{19}{25}$	13.	$\frac{5}{7}$	20.	2
7.	$\frac{27}{64}$	14.	$\frac{5}{8}$		

Miscellaneous Exercise 3

1. (a) $\frac{3}{4}$ (b) $\frac{3}{20}$ (c) $\frac{9}{20}$ (d) $\frac{12}{13}$
2. (a) $\frac{2}{7}$ (b) $\frac{5}{22}$ (c) $\frac{5}{24}$ (d) $4\frac{1}{12}$
3. $\frac{1}{2}$
4. $3\frac{3}{8}$, $3\frac{3}{4}$, $4\frac{1}{8}$
5. 20
6. $\frac{3}{16}$
7. $\frac{17}{32}$
8. $1\frac{1}{2}$
9. £2500
10. $5\frac{1}{2}$
11. $3\frac{1}{2}$
12. £750
13. $106\frac{2}{3}$ ft
14. A receives £200, B receives £200, C receives £800
15. $2\frac{3}{10}$
16. £160
17. $\frac{1}{16}$
18. £1800

Mental Test 3

1. 6   3. $1\frac{1}{4}$ 5. No   7. $\frac{2}{3}$ 9. 2
2. $\frac{1}{6}$ 4. $\frac{7}{2}$ 6. $\frac{3}{4}$ 8. 5   10. $2\frac{1}{2}$

ANSWERS TO CHAPTER 4

Exercise 4.1

1. (a) seven hundredths   (b) seven thousandths   (c) seven tens
2. (a) five hundreds   (b) five hundredths   (c) five thousandths
3. (a) eight thousandths   (b) eight tenths   (c) eight hundreds
4. $\frac{3}{10}$
5. $3\frac{7}{10}$
6. $20\frac{8}{100}$
7. $25\frac{27}{100}$
8. $\frac{308}{1000}$
9. $60\frac{9}{1000}$
10. $\frac{4}{1000}$
11. 7992
12. (a) 5   (b) 6   (c) 8
13. (a) 0.09   (b) 0.273   (c) 0.45
14. (a) $\frac{2}{5}$ (b) $\frac{7}{20}$ (c) $\frac{7}{8}$

Exercise 4.2

1. 7.9
2. 18.09
3. 13
4. 32.038
5. 22.28
6. 683.097
7. 0.11
8. 9.332
9. 2
10. 1.8
11. 1.5
12. 0.012
13. 0.01
14. 0.000 12
15. 0.016
16. 0.9
17. 0.5
18. 2.3
19. 0.8
20. 2
21. 0.3
22. 3000
23. 70
24. 12
25. 60
26. 29.856
27. 2.146
28. 22.28
29. 672.102
30. 4072.8
31. 26.7858
32. 3.822 594
33. 1.38
34. 112.4
35. 0.001 36

Exercise 4.3

1. (a) 3.5   (b) 35   (c) 350
2. (a) 59.83   (b) 598.3   (c) 5983
3. (a) 0.38   (b) 3.8   (c) 38
4. (a) 982.345   (b) 9823.45   (c) 98 234.5
5. (a) 81.624   (b) 816.24   (c) 8162.4
6. (a) 0.46   (b) 4.6   (c) 46
7. (a) 0.0058   (b) 0.058   (c) 0.58
8. (a) 0.09   (b) 0.9   (c) 9
9. (a) 18.9   (b) 1.89   (c) 0.189
10. (a) 1.813   (b) 0.1813   (c) 0.018 13
11. (a) 52.731   (b) 5.2731   (c) 0.527 31
12. (a) 0.003   (b) 0.0003   (c) 0.000 03
13. (a) 0.0325   (b) 0.003 25   (c) 0.000 325
14. (a) 0.000 28   (b) 0.000 028   (c) 0.000 002 8
15. (a) 0.562   (b) 0.0562   (c) 0.005 62

Exercise 4.4

1. (a) 19.37   (b) 19.4
2. (a) 0.007 52   (b) 0.008   (c) 0.01
3. (a) 4.970   (b) 4.97
4. (a) 153.232   (b) 153.26   (c) 153.3
5. 33.1
6. 0.016
7. 23.53
8. 0.0025
9. (a) 24.94   (b) 25
10. (a) 0.007 33   (b) 0.0073   (c) 0.007
11. (a) 35.60   (b) 35.6
12. (a) 35 680   (b) 35 700   (c) 36 000
13. (a) 13 360 000   (b) 13 400 000   (c) 13 000 000
14. (a) 48.9   (b) 4   (c) 0.5   (d) 600   (e) 0.0073   (f) 108.07
15. 111
16. 224
17. 33
18. 47
19. 13
20. 70

Exercise 4.5

1. $20 + 40 + 430 = 490$; 487
2. $80 - 60 - 10 = 10$; 9.96
3. $20 \times 0.6 = 12$; 13
4. $40 \times 0.25 = 10$; 11
5. $0.7 \times 0.1 \times 2 = 0.14$; 0.16
6. $90 \div 30 = 3$; 2.931
7. $0.09 \div 0.03 = 9 \div 3 = 3$; 2.6
8. $(30 \times 30) \div 0.05 = 18\,000$; 14\,900
9. $(1.5 \times 0.01) \div 0.5 = 0.3$; 0.342
10. $(30 \times 30) \div (10 \times 3) = 30$; 29.2

Exercise 4.6

1. (a) 0.25   (b) 0.875
   (c) 2.593 75   (d) 3.234 375
2. (a) (i) 0.555 56   (ii) 0.555 556
   (b) (i) 0.171 72   (ii) 0.171 717
   (c) (i) 0.353 54   (ii) 0.353 535
   (d) (i) 0.212 12   (ii) 0.212 121
   (e) (i) 0.428 43   (ii) 0.428 428
   (f) (i) 0.563 64   (ii) 0.563 636
   (g) (i) 0.567 17   (ii) 0.567 167
   (h) (i) 0.032 32   (ii) 0.032 323 2
3. (a) $0.\dot{2}$ (b) $0.\dot{4}\dot{5}$ (c) $0.4\dot{6}$ (d) $0.4\dot{0}\dot{9}$
4. (a) $\frac{3}{10}$ (b) $\frac{13}{20}$ (c) $\frac{3}{8}$ (d) $\frac{7}{16}$
   (e) $1\frac{3}{4}$ (f) $7\frac{9}{25}$
5. 0.0175
6. 1.252
7. 4.5945
8. 0.276 875

Exercise 4.7

1. 0.1221
2. 0.1082
3. 0.011 21
4. 0.000 139 8
5. 6.506
6. 25.34
7. 641.0
8. 0.000 061 30
9. 5.977
10. 0.004 283
11. 53.12
12. 0.053 39
13. 55.62
14. 0.223 0
15. 2.384

Exercise 4.8

1. 4.676 tons
2. 18.3 litres
3. 12.75 km
4. 2350
5. £39.38
6. 980.9 kg
7. 288.84 min
8. 3400
9. 2916
10. 184 min

Miscellaneous Exercise 4

1. (a) 3.317   (b) 3.32
2. (a) $\frac{22}{25}$ (b) $\frac{13}{500}$
3. (a) 0.1778   (b) 0.215 22
4. (a) $\frac{5}{6}$ (b) 0.833

5. 9
6. 0.02
7. 57.425
8. 512
9. (a) $\frac{1}{3}$ (b) 0.333
10. 9.291

Mental Test 4

1. 4
2. 0.25
3. 0.5
4. 10.5
5. 0.06
6. $\frac{3}{5}$
7. 0.53
8. 0.6
9. 9.3
10. 457
11. 0.4738
12. 5.69
13. 38.7
14. 27.50
15. 49.8

ANSWERS TO CHAPTER 5

Exercise 5.1

1. (a) 30 mm   (b) 280 mm   (c) 1340 mm
   (d) 5000 mm   (e) 63 000 mm   (f) 4600 mm
2. (a) 6 cm   (b) 24 cm   (c) 72 cm
   (d) 400 cm   (e) 5600 cm   (f) 374 cm
3. (a) 5 m   (b) 7 m   (c) 8.9 m
   (d) 5.643 m   (e) 5000 m   (f) 6420 m
4. (a) 7 km   (b) 6.34 km   (c) 8.325 km

Exercise 5.2

1. (a) 2 ft   (b) 5 ft   (c) 12 ft
   (d) 15 ft   (e) 240 ft
2. (a) 2 yd   (b) 24 yd   (c) 300 yd
   (d) 3520 yd   (e) 49 280 yd
3. (a) 60 in   (b) 240 in   (c) 408 in
   (d) 108 in   (e) 540 in
4. (a) 3 miles   (b) 9 miles   (c) 20 miles

Exercise 5.3

1. (a) 8000 g   (b) 19 000 g   (c) 15 000 g
   (d) 12 g   (e) 27 g
2. (a) 5 kg   (b) 18 kg   (c) 3000 kg
   (d) 18 000 kg
3. (a) 7000 mg   (b) 24 000 mg   (c) 500 mg
4. (a) 8 t   (b) 427 t   (c) 0.6 t

Exercise 5.4

1. (a) 4 oz   (b) 8 oz   (c) 72 oz
   (d) 80 oz   (e) 128 oz
2. (a) 0.75 lb   (b) 3 lb   (c) 0.5 lb
   (d) 6 lb   (e) 560 lb   (f) 6720 lb
3. (a) 100 cwt   (b) 160 cwt   (c) 5 cwt
4. (a) 3 ton   (b) 3 ton   (c) 7.63 ton

Exercise 5.5

1. **(a)** 7 cl   **(b)** 56 cl   **(c)** 600 cl
2. **(a)** 50 ml   **(b)** 260 ml   **(c)** 8000 ml
3. **(a)** 6 l   **(b)** 0.5 l   **(c)** 3 l
4. **(a)** 60 fl oz   **(b)** 10 fl oz   **(c)** 320 fl oz
5. **(a)** 2 pt   **(b)** 6 pt   **(c)** 48 pt
6. **(a)** 2 gal   **(b)** 8 gal

Exercise 5.6

1. 144 lb
2. 150 cm
3. 3 ft
4. 200 yd
5. 8 kg
6. 112 km/h
7. 150 ml
8. 12 l
9. 21 pt
10. 6 gal

Exercise 5.7

1. 6.7 m
2. 19 cm
3. 23 m
4. 150
5. 1.85 l
6. 12.065 m
7. 282.15 m
8. 468 full jars
9. 7
10. 1500

Miscellaneous Exercise 5

1. **(a)** 4000 m   **(b)** 3056 m
   (c) 8.93 m   **(d)** 28.4 m
2. 400
3. 20
4. $\frac{11}{40}$
5. 90 mg, 0.9 g, 90 g, 0.9 kg
6. 7864.5 g
7. 900 g
8. 120 miles

Mental Test 5

1. 400 cm
2. 7000 mm
3. 8 km
4. 7300 m
5. 2 cm
6. 90 mm
7. 4 ft
8. 5280 ft
9. 2 yd
10. 8 kg
11. 6000 g
12. 7 g
13. 6500 mg
14. 48 oz
15. 224 lb
16. 2 pt
17. 400 cl
18. 3000 ml
19. 8 l
20. 50 ml
21. 10 m
22. 100 mm
23. 2.6 m
24. 200
25. 2 fl oz

ANSWERS TO CHAPTER 6

Exercise 6.1

1. £21.22
2. £9.80
3. £4.33
4. £4.78
5. £1.18
6. £190.89
7. £128.76
8. £3.46
9. £2.70
10. £219.48
11. £12.80
12. 31 p
13. 92 p
14. 50 p, 20 p, 5 p, 2 p
15. £3.51

Exercise 6.2

1.

	Postage	Office tea	Stationery	Cleaner's pay	Sundries	Totals
Week 1	£44.50	£6.32	£9.60	£30.00	£4.05	£94.47
Week 2	£39.25	£5.02	£12.48	£30.00	£2.34	£89.09
Week 3	£46.80	£9.96	£11.34	£30.00	£1.68	£99.78
Week 4	£43.15	£4.26	£15.18	£30.00	£3.75	£96.34
TOTALS	£173.70	£25.56	£48.60	£120.00	£11.82	£379.68

2.

	Man A	Man B	Man C	Man D	Man E	Totals
Week 1	£45.76	£39.88	£51.63	£87.62	£49.88	£274.77
Week 2	£42.89	£43.67	£54.68	£78.90	£51.27	£271.41
Week 3	£52.78	£64.68	£53.22	£80.81	£48.69	£300.18
Week 4	£77.83	£49.73	£50.00	£71.42	£36.25	£285.23
Totals	£219.26	£197.96	£209.53	£318.75	£186.09	£1131.59

3.

	Week 1	Week 2	Week 3	Week 4	Week 5	Totals
April	—	£47.49	£42.80	£39.81	—	£130.10
May	£40.37	£41.63	£40.85	£42.70	—	£165.55
June	£37.93	£38.93	£43.37	£37.89	—	£158.12
July	£41.65	£41.20	£41.35	£43.37	£38.80	£206.37
August	£37.71	£62.35	£40.89	£37.73	—	£178.68
Sept.	£39.90	£44.30	£40.05	£37.92	—	£162.17
Totals	£197.56	£275.90	£249.31	£239.42	£38.80	£1000.99

Exercise 6.3

1.

Date	Particulars	Receipts	Date	Particulars	Payments
1/9	Annual subs 32 members @ £9.50	£304.00	10/9	Cost of teas for game v Old Manorians	£18.70
10/9	Match fees v Old Manorians	£16.50	10/9	Umpires expenses	£3.50
17/9	Match fees v Moorpark	£14.30	17/9	Cost of teas	£19.80
			17/9	Umpires expenses	£3.00
					£45.00
				Balance carried down	£289.80
	Total	£334.80			£334.80

2.

Date	Particulars	Receipts	Date	Particulars	Payments
5/7	Payments @ 2.95 from from 70 members	£206.50	9/7	Hire of 2 coaches and drivers	£172.50
7/7	Subsidy from General Committee	£75.00	9/7	Cost of 72 teas @ 1.20 each	£86.40
					£258.90
				Balance carried down	£22.60
	Total	£281.50			£281.50

3.

Date	Particulars	Receipts	Date	Particulars	Payments
3/6	Subsidy from directors	£100.00	8/6	Hire of tents	£58.00
5/6	Entry fee from competitors	£62.00	8/6	Competitors prizes	£146.00
8/6	Sale of raffle tickets	£54.60	8/6	Raffle tickets & prizes	£17.20
		£216.60			
	Balance carried down	£4.60			
	Total	£221.20			£221.20

4.

Dr		£		Cash a/c	Cr £
Jan 1	To balance b/d	39.47	Jan 5	By telephone	37.89
Jan 8	To P. Smith	62.00	Jan 12	By purchases	53.25
Jan 29	To sales	108.75	Jan 31	By bank	105.00
					196.14
				By balance c/d	14.08
		210.22			210.22

5.

Dr		£		Cash a/c	Cr £
March 3	To balance b/d	97.57	March 9	By purchases	73.78
March 16	To sales	128.97			
March 18	To T. Barnes	54.00			
			March 28	By bank	175.00
			March 30	By stamps	3.40
				By balance c/d	28.36
		280.54			280.54

Exercise 6.4

1.

Receipts	Date	Particulars	Payments	Postage	Stationery	Travelling expenses	Cleaning	Office expenses
72.00	3 Feb	Balance in hand						
	4 Feb	Postage	5.64	5.64				
	4 Feb	Xerox copying	3.84					3.84
	5 Feb	Pencils	2.88		2.88			
	5 Feb	Train fare	4.68			4.68		
	5 Feb	Office teas	4.08					4.08
	6 Feb	Window cleaning	8.00				8.00	
	6 Feb	Notepaper	4.80		4.80			
	7 Feb	Parcel postage	5.02	5.02				
	7 Feb	Typewriter ribbons	4.50		4.50			
	8 Feb	Office teas	4.50					4.50
	8 Feb	Cleaner's wages	21.00				21.00	
		Totals	68.94	10.66	12.18	4.68	29.00	12.42
68.94	10 Feb	Reimbursement						

227

2.

Receipts	Date	Particulars	Payments	Postage	Stationery	Travelling expenses
96.00	5 June	Balance in hand				
	6 June	Postage stamps	12.00	12.00		
	6 June	Envelopes	3.78		3.78	
	6 June	Bus fares	1.68			1.68
	7 June	Notepaper	2.70		2.70	
	7 June	Parcel post	5.88	5.88		
	8 June	Erasers	2.10		2.10	
	8 June	Railway fares	2.76			2.76
	8 June	Ball pens	2.70		2.70	
	9 June	Envelopes	3.24		3.24	
	9 June	Carbon paper	3.05		3.05	
		Totals	39.89	17.88	17.57	4.44
39.89	13 June	Reimbursement				

3.

Receipts	Date	Particulars	Payments
28.00	8 Jan	Cash in hand	
	9 Jan	Postage	0.57
	10 Jan	Parcel post	2.10
	11 Jan	Window cleaner	5.00
	12 Jan	Stationery	2.99
	14 Jan	Cleaner's wages	12.00
		Total	22.66
22.66	15 Jan	Reimbursement	
		Balance carried down	28.00
50.66			50.66

4.

DETAILS	PAYMENTS	RECEIPTS	DATE	BALANCE
BALANCE FORWARD			8 Aug	1702.31
	79.42		9 Aug	1622.89
	900.26		10 Aug	722.63
	1233.34		17 Aug	510.71 DR
		800.00	25 Aug	289.29

Miscellaneous Exercise 6

1. (a) 15.9 (b) £13.53 (c) £0.88 **2.** £4.97 **3.** £69.45 **4.** 10.5 p **5.** (a) £90.10 (b) £21.37
6.

DETAILS	PAYMENTS	RECEIPTS	DATE	BALANCE
BALANCE FORWARD			9 Apr	3782.95
		88.07	10 Apr	3871.02
	34.87		12 Apr	3836.15
	3000.00		14 Apr	836.15
	77.19		20 Apr	758.96
		200.00	27 Apr	958.96

7.

Receipts	Date	Particulars	Payments
50.00	4 Aug	Cash in hand	
	6 Aug	Postage stamps	5.40
	8 Aug	Stationery	12.30
	8 Aug	Parcel post	3.69
	11 Aug	Window cleaner	5.00
	11 Aug	Travelling expenses	3.69
	15 Aug	Office cleaner	12.00
	15 Aug	Ballpoint pens	2.40
		Total	44.48
44.48		Reimbursement	
		Balance carried down	50.00
94.48			94.48

Mental Test 6

1. £3.95
2. £1.13
3. £13.50
4. 50 p
5. 12 p
6. 20 p
7. £6.00
8. £4.95
9. £95.00
10. £3.98

ANSWERS TO CHAPTER 7

Exercise 7.1

1. (a) 120 kg, 200 kg　(b) 360 kg
2. (a) £6 000　(b) £15 000　(c) £24 000
3. (a) 15 kg　(b) 20 kg
4. 1:4
5. 1:3
6. 6:7
7. 5:6
8. 8:7
9. 4:6:9
10. 4:5:6:7

Exercise 7.2

1. $\frac{9}{7}$　　3. $\frac{2}{1}$　　5. $\frac{2}{3}$　　7. $\frac{1}{3}$　　9. $\frac{7}{8}$
2. $\frac{1}{2}$　　4. $\frac{4}{5}$　　6. $\frac{4}{5}$　　8. $\frac{5}{6}$　　10. $\frac{5}{9}$

Exercise 7.3

1. 9:4
2. 4:3
3. 4:3
4. 2:5
5. 9:1
6. 7:3
7. 1:2
8. 11:6
9. 16:39
10. 48:103
11. 4:1
12. 1:2
13. 3:100
14. 3:1
15. 20:1
16. 1:10
17. 4:1
18. 10:3
19. 32:1
20. 100:3

Exercise 7.4

1. £500:£300
2. 112 kg, 48 kg
3. 24 m, 36 m, 60 m
4. 33.6 cm, 117.6 cm, 16.8 cm
5. £2 800
6. 15 kg, 22.5 kg, 37.5 kg
7. £88
8. £10.80

Exercise 7.5

1. £8.48
2. 36 litres
3. 7 hours
4. 200 grams each of butter, caster sugar and flour, 4 eggs and 160 grams of chocolate chips
5. 120
6. 16 days
7. $13\frac{1}{2}$ days
8. 6
9. $10\frac{1}{2}$ mins
10. 24
11. 80
12. 10 hours

Exercise 7.6

1. 50 grams for £1.00
2. 850 grams for £2.04
3. 250 grams for 38 p
4. 750 grams for £1.12
5. 200 millilitres for £2.50

Exercise 7.7

1. 10 min
2. 6 gallons
3. (a) 2 m/s　(b) 90 s
4. 8100 kg
5. (a) 60 lb　(b) 4 sq ft

Exercise 7.8

1. 48.60
2. 5325
3. $87.84
4. 6432.05
5. 137 700
6. £38.20
7. $92.05

Miscellaneous Exercise 7

1. 1008 km
2. 4.5 km
3. 7:8
4. (a) £50　(b) 9600 pts　(c) £752.08

5. £3.84
6. (a) 10.5 p   (b) £32.55
7. £170
8. 32 p
9. 100 g for 35 p
10. 27.3 m
11. 1261.11 lire
12. £110.08
13. £14 400, £8400
14. 3 hours
15. 18 litres

Mental Test 7

1. 5 kg
2. 3:4
3. $\frac{4}{5}$
4. 6:1
5. £70, £30
6. 50 p
7. 4 days
8. 50
9. £6.00
10. 12 kg, 8 kg
11. 3 gallons
12. 4 hours

ANSWERS TO CHAPTER 8

Exercise 8.1

	Fraction	Decimal	Percentage
1.	$\frac{1}{4}$	0.25	25%
2.	$\frac{11}{20}$	0.55	55%
3.	$\frac{7}{8}$	0.875	87.5%
4.	$\frac{2}{3}$	0.\dot{6}	$66\frac{2}{3}\%$ = 66.\dot{6}%
5.	$\frac{2}{25}$	0.08	8%
6.	$\frac{24}{125}$	0.192	19.2%
7.	$\frac{3}{20}$	0.15	15%
8.	$\frac{27}{100}$	0.27	27%
9.	$\frac{5}{8}$	0.625	62.5%
10.	$\frac{33}{400}$	0.0825	$8\frac{1}{4}\%$ = 8.25%
11.	$\frac{79}{800}$	0.09875	$9\frac{7}{8}\%$ = 9.875%
12.	$\frac{1}{15}$	0.06\dot{6}	$6\frac{2}{3}\%$ = 6.\dot{6}%

Exercise 8.2

1. (a) 10   (b) 24   (c) 6
   (d) 2.4   (e) 21.315   (f) 2.516
   (g) 4   (h) 3
2. (a) 12.5%   (b) 20%   (c) 16%
   (d) 16.292%   (e) 45.455%
3. (a) 60%   (b) 27
4. 115 cm
5. 88.67 cm
6. (a) £7.20   (b) £13.20   (c) £187.50
7. 584 kg
8. 39 643

Exercise 8.3

1. £800
2. £20
3. £1000
4. 800
5. £1600
6. 6000
7. £8 000

Miscellaneous Exercise 8

1. £13
2. 90%
3. £65.25
4. £144
5. 1100
6. 28%
7. (a) £120   (b) £110.40
8. (a) 55%   (b) 54
9. (a) 12   (b) 60%
10. (a) 7500 kg   (b) 6000 kg

Mental Test 8

1. 80%
2. 70%
3. 0.3
4. 24
5. £3.20
6. 18%
7. 0.37
8. 60 cm
9. 18 mm
10. $\frac{3}{5}$

ANSWERS TO CHAPTER 9

Exercise 9.1

1.		Basic week	Basic rate	Weekly wage
	(a)	35	£3	£105
	(b)	40	£5	£200
	(c)	36	£4	£144
	(d)	32	£6	£192
	(e)	40	£5	£200
	(f)	38	£4.50	£171

2. (a) £6.25   (b) £7.50   (c) £10
3. (a) £3   (b) £3.75   (c) £18.75
   (d) £138.75
4. (a) £10.72 per hour   (b) £117.92   (c) £305.52

Exercise 9.2

1. £13.50
2. (a) £17.40   (b) £24.80   (c) £36.30
3. £43.50
4. £18.50

Exercise 9.3

1. (a) £10.00   (b) £25.00
   (c) £40.00   (d) £15.00
2. £422
3. (a) £105   (b) £155
4. £230
5. £123.00

Exercise 9.4

1. £500   3. £782   5. £2274
2. £700   4. £989

Exercise 9.5

1. (a) £630, £882, £1327.50   (b) £350, £490, £737.50
2. (a) £4395   (b) £1274.55
3. (a) £4815   (b) £7185   (c) £1796.25
4. (a) £7100   (b) £5900   (c) £1475

Miscellaneous Exercise 9

1. (a) £6000   (b) £1620
2. (a) £3.00   (b) £4.50   (c) £147.00
3. £1400
4. £23.20
5. (a) £3150   (b) £5850   (c) £487.50
6. £8244
7. (a) £133   (b) £5.12   (c) £110.58
8. £231.25

Mental Test 9

1. £6   3. £3   5. £20   7. £540
2. £170   4. £20   6. £75   8. £100

ANSWERS TO CHAPTER 10

Exercise 10.1

1. £60
2. 15 p
3. 25%
4. (a) 20%   (b) 16.7%
5. (a) 20%   (b) 25%
6. 12.5%
7. 16.7%
8. (a) £20   (b) $33\frac{1}{3}$%

Exercise 10.2

1. 20%   6. £32
2. 25%   7. £70
3. £9.00   8. £11.85
4. £351   9. £675
5. £11.25   10. £4154

Exercise 10.3

1. £600
2. (a) £187.50   (b) £562.50   (c) $33\frac{1}{3}$%
3. 28.6%
4. 25%
5. £6750
6. (a) 53.8%   (b) £18 550
7. 23.08%
8. 20%

Exercise 10.4

1. (a) £15 000   (b) £8000
   (c) 39.5%   (d) 21.1%
2. (a) £1250   (b) £850
   (c) 17%
3. (a) £104 800   (b) 16.03%
4. (a) £280   (b) 20%
   (c) 31.82%
5. (a) £40 000   (b) £12 760
   (c) £27 240   (d) 24.76%
   (e) 38.91%

Exercise 10.5

1. £25.20   3. £390.00   5. £83.70
2. £57.00   4. £23.75

Exercise 10.6

1.

50 pairs of double sheets at £16.00 per pair	£800
30 pairs of single sheets at £12.00 per pair	£360
80 pillowcases at £5 each	£400
20 duvets at £35 each	£700
	£2260
Less 25% discount	£565
	£1695

2. £414.00   6. £60
3. £93.91   7. £10.44
4. £368.00   8. £400.00
5. £69

Exercise 10.7

1. £504
2. £240
3. £1.20 in the £1
4. 31.25 p in the £1
5. £2 322 000
6. 9.1 p in the £1
7. £850 000
8. (a) £87 960   (b) 55 p in the £1
9. £117 300
10. 5.8 p

Exercise 10.8

1. (a) £64   (b) £5.33
2. £66
3. £2320
4. (a) 500   (b) £875
5. (a) £237.50   (b) £582.50   (c) 5.8 p
6. (a) £1971   (b) £8029
7. £21.33

Miscellaneous Exercise 10

1. £126
2. £9
3. £1380
4. £85.50
5. 20%
6. £480
7. (a) £1760   (b) 22 p
8. 12.5%

Mental Test 10

1. 8 p
2. £45
3. £1000
4. 10%
5. £450
6. 10%
7. £75
8. £200

ANSWERS TO CHAPTER 11

Exercise 11.1

1. (a) (i) £139.40   (ii) £10.40
   (b) (i) £245   (ii) £46
   (c) (i) £177.46   (ii) £17.46
2. (a) (i) £330.24   (ii) £1042.56   (iii) £1199.52
   (b) £599.76; £99.76
3. (a) £60   (b) £240
   (c) £287.28   (d) £23.94
4. (a) £520   (b) £120
5. (a) £187.50   (b) £562.50
   (c) £675   (d) £168.75
6. £60

7. (a) £120   (b) £13.20
   (c) £133.20   (d) £13.32
8. (a) £128   (b) £512   (c) £38.40
   (d) £550.40 (e) £137.60
9. (a) £24   (b) £264   (c) £66
   (d) £150   (e) 16%
10. £60; $26\frac{2}{3}\%$

Exercise 11.2

1. (a) £19   (b) £23.50   (c) £35.50
2. £50.07
3. (a) £310.08   (b) £55.32
4. (a) £156.66   (b) £443.95   (c) £254.63
5. £361.35
6. £225.31

Exercise 11.3

1. (a) £1563   (b) £123
   (c) £140.50   (d) £146.12

2.

Charge per therm (p)	Number of therms used	Cost of gas used in pence	in pounds
38	110	4180	41.8
43	215	9245	92.45
36.2	87	3149	31.49
39.8	108	4298	42.98

3. £470
4. (a) 445   (b) 461   (c) £194.46
5. (a)

(b)

(c)

6. (a) 2508   (b) 2712   (c) 2000

7.

Charge per unit (p)	Number of units used	Cost of electricity in pence	in pounds
4.65	200	930	9.30
5.20	120	624	6.24
4.93	206	1016	10.16
5.91	569	3363	33.63

8. £125.53
9. £8.57
10. (a)

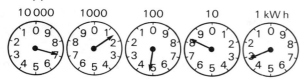

(b)

(c)

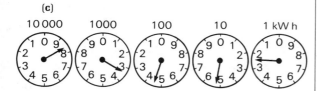

11. (a) 23 968   (b) 85 037   (c) 46 036
12. (a) 50.4   (b) £2.58
13. 1200

Exercise 11.4

1. £18.75
2. £40.46
3. £10
4. (a) £872.40   (b) £133.20
5. (a) £442   (b) £66.30
     (c) £508.30
6. (a) £19.60   (b) £21.11
7. (a) £32.43   (b) £48.83
     (c) £7.32   (d) £56.15
8. (a) 21   (b) 92 p
9. (a) (i) 67 p   (ii) 52 p
     (b) (i) £1.20   (ii) 90 p
     (c) £5.50
10. (a) £3.30   (b) £3.60
11. (a) 73 p   (b) 90 p   (c) 73 p

Miscellaneous Exercise 11

1. £157.67
2. £50.17
3. (a) £298.08   (b) £412.68   (c) £34.39
4. (a) £92.84   (b) 21
5. £168.20
6. (a) 72.5 p in the £1   (b) £226.20   (c) £33 800
7. £946
8. (a)

	Reading		Units used	Pence per unit	Cost
	This time	Last time			
	72864	68992 (E)	3872	2.34	£90.60
	53572	52932 (S)	640	5.61	£35.90

(b) £136.64

ANSWERS TO CHAPTER 12

Exercise 12.1

1. (a) 300   (b) 270
     (c) 12
2. (a) 180   (b) 330
     (c) 3600   (d) 11 700
3. (a) 5   (b) $2\frac{1}{2}$
     (c) $3\frac{1}{4}$
4. (a) £455   (b) £105
5. £8
6. £2.80
7. cartoons: 42 min, plays: 105 min, music and dancing: 63 min
8. (a) Yes   (b) No
     (c) Yes   (d) Yes
     (e) Yes   (f) No
9. 95
10. £89.66

Exercise 12.2

1. 4 h 6 min   **5.** 15 h 6 min
2. 5 h 16 min   **6.** 1210 hours
3. 17 h 51 min   **7.** 12.24 p.m.
4. 9 h 48 min   **8.** 8.50 a.m.

Exercise 12.3

1. 1030, 28 min   **6.** 1107
2. 58 min   **7.** 50 min
3. 32 min   **8.** 1013
4. 1100   **9.** 1222
5. 25 min   **10.** 2 h 21 min

Exercise 12.4

	Distance	Time	Average speed
1.	10 miles	2 h	5 mile/h
2.	40 km	5 h	8 km/h
3.	90 m	6 s	15 m/s
4.	200 ft	4 s	50 ft/s
5.	150 miles	$2\frac{1}{2}$ h	60 mile/h

	Average speed	Time	Distance travelled
6.	30 km/h	4 h	120 km
7.	50 mile/h	8 h	400 mile
8.	35 m/s	3 s	105 m
9.	25 m/s	4 s	100 m
10.	60 km/h	$3\frac{1}{2}$ h	210 km

	Distance travelled	Average speed	Time taken
11.	40 km	20 km/h	2 h
12.	80 miles	40 mile/h	2 h
13.	60 ft	30 ft/s	2 s
14.	120 m	40 m/s	3 s
15.	10 miles	4 mile/h	2.5 h

16. 48.8 mile/h
17. (a) 11.45 a.m.   (b) 40.8 mile/h
18. 50 km/h
19. 5 min
20. 335 miles
21. (a) 150 miles   (b) 270 miles
    (c) 5 h   (d) 54 mile/h
22. (a) 4 h   (b) 64 km/h
23. (a) 260 miles   (b) 5 h
    (c) 52 mile/h

Miscellaneous Exercise 12

1. (a) 2015   (b) 40 mile/h
2. (a) 1605   (b) 500 mile/h
3. (a) 4 h 15 min   (b) 36 mile/h
4. (a) 20 min   (b) 2 h   (c) 51.43 km/h
5. (a) 8 m/s   (b) 28.8 km/h
6. 60 km/h
7. (a) 180 miles   (b) 36 min

Mental Test 12

1. 3
2. 300
3. 4
4. 300
5. 10
6. 2 h 15 min
7. 3 h 30 min
8. 3 h 8 min
9. 70 km/h
10. 50 mile/h
11. 120 miles
12. 2 h
13. 800 miles
14. 60 mile/h
15. 5 h

ANSWERS TO CHAPTER 13

Exercise 13.1

1. $5a$
2. $6m + 7$
3. $3x - 4$
4. $4m + 3n$
5. abc
6. $\dfrac{2m}{n}$
7. $7p - 8q$
8. $\dfrac{mn}{3p}$

Exercise 13.2

1. 9
2. 3
3. 3
4. 18
5. 45
6. 6
7. 45
8. 30
9. 23
10. 26
11. 33
12. 33
13. 28
14. 1
15. $\frac{3}{4}$
16. 5
17. 5
18. 8

Exercise 13.3

1. b^2
2. c^3
3. n^4
4. p^6
5. q^5
6. 4
7. 81
8. 54
9. 32
10. 1152
11. 74
12. 20
13. 3024
14. 3
15. 16

Exercise 13.4

1. 32
2. 360
3. 80
4. 21
5. 17
6. 18.852
7. 252
8. 1200
9. 1875
10. 6

Exercise 13.5

1. 8.27×10^2
2. 2.937×10^3
3. 4.7734×10^4
4. $9.832\,67 \times 10^5$
5. 7.089×10^6
6. 3400
7. 800
8. 3 780 000
9. 23 500
10. 267 800

Exercise 13.6

1. 3.2×10^3 by 2.52×10^3
2. 8.7×10^4 by 7.77×10^4
3. 8.79×10^4 by 8.6902×10^4
4. 3.1×10^4 by 2.46×10^4
5. 9.73×10^3 by 7.47×10^3
6. 7.469×10^3
7. 1.931×10^3
8. 1.026×10^2
9. 4×10^1
10. 3.958×10^3
11. 8.5853×10^4
12. 7.237×10^3

Miscellaneous Exercise 13

1. 100 min
2. 165 °C
3. 33
4. 54
5. 30
6. 108
7. £13
8. 1.25×10^6
9. 8.62×10^3
10. 700

ANSWERS TO CHAPTER 14

Exercise 14.1

1. £25
2. £160
3. £400
4. £960
5. £3000
6. £150
7. £15
8. £3000
9. £3920
10. £22.50

Exercise 14.2

1. £367.33
2. £7312.16
3. £3766.11
4. £2294.08
5. £668.56
6. £6963.32
7. £11 958
8. £44 050
9. £7755
10. £205.45
11. £5866
12. £54 140

Exercise 14.3

1. £7594
2. £3617
3. £4608
4. £11 093
5. £7087

Miscellaneous Exercise 14

1. £275
2. £14 494.59
3. £31 000
4. £8977
5. (a) £412.50 (b) £550 − £148.50 = £401.50

ANSWERS TO CHAPTER 15

Exercise 15.1

1. £32.50
2. (a) £155 (b) £38.75
3. £8817.98
4. £2120
5. (a) £960 (b) £720
6. Value after 1 year = £21.30
   Value after 2 years = £22.90
   Value after 3 years = £25.02
   Value after 4 years = £27.72
   Value after 5 years = £30.77

7. (a) £2551 (b) £229.59
8. (a) £6667 (b) £533.36
9. (a) £2700 (b) £140
   (c) 5.19%
10. (a) £525 (b) £27
    (c) 3.6% (d) 5.14%
11. (a) £291 (b) £273
12. (a) £6375 (b) £320
    (c) 125
13. (a) £60.50 (b) £36.30
14. £36.73
15. £62.10

ANSWERS TO CHAPTER 16

Exercise 16.1

1. (a) £4.07 (b) £70.56 (c) £3.85
   (d) £81.15 (e) £24.40 (f) £43.44
2. (a) 28.3 °C (b) 45.9 °C (c) 131 °F
   (d) 155.7 °F
3. (a) 488 miles (b) 130 miles (c) 63 miles
4. (a) 14.2% (b) 1:14
5. (a) 1.8 kg (b) 258 kg (c) 8.4 lb
   (d) 0.5 lb
6. (a) 24.13 km (b) 30 mile/h (c) 93.33 km
   (d) 913.1 km/h
7. (a) 38 °C (b) 176 °F (c) 18 °C
   (d) 118 °F
8. (a) 1.54 kg/cm^2 (b) 30 lb/in^2

Exercise 16.2

2. (a) 40 (b) 11
5. household goods: 90°; clothing: 81°; furniture: 108°; stationery: 27°; sports equipment: 54°

Mental Test 16

1. (a) 115 miles (b) 272 miles (c) 326 miles
2. (a) 122 °F (b) 68 °F (c) 10 °C
3. (a) 2 (b) 17
4. (a) 25% (b) $\frac{1}{3}$
5. (a) 36° (b) 90°
6. (a) 1978 (b) 50 000 (c) 35 000
7. 72°

ANSWERS TO CHAPTER 17

Exercise 17.1

1. A(1, 1), B(2, 3), C(3, 4), D(4, 5), E(5, 2), F(5, 1)
2. R(2, 25), S(4, 10), T(8, 20), U(6, 5), V(10, 15)

Exercise 17.2

1. (a) 8, 14, 22   (b) 3.5, 5.5, 11.5
2. (a) 10 m, 18 m, 40 m   (b) 4 s, 6 s, 7 s
3. (a) 5 years   (b) 122 cm
4. (a) £18   (b) 500
5. (b) (i) 38 mile/gal   (ii) 17 mile/h, 77 mile/h
   (iii) 50 mile/h
6. (a) 0.7   (b) 4.8
7. 3.1 min

Exercise 17.3

1. (a) 80 marks   (b) £35
2. (a) £10   (b) 40 p per therm
   (c) £110   (d) 200 therms
3. (a) £12.50   (b) 100 units
   (c) £10
4. (c) (i) 200 mm   (ii) 16 in
5. (b) (i) 64 °F   (ii) 27 °C
6. (c) (i) £39   (ii) 400 units
7. (c) (i) $12.6   (ii) £11.10

Miscellaneous Exercise 17

1. $v = 9.7$ m/s; $t = 6.7$ s
2. (a) D3   (b) E9   (c) A8
3. 100 francs
4. (a) W(1, 2)   (b) T(4, 1)
5. 19.3 amp
6. AB = 2 units; AC = 2 units
7. 22.45 ohms

ANSWERS TO CHAPTER 18

Exercise 18.1

1. 240°   6. 71.9°
2. 225°   7. 122.5°
3. 108°   8. 135.7°
4. 252°   9. 45.3°
5. 126°   10. 10.4°

Exercise 18.2

1. A acute   B reflex   C acute   D obtuse
   E reflex   F acute   G right angle
2. (a) 60°   (b) 72°   (c) 45°
3. (a) equilateral: G, I
   (b) acute-angled: B, H
   (c) right-angled: A, C, E
   (d) isosceles: F, K
   (e) obtuse-angled: D, J, L
4. A. 43°   B. 112°   C. 125°   D. 320°   E. 78°

5.

Acute	Obtuse	Reflex
31°	156°	186°
63°	163°	217°
62°	116°	235°
81°	143°	279°
16°	168°	315°
20°	120°	340°
16°	96°	225°

Exercise 18.3

1. ∠C = 80°   5. ∠C = 67°
   AC = 4.1 cm   ∠A = 43°
   CB = 7.5 cm   AC = 8.2 cm
2. ∠C = 40°   6. BC = 4.4 in
   AC = 13.8 cm   ∠B = 23°
   BC = 9.0 cm   ∠C = 37°
3. ∠A = 56°   7. ∠A = 65°
   ∠B = 78°   AB = 6.4 cm
   ∠C = 46°   AC = 5.7 cm
4. AB = 5.6 cm   8. A = 86°
   ∠A = 51°   B = 36°
   ∠B = 69°   C = 58°

Exercise 18.4

1. (a) CB   (b) QR   (c) XY
   (d) CE   (e) LN
2. (a) 13   (b) 9.7   (c) 11.49
   (d) 13.23   (e) 9.82
3. (a) 7.42   (b) 9.17   (c) 6.32
   (d) 10.51
4. (a) 7.62   (b) 9.85   (c) 11.88
   (d) 13.20
5. (a) 5.20   (b) 10.39   (c) 12.99
6. 6.93 ft

Exercise 18.5

1. 13.42 cm   4. CD = 15 cm   AD = 8.54 cm
2. 6.24 ft   5. 6.36 in
3. 8.49 in   6. 6.71 ft

Miscellaneous Exercise 18

1. (a) 270°   (b) 162°   (c) 180°
2. (a) 48.14°   (b) 58.3°
3. (a) 55°   (b) 135°   (c) 310°
4. ∠A = 75°
   ∠B = 58°
   ∠C = 47°
5. 150°
6. 215 yd
7. 12.49 cm
8. 11.31 cm

Mental Test 18

1.	60°	**6.**	37°
2.	108°	**7.**	10 in
3.	obtuse	**8.**	square
4.	60°	**9.**	obtuse-angled triangle
5.	80°	**10.**	60°

6.	N 36° E
7.	S 51° W
8.	Due E
9.	S 48° E
10.	N 63° W

ANSWERS TO CHAPTER 19

Exercise 19.1

1. 90 miles
2. 220 km
3. 1:1 520 640
4. 28 miles
5. 1:1 200 000
6. 12.5 km
7. 1:12 000 000
8. (a) 9   (b) 6   (c) $4\frac{1}{2}$

Exercise 19.2

1.

2.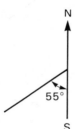

3.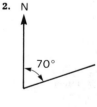

4.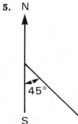

5.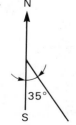

Exercise 19.3

1.

2.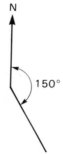

3.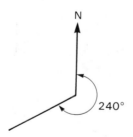

4.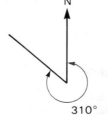

237

5.

350°

6. 050°
7. 085°
8. 155°
9. 220°
10. 340°

Exercise 19.4

1. (a) N 48° E (048°)   (b) S 48° W (228°)
   (c) 42½ miles   (d) N 80° W (280°)
2. 009°
3. 256°
4.

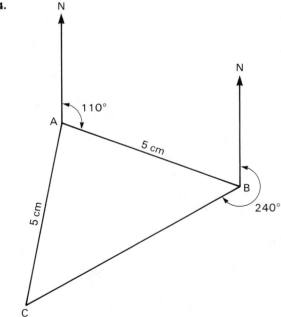

(a) 290°   (b) 50°
(c) 260 km
5. (a) 240°   (b) 060°
   (c) 340°   (d) 315°

Miscellaneous Exercise 19

1. (a) 135°   (b) 045°
2. (a) Pylon   (b) 045°
   (c) 135°
3. 90 km
4. (a) 1 : 633 600   (b) 136°
   (c) 12 miles   (d) 220°
5. (a) 1 : 2 560 000   (b) 80 miles
   (c) 40°   (d) 32 miles
6. (a)

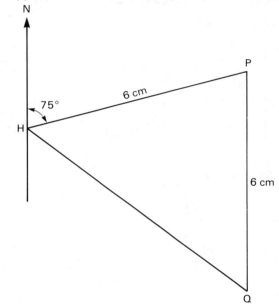

(b) (i) 128°   (ii) 14.6 miles
7. (a) 325 km   (b) 062°
8. 48 min
9. (a) $\frac{9}{16}$ (b) $\frac{7}{16}$
   (c) $\frac{3}{4}$ (d) $\frac{1}{2}$
   (e) 225, 175, 300 and 200 miles
10. (a) 325 miles   (b) 125 miles
    (c) 200 miles   (d) 200 miles
    (e) 200 miles   (f) 1050 miles

Mental Test 19

1. (a) 1 m   (b) 3 m   (c) ½ m
2. (a) 15 km   (b) 2 km
3. (a) 2 cm   (b) 0.5 cm
4. (a) ½ mile   (b) ½ mile   (c) ½ mile
5. (a) 225°   (b) 315°
6. (a) 040°   (b) 160°
   (c) 250°
7. (a) 050°   (b) 230°
8. (a) 110°   (b) 315°

ANSWERS TO CHAPTER 20

Exercise 20.1

1. (a) 16 cm   (b) 30 cm   (c) 24 cm
   (d) 23 cm   (e) 16 cm
2. (a) 16 ft   (b) 20 m   (c) 36 in
   (d) 32 yd   (e) 26 cm
3. (a) 22 cm   (b) 24 cm   (c) 25.4 cm
   (d) 16.8 in
4. (a) 24 ft   (b) 172 mm   (c) 36.8 in
5. (a) 18 cm   (b) 12 cm   (c) 16 cm
6. (a) 25.12 cm   (b) 9.42 ft   (c) 14.444 in
   (d) 30.772 cm   (e) 12.56 in   (f) 31.4 cm
   (g) 42.076 in   (h) 37.052 m
7. (a) 88 cm   (b) 264 in   (c) 308 mm
   (d) 396 in
8. 22 ft
9. 56.52 ft
10. 220 cm
11. 37.68 cm
12. (a) 22 cm   (b) 22 cm   (c) 20 cm
13. 63.12 cm
14. 28.84 in

Exercise 20.2

1. (a) 15 cm^2 (b) 8 cm^2
   (c) 18 ft^2 (d) 28 in^2
2. (a) 450 mm^2 (b) 324 ft^2
   (c) 165.48 in^2 (d) 41.87 cm^2
   (e) 118.58 ft^2
3. 178.54 cm^2
4. 186.3 ft^2
5. 64 in^2
6. 900 cm^2
7. B, D
8. (a) 18 cm^2 (b) 32 cm^2
   (c) 20 cm^2
9. $33\,750 \text{ cm}^2$
10. £133.20

Exercise 20.3

1. 29 cm^2 4. 52 mm^2
2. 103 m^2 5. 72 mm^2
3. 56 in^2 6. 68 cm^2

Exercise 20.4

1. 14 cm^2 6. 24 cm^2
2. 12 cm^2 7. 66 in^2
3. 18 ft^2 8. 296 yd^2
4. 20 m^2 9. 22 m^2
5. 18 in^2 10. 219 yd^2

Exercise 20.5

1. 192
2. 390
3. (a) 12   (b) 576
4. 10
5. (a) 65.8 m^2 (b) 3

Exercise 20.6

1. 56 cm^2 3. 46.11 ft^2
2. 108 in^2 4. 52 cm^2

Exercise 20.7

1. (a) 20 cm^2 (b) 10 in^2
   (c) 31.5 ft^2 (d) 9 m^2
2. (a) 35 cm^2 (b) 9 in^2
   (c) 6 m^2 (d) 15 ft^2
   (e) 5 m^2
3. (a) 14 cm^2 (b) 36 cm^2
   (c) 11.13 in^2 (d) 19.575 ft^2

Exercise 20.8

1. 144 cm^2 4. 1785 yd^2
2. 80 in^2 5. 500 ft^2
3. 55 cm^2

Exercise 20.9

1. (a) 154 cm^2 (b) 2464 in^2
   (c) $61\,600 \text{ mm}^2$ (d) 1386 ft^2
   (e) 3850 m^2
2. (a) 28.26 cm^2 (b) 98.47 in^2
   (c) 176.625 ft^2 (d) 69.363 m^2
3. 62.8 in^2
4. 550 mm^2
5. 40.82 m^2

Exercise 20.10

1. 7.75 acres   4. 28.26 mile^2
2. 14 ha   5. 4900 km^2
3. 20.7 ha

Exercise 20.11

1. 14.28 cm^2 5. 13.76 cm^2
2. 76.27 cm^2 6. 23.44 cm^2
3. 292.3 cm^2 7. 57.72 cm^2
4. 5.38 cm^2 8. 42.14 cm^2

Miscellaneous Exercise 20

1. (a) 21.2 in   (b) 25.53 in^2
2. (a) 28 m   (b) 88 m
   (c) 616 m^2
3. (a) 18 cm   (b) 18 cm^2
   (c) 7 m by 2 m, 4 m by 5 m, 1 m by 8 m
4. R, S
5. 48 ft^2
6. 25 cm^2
7. 204 in^2
8. 84 cm^2
9. 8.4 ha
10. 64.26 cm^2

Mental Test 20

1. 40 cm^2
2. (a) 24 cm   (b) 36 cm^2
3. 42 in^2
4. 12 cm^2
5. 18 cm
6. 20 cm^2
7. 10 in^2
8. 50 cm

ANSWERS TO CHAPTER 21

Exercise 21.1

1. 12 edges, 6 faces, 8 vertices
2. 12 edges, 6 faces, 8 vertices
3. 8 edges, 5 faces, 5 vertices
4. 9 edges, 5 faces, 6 vertices

Exercise 21.2

1. 76 cm^2
2. 59.08 in^2
3. 484.5 cm^2
4. (a) cylinder   (b) pyramid   (c) cuboid
5. 216 cm^2

Exercise 21.3

1. 440 cm^3
2. 360 cm^3
3. 936 in^3
4. 300 ft^3
5. 306 cm^3
6. 162 000 mm^3
7. 183 200 mm^3
8. 122.8 m^3

Exercise 21.4

1. 307.72 in^3
2. 75 360 mm^3
3. 3014.4 cm^3
4. 1643 cm^3
5. 35 ft^3
6. 4.41 m^3
7. 180 ft^3
8. 4292.6 cm^3

Exercise 21.5

1. (a) 1386 cm^3 (b) 1.386 l
2. (a) 24 000 000 cm^3 (b) 24 000 l
3. 46 l
4. 21 195 l
5. (a) 38.4 cl   (b) 76 complete doses
6. (a) 3.18 cl   (b) 22
7. 11.3 l

Miscellaneous Exercise 21

1. 64
2. 8 edges 5 faces
3. 117.75 ft^3
4. 640 cm^2
5. 900 in^3
6. (a) 75.36 m^3 (b) 75 360 l
7. (a) 250 cm^3 (b) 132 cm^2 (c) 60 cm^3
8. 0.385 l

Mental Test 21

1. 27 cm^3
2. 210 cm^3
3. 5
4. 24 cm^3
5. 96 cm^3
6. 35 in^3
7. 40 cm^3
8. 3 l

ANSWERS TO CHAPTER 22

Exercise 22.1

1.

Time (seconds)	Frequency
24	1
25	2
26	4
27	3
28	1
29	2
30	1
31	3
32	3

2.

No. of goals	0	1	2	3	4	5
Frequency	7	13	5	1	2	2

3.

Height (cm)	150	151	152	153	154	155
Frequency	2	3	4	5	6	7
Height	156	157	158	159	160	161
Frequency	8	6	5	4	3	1

5.

Age (years)	14	15	16	17	18
Frequency	10	9	5	4	2

6. (a) 20.5, 25.5 cm   (b) 5 cm

7. (a) 10 cm

Exercise 22.2

1. 9
2. £29
3. 175 cm
4. 4
5. 6.5
6. 6
7. (a) $2\frac{1}{2}$ lb   (b) $3\frac{1}{2}$ lb   (c) $2\frac{1}{2}$ lb
8. (a) 30   (b) 4   (c) 3.2   (d) 3
9. (a) 4.09   (b) 4   (c) 4
10. (a) 134   (b) 22   (c) 22   (d) 21.7

Exercise 22.3

1. (a) $\frac{1}{6}$ (b) $\frac{1}{2}$ (c) $\frac{1}{2}$
2. (a) $\frac{1}{8}$ (b) $\frac{1}{4}$
3. (a) $\frac{1}{52}$ (b) $\frac{1}{13}$ (c) $\frac{1}{2}$ (d) $\frac{1}{4}$
    (e) $\frac{4}{13}$
4. (a) $\frac{1}{2}$ (b) $\frac{1}{5}$ (c) $\frac{3}{10}$ (d) $\frac{7}{10}$

5. 0.3
6. 0.6
7. $\frac{4}{9}$
8. (a) $\frac{1}{2}$ (b) $\frac{13}{20}$ (c) $\frac{3}{10}$

Miscellaneous Exercise 22

1. (b) 1 mm   (c) 299 mm   (d) 299 mm
2. 61
3. 2134
4. (a) $\frac{1}{6}$ (b) $\frac{7}{12}$
5.

Length (mm)	120–129	130–139	140–149
Frequency	4	7	14

Length (mm)	150–159	160–169	170–179
Frequency	8	5	2

6. 4
7. 0.86
8. (a) 163 cm   (b) 163 cm   (c) 163 cm

Mental Test 22

1. (a) 7   (b) 36   **5.** 2
2. 7   **6.** $\frac{3}{10}$
3. £15   **7.** $\frac{1}{3}$
4. 2   **8.** 8

Index